The Armchair Esquire

ESQUIRE BOOKS

EDITED BY

ARNOLD GINGRICH

The Bedside Esquire
The Esquire Treasury
The Esquire Cartoon Album
The Armchair Esquire

The Armchair Esquire

Edited by Arnold Gingrich
and L. Rust Hills

HEINEMANN

LONDON MELBOURNE TORONTO

William Heinemann Ltd
LONDON MELBOURNE TORONTO

CAPETOWN AUCKLAND

THE HAGUE

First published in Great Britain 1959

© 1958 by ESQUIRE, INC.

Copyright © 1934, 1935, 1936, 1937, 1938, 1939,
1942, 1943, 1945, 1953, 1956, 1957, 1958, by Esquire,
Inc.

Printed in Great Britain
by The Windmill Press Ltd
Kingswood, Surrey

ACKNOWLEDGMENTS

'With Other Eyes' by Luigi Pirandello, reprinted by permission of the author's heirs, © 1934 by Esquire, Inc.

'Turnabout is Fair' by D. H. Lawrence, reprinted by permission of the author's estate, © 1934 by Esquire, Inc.

'Fly Away Ladybird' by Conrad Aiken, reprinted by permission of author, © 1934 by Esquire, Inc.

'Reflexshuns on Iggurunce" by Ezra Pound, reprinted by permission of the author, © 1934 by Esquire, Inc.

'Exit the Boob' reprinted from *E. E. Cummings: A Miscellany*, The Argophile Press, by E. E. Cummings, reprinted by permission of Brandt & Brandt, © 1935 by Esquire, Inc.

'Arnold Pentland' ('A Kinsman of his Blood'), from *The Hills Beyond* by Thomas Wolfe, reprinted by permission of Harper & Brothers, © 1935 by Maxwell Perkins, as Executor.

'The Celebrity' reprinted from *U. S. A.* by John Dos Passos, published by Houghton Mifflin Co., © 1935 by John Dos Passos.

'The Godly Warrior' reprinted from *Stories of Three Decades* under the title 'Gladius Dei' by Thomas Mann, translated by H. T. Lowe-Porter by permission of Alfred A. Knopf, Inc., © 1936 Alfred A. Knopf, Inc.

'Three Acts of Music' by F. Scott Fitzgerald, reprinted by permission of Harold Ober Associates, Inc., © 1936 by Frances S. F. Lanahan.

'Life in a Prison Cell' by Maxim Gorki, reprinted by permission of Am-Rus Literary and Music Agency, © 1937 by Esquire, Inc.

'Heavenly and Earthly Love' by Ferenc Molnar, reprinted by permission of the estate of Ferenc Molnar, deceased, © 1935 by Review of Reviews Corporation.

'The Tithe of the Lord' by Theodore Dreiser, reprinted by permission of the author's estate, © 1938 by Esquire, Inc.

'The Butterfly and the Tank' by Ernest Hemingway, reprinted by permission of the author, © 1938 by Ernest Hemingway.

'Dreiser at Spoon River' by Edgar Lee Masters, reprinted by permission of Mrs. Edgar Lee Masters, © 1939 by Esquire, Inc.

CONTENTS

INTRODUCTION

The Literary Scene, 1933–1958

THE READER has only to glance at the table of contents of this anthology to see how many distinguished contributors *Esquire* has had in the twenty-five years of its existence. Here is rich fare, a strikingly diversified collection of stories and articles, many of which have not previously appeared in book form. The selections are fresh and remarkably readable, and the volume makes a most satisfactory armchair companion.

The volume also belongs to literary history.

The autumn of 1933 seems, as one takes the first look backward, an inauspicious time for the introduction of a magazine such as *Esquire* aspired to be. Although Franklin D. Roosevelt had been in office for a few months, and had introduced some of the measures that enraged so many of the wealthy and encouraged millions of other Americans, the depression had continued to deepen. If the magazine had been started in 1923, it would have had six boom years in which to entertain and instruct a generation of young men with money in their pockets. A decade later its potential audience had shrunk and seemed likely to go on shrinking. In an autumn in which the word 'revolution' was often heard, spoken now with horror and now with hope, the publication of *Esquire* seemed either a piece of unpardonable insolence or a gallant but futile gesture.

However, we can now see that in one important way the young *Esquire* had the best luck a magazine can have: a supply of good writers. The 1920s had confirmed the reputations of a number of men who had begun writing before the First World War, among them Theodore Dreiser, Sherwood Anderson, Sinclair Lewis, H. L. Mencken. Moreover, the twenties themselves had suddenly and richly brought forth John Dos Passos, F. Scott Fitzgerald, Ernest Hemingway, William Faulkner, Cummings, and Thomas Wolfe. Beginning their careers almost as *Esquire* began its career were John Steinbeck and James T. Farrell. With the exception of Faulkner, all the men I have mentioned contributed to *Esquire* at one time or another. Some of them made many contributions, and, I am sure, were grateful for the existence, in a world of earnest, insolvent little magazines, of a magazine that paid cash.

It was never the purpose of the magazine to represent American literature according to some comprehensive scheme; the editors sought to find contributions that they liked and hoped the readers would like. Yet it is interesting to notice how often, especially in its first half-dozen years and again in recent years, contributions to *Esquire* have belonged in the literary mainstream.

Take the case of John Dos Passos. Disillusioned by the First World War, he began asking himself, even in the prosperous twenties, whether fundamental economic and social changes were not needed in America, and when the depression began, he was one of the first American writers to ask, Why not communism? Never firmly committed to the communist cause, and as much a pioneer in disillusionment as he had been in involvement, Dos Passos nevertheless strongly influenced the intellectuals who moved leftward in the thirties. *The Big Money*, the third of the novels that compose *U.S.A.*, came out of a mood somewhere between sympathy and disenchantment, but it is sternly critical of capitalist economics and especially capitalist culture. The story published here, 'The Celebrity', is a considerably altered version of an episode in that novel. Its theme is fraud, a kind of accidental, aimless fraud, a fraud really forced upon rather than chosen by the young man from the sticks, and exactly this kind of fraud is central in *The Big Money*.

Ernest Hemingway was slower than Dos Passos in arriving at what the jargon of the times called 'social consciousness', but he did have his moment of snow blindness—to use Edmund Wilson's phrase. Hemingway was a natural for *Esquire*, a good writer who was also a sort of self-fashioned image of masculinity, a man interested in everything that is supposed to interest men. To *Esquire* he contributed articles, usually short, on many topics, from the art of writing to the art of deep-sea fishing, and in some of these one finds material of which he made use in *To Have and Have Not*, which was published in 1937. It was not until he served as a journalist in Spain during the Civil War that Hemingway definitely took sides. As is well known, he was able to curb his partisanship by the time he wrote *For Whom the Bell Tolls*, published in 1940, but it is interesting to see that in 'The Butterfly and the Tank', one of 'Three Stories of Chicote's', written while his sympathy for the Loyalists was at its height, objectivity triumphs.

Of course, there were many American writers in the thirties who were indifferent or hostile to Marxism. Conrad Aiken, for instance, went his own way in both poetry and prose. Then there was E. E. Cummings. He had gone to the Soviet Union in the early thirties, and, as *Eimi* demonstrated, had not been impressed. In 'Exit the Boob' one finds him saying in 1935 the same things he was to say twenty years later in his 'nonlectures' at Harvard and saying them in the same tone of voice. But in the thirties such sentiments were less generally acceptable than they are, at least in literary circles, in the fifties, and Cummings was often attacked as irresponsible and anti-social.

Ezra Pound was also preaching individualism in *Esquire* in the early thirties, but his brand of individualism, by a curious process described by Richard H. Rovere in his contribution to the book, was to lead him to become an apologist for Mussolini's Corporate State. Like Cummings, Pound was primarily a poet, but, unlike Cummings, he was also a reformer, and it was his passion for reform that got him into trouble. Since his 'Reflexshuns on Iggurunce' eventually tackles the problem of money, note what Rovere says: "It was no doubt always in the cards that Pound would reach for the purely mechanical device—currency reform—for righting social wrongs." He moved from discontent with society to an interest in Social Credit, to a hatred of those he called usurers, to anti-Semitism, to advocacy of Fascism.

As Rovere points out, Pound's course toward Fascism parallels the course taken by many of his younger contemporaries toward communism. The creative writer is perhaps particularly likely to be misled by systems of universal reform. The writer does not ordinarily have an acute interest in social questions as such—he is too much absorbed by his own problems; but he does have eyes, and he may have a conscience; and when he sees a people suffering as the American people suffered in the Great Depression, he can easily be convinced that something must be done. What makes him accept some all-inclusive remedy is his desire to have social questions disposed of once and for all, so that he can go about what he regards as his proper business. But fortunately the creative writer, as a general rule, cannot long be comfortable with dogma. Of the writers who were attracted to communism in the thirties, a few were destroyed as writers and a few maintained a schizoid existence for some length of time, but the majority saw relatively soon that, whether or not communism would dispose of the social questions that were bothering them, it would certainly dispose of the values to which they as writers adhered.

Among the other famous writers of the twenties and thirties we have Wolfe and Fitzgerald. The latter wrote a great deal for the magazine, and from the contributions, which include the famous autobiographical essay, 'The Crack-Up', one can document some aspects of his decline. 'Three Acts of Music' is an attempt to re-capture, by an act of will, the mood of some of the stories on which his popularity was founded. As for 'Arnold Pentland', it is pure Tom Wolfe, full of his passion for the grotesque and the pathetic.

Of the writers a little older than those I have been discussing, we have Sinclair Lewis, Theodore Dreiser, and Edgar Lee Masters. Lewis served for a time as *Esquire*'s book reviewer, and his review of books on the Negro problem is marked by a characteristic acerbity and looks forward to a famous novel, *Kingsblood Royal*. Dreiser's 'The Tithe of the Lord' has exactly the quality of his best work, the wondering, blundering pity that sometimes turns his harshest prose into music. As for Masters' reminiscence of Dreiser in the Lincoln country, it tells us something about two men of letters and intro-duces the fascinating figure of John Armstrong.

Another reminiscence is H. L. Mencken's 'An Evening on the House'. Although Mencken retained his powers of vituperation long after 1943, when this piece appeared, he was at his best in the later years in his recollections of the past. A first-class brawl at a rowdy resort at the turn of the century was a subject to call forth his humour and extravagance. But there is a fine note of nostalgia in the piece—as of course there is in the recollections that Mencken's old partner, George Jean Nathan, wrote many years later about Mencken himself and about Scott Fitzgerald.

Something should be said about the stories that came from outside America during the publication's early years. The names are notable—Pirandello, Lawrence, Mann, Gorki, Molnar—and so are the contributions, but it would be hard to argue that they constitute a pattern. At any rate the variety is impressive: Gorki's harsh realism, Pirandello's careful fantasy, Molnar's playfulness. The D. H. Lawrence story, an early one somehow made available for posthumous publication, has a great freshness about it that takes the reader back to the less turgid pages of *Sons and Lovers*. Thomas Mann's warning against life-denying fanaticism is as pertinent now as it was in the days when Nazism was spreading through Europe. It is impressive to think that all of these stories were set before readers of *Esquire* in a period of less than four years—all this in addition to the rich selection from American literature.

The early years of *Esquire* were great years. Why between 1940 and 1950 so much less was published that today seems worth reprinting is a question for which there must be several answers. One of them is that many of the new writers didn't seem to be *Esquire* writers. If only because so many men were involved in the war, many of the new voices in the early forties were women's voices. Consider Carson McCullers' *The Heart is a Lonely Hunter* (1940), Eudora Welty's *Curtain of Green* (1941), and Jean Stafford's *Boston Adventure* (1944). I admired Mrs. McCullers, Miss Welty, and Miss Stafford, as of course I still do, but I should have been surprised to find their work in *Esquire*.

Of the contributions we do have from the forties, one is Nelson Algren's account of a police line-up. This is interesting in itself because he has made use of the material elsewhere, and it is also interesting as it displays Algren in transition. Algren was one of the socially conscious writers of the thirties, but his social consciousness was based less on a reading of Marx and Lenin than on first-hand acquaintance with suffering and exploited human beings. His sympathy with the underdog has survived whatever changes may have taken place in his political thinking and has remained the strongest force in his fiction up to and including *A Walk on the Wild Side*.

Another striking contribution from the forties is J. D. Salinger's 'This Sandwich Has No Mayonnaise'. A more modest story than some he has written in recent years, it is poignant and neatly turned. Admirers of *The Catcher in the Rye* will be struck by the fact that in this story, published six years before the novel, Salinger introduced the character of Holden Caulfield—not that Holden is physically present, which is the point of the story.

Norman Mailer was the first young writer, the first young veteran of World War II, to produce a war novel that made a strong general impression. Although in *The Naked and the Dead* he sometimes sounded like the early Dos Passos and although he has continued to have a strong interest in social problems, he has always been an individualist. His story, 'The Language of Men', neatly poses the problem of the man who is an individualist in spite of himself.

The emphasis on individualism is strong in the second part of this anthology. Arthur Miller flirted with Marxism in the post-war period, but he is obviously an individualist interested in a means for the emancipation of the individual. 'The Misfits' is that rare creation, a story that succeeds as a fable without losing any of its force as a story.

Saul Bellow might almost be called a connoisseur of individualism. In all his major works, and especially in *The Adventures of Augie March*, he is concerned not with the obvious pressures towards conformity but with the subtle temptations that can rob a man of his identity. For him, as he shows in *Seize the Day*, individuality is not something that can be given or taken away; it is something that must be achieved. In 'Leaving the Yellow House' he portrays a tough old warhorse, a woman who refuses to give in to either circumstance or physical infirmity and whose refusal becomes in the end both pathetic and heroic.

It is not hard to understand why today such writers as Mailer and Miller and Bellow and Salinger are attracted to dissenters. (Note also how strongly Nathan's reminiscences of Mencken and Fitzgerald emphasise their nonconformity.) I do not accept the theory, popular in some quarters, that a conspiratorial élite is systematically trying to reduce the American people to the condition of robots. But a society based on mass production, a society with a generous amount of leisure and with mass media to occupy that leisure, is not a society in which individualism naturally flowers. As David Riesman soberly sets forth in *The Lonely Crowd*, such a society tends to create the kind of character to which conformity seems both desirable and inevitable. The writer knows that resistance is possible because he himself resists, although probably not all pressures all the time. He believes it is important because he believes the individual is important, and he is likely to seek out figures to serve as examples or even as symbols of resistance.

The preoccupation with dissent adds point to the significance of the pieces by John Steinbeck and Richard Rovere. Steinbeck has taken a single incident in Arthur Miller's career, his refusal to name names before a Congressional investigating committee, and has defended the dramatist on the ground that his defiance serves the cause of morality. Rovere has examined critically the whole complicated career of Ezra Pound, and in doing so he has illuminated one of the perennial problems of the past quarter-century—the problem of the author who allies himself with a movement hostile to the theory and practice of individualism. As I write this, it happily appears that the case of Ezra Pound has been settled, but the problems the case raised continue to deserve our scrutiny.

Again it becomes necessary to comment on the contributions from Europe, and again one must say that they are distinguished and miscellaneous. Shaw's letters, written before he had created the legendary George Bernard Shaw, have charm and interest, if only because so many of us had come to feel that the legendary Shaw must always have existed. Waugh on Goa writes brilliant description and reveals something of his philosophy, while Camus characteristically turns description to the service of philosophical generalisation.

Most striking is Aldous Huxley's revisitation of *Brave New World*: the article is so much less cocksure than the book. Huxley was not, of course, one of the dogmatic young revolutionaries back in 1932. On the contrary, he was setting out to tell the revolutionaries where they had gone wrong. The problem, he said, was not how to bring about but how to avoid utopia, and the novel resolved itself into a defence of the right to suffer. Looking back, he observes, with a mixture of satisfaction and dismay, that some of his predictions have been fulfilled, but now he seems to have no doubt that the future will hold suffering enough for everyone, and he devotes much of his article to the discussion of the possibility of developing something like the Soma of his novel, a superior kind of tranquilliser, with all of the advantages and none of the disadvantages of alcohol. The reader will have to decide for himself whether Huxley has advanced or regressed in the quarter-century.

It is obvious that no anthology, much less an anthology chosen from the pages of a single magazine, can represent the diversity of the past twenty-five years. What one can say is that, of the names that come to mind when one thinks back over those years, a surprising portion are represented in this volume. One can also say that the selections are extremely good reading.

GRANVILLE HICKS

PREFACE

The Vintage Years

ESQUIRE's twenty-fifth year, which culminates with the publication of this volume, began with the issuance of a cartoon album. Both books were derived from the pages of *Esquire*. But anybody who had never seen the magazine, and had only the two books to go by, would find it hard to believe.

The disparity between the magazine's lettered side and its pictured side has long been a cause of comment and wonder. We commented on it ourselves, with some wryness, as long ago as 1940, in the course of the Introduction to the first volume of writings collected from *Esquire*, saying that we were (already) "weary of hearing the cartoons talked about as if they characterised the contents as a whole".

In that earlier collection, *The Bedside Esquire*, we had wanted to include 'The Godly Warrior' by Thomas Mann, which had appeared in the April '36 issue, and Alfred Knopf, who had received a copyright assignment from us to include the story in his volume of Thomas Mann's *Stories of Three Decades*, refused to return the courtesy for its inclusion in our collection.

The years between have either mellowed Alfred Knopf or added stature to *Esquire*'s literary standing, because the Thomas Mann story is in, this time, without dispute.

Until the marriage of Arthur Miller and Marilyn Monroe there had never been such a surprising combination of intellectual and pictorial elements as was represented by the teaming up between the same covers of *Esquire*'s words and its pictures. But the sad truth that brains wear better than beauty was never more evident than in looking back over old issues, and seeing how much better the sober side of the magazine stands up under critical re-examination today, after a lapse of anywhere up to two and a half decades, than the flashy side does. For the pictures were reflections of the passing moment, the fads and foibles and the fleeting fancies of the stage and screen, whereas the words were concerned, in major part, with the verities that are eternal.

This is not to say that all the words added up to spell literature with a capital L, but merely that much of the verbal ore now assays to a remarkably high percentage of literary gold, whether or not it was consciously presented as Literature in the first place.

For proud as we are of the 'names' we have published, we are even prouder of the stories by authors who only later became famous, and a number of the items listed in the appendix and dating back to the thirties or early forties serve as prime examples.

There are other instances where early contributions to the magazine's pages are now chiefly of interest as literary curiosities, and are here presented as such, as the head notes in those cases point out.

In any case, there are representative selections here dating over the last twenty-five years, with especial concentration in the first five and the last five. As Granville Hicks has said in his Introduction relating them to the literary scene, it would be hard to argue that they constitute a pattern.

And perhaps it would be sad if they did. American magazines, like American cars, seem to be increasingly characterised by their resemblances rather than their differences. Looking at the older examples, you may feel inclined to say, "They don't build 'em like that any more." But don't forget, what you're looking at today is the survivor. The overwhelming success of a few makers, of magazines as well as cars, results in an increasing conformism to success patterns, and a resultant killing off of the hindmost. The off-beat, the irregular, the unorthodox, seem to be acquiring an unenviable scarcity value.

Our only pattern, or touchstone, or divining rod, in assembling the contents of *Esquire* has always been the homely rule of looking for 'a good story, even if it *is* Literature'. We haven't always achieved an exact fit. But the aim, at least, was to see to it that if all our good stories couldn't be literature, at least all our literature would be good stories.

Literature, of course, is anything but an exact science. And as an English judge said, not long ago, "Every age gets the literature it deserves." He surely could not have known that his thought had been anticipated, by better than a decade, by a letter writer in our correspondence columns who said, "I find no fault with *Esquire* that I do not find with the age that produced it." But then, Whitman was ahead of both of them, with "To have great poets, we must have great audiences."

So when you hear, as one often does, of *Esquire*'s 'great years', you begin to wonder which was great, the magazine, or the audience, or the year itself. Magazines are like vineyards, in that you work just as hard one year as another, only sometimes the sun shines more kindly on your efforts. That's when the great years just happen. Sweating double won't help. It's either a great year or it isn't.

Granted *Esquire*'s middle years were not great. From, roughly, '42 to '52, or approximately the magazine's second decade, our grapes weren't tended as carefully as they had been before and have been since. Some of us turned our backs on the vineyard for too long a time, and thought the vines would tend themselves. So you can throw out those middle years, as, by no great coincidence, this book has pretty much done.

But a fair case could be made for the last five years, as against even the first five that are by now with such uniform nostalgia commonly considered the great years.

Maybe this is wrong to do. Maybe one should no more attempt to treat literature as a competitive sport than as an exact science. And after all, you won't read this book as you would attend a game or a match, disappointed if one half of it doesn't beat the other.

But in looking down a table of contents, as in looking down a bill of fare, it is only natural that you tend to 'like' one section more than another. And when, as in this case, the names read down from the past to the present, yet are all from the same magazine, the tendency is equally natural to look up to the older ones and down at the newer ones.

That's where the perspective can get tricky on this business of great years. Vintage labels can pre-condition the palate to too much respect.

An Arthur Miller or a Saul Bellow may not be as much fun to sit around and drink with as a Dreiser was, and neither could or would roll and unroll that white handkerchief over and over again half as fascinatingly, but either could be more fun to read, now or twenty-five years hence.

Reading Dreiser again today it's hard to remember that he talked well, because his *written* speech patterns now seem as alien to the mid-century tongue as those of some of the Elizabethans.

But, against that, Fitzgerald's, after twenty-two years, seem astonishingly natural, so maybe it would be better to drop the whole line of argument.

The only thing these writings have in common is their original appearance in the pages of *Esquire*. It is foolish and futile to try to rank them or set them off against each other, either by era or by school or type.

They are twenty-nine milestones or landmarks in the literary history of *Esquire*, to make the most interesting and unfamiliar reading. We have deliberately avoided those apparent 'naturals' that have been over-often included in other collections, including the last two of our own.

To have tried to include everything worthy of anthologising that has appeared in *Esquire*'s pages over the past quarter-century would have been to make a book too big to sell at anything like a price you could conceivably care to pay.

So we've had to content ourselves with a roll of honour that was tantamount to confining our citations to officers above the rank of major-general. There were an awful lot of brigadiers and colonels we would at least have liked to list.

With this aim, we have included in the body of this book a check-list of contributions of literary distinction, which was contributed to the *Bulletin of Bibliography* in 1957. It was compiled by two scholars at the University of California, E. R. Hagemann and James E. Marsh, and appeared in two parts, in the *Bulletin*'s issues for January–April '57 and May–July '57, although it covered only the 'vintage years', from '33 through '41. Since then, however, and for the purpose of its inclusion in this volume, Messrs. Hagemann and Marsh have obligingly brought it up to date.

Depending not on any say-so of ours, but on their own taste and judgment, they attempted to skim the literary cream off the top of the entire textual content of *Esquire*'s first three hundred issues, and to show where else it has been bottled, or otherwise served up, since its first appearance in the magazine. Thus they have listed, not only the original *Esquire* volume, issue, and page numbers of all contributions they considered to be of literary import, but have also attempted to indicate all subsequent reprintings in book form.

Viewed as an honour roll it is undoubtedly as unbiased as any listing can be that depends on two persons' appraisals. But its value to this book seems to us to be greater than that, because it is also useful as a reference guide.

Esquire is not now and never has been listed in either the *International Index* or the *Reader's Guide*, probably because in both instances they took one look at the pictures twenty-five years ago and never looked beyond them to notice that the magazine also contained words. And while most libraries have complete collections of *Esquire*, many have developed the habit of keeping them in their rare-book rooms, presumably because people took to cutting out the pictures.

So the serious reader, interested in *Esquire*'s lettered side and trying to look up something like 'The Crack-Up' or 'The Snows of Kilimanjaro', is hard put to it to know what issues to ask for, even after obtaining access to a complete back file.

The Hagemann and Marsh check-list at the back of this volume now solves that problem. If you like the authors represented in this book enough to want to seek out their other *Esquire* writings, either in bound volumes in libraries or on the dusty shelves of second-hand magazine dealers, this list will lead you to them.

Or if you don't like the writings that Rust Hills and I have here garnered, after a trip through twenty-five years' worth of issues, then armed with this list you can make your own selection. As a do-it-yourself project, it might be more fun. You could call it, after the exhilarating sport of tracking down your choices, no longer the *Armchair*, but rather the *Wheelchair*, *Esquire*.

ARNOLD GINGRICH

LUIGI PIRANDELLO

—————————————◦◦◦————————————

With Other Eyes

Under its Italian title, '*Con Altri Occhi*', this story of Pirandello's is dated July 28, 1901; and, under the title 'Through the Other Wife's Eyes', it appeared in the English magazine *Fortnightly Review* in 1933; the first American appearance was in *Esquire* in July, 1934.

One of Pirandello's early stories (he wrote over 300), 'With Other Eyes' was written well before any of his celebrated plays (*Six Characters in Search of an Author*, for instance, appeared in 1921). It nevertheless reflects many of Pirandello's preoccupations and methods. In 1902 he published a novel called *His Turn*, which considered the situation of 'With Other Eyes' in reverse: a woman's second husband torments himself speculating on his wife's previous marriage. Another interesting parallel, this one demonstrating once again how Nature imitates Art, is with Pirandello's own marriage. Supported by their wealthy parents, Pirandello and his wife lived together happily until 1904, when their parents' mines were flooded and they were faced with financial disaster. Consequent worry and anxiety affected his wife's mind and gradually drove her into hysteria and fits of jealousy; maniacally she would accuse her husband of treachery, unfaithfulness; and in her insanity she drove her own daughter to attempt suicide. The preoccupation with unfaithfulness in 'With Other Eyes' appeared, of course, several years earlier.

Pirandello's characteristic interest in the problems of illusion *versus* reality is present here too, as is his constant theme (in Walter Starkie's words) that "what makes life is the reality you give to it. Every character suffers from some fixation to the point of madness. Life seems to be a hideous nightmare and everything is out of focus."

————————————◦◦◦————————————

As she turned away from the window, with a sigh, Anna noticed that her husband had forgotten that morning to disturb his bed, as was his custom when he did not want the servants to know that he had not slept in his own bedroom. She leaned her elbows on the bed and then stretched out, pressing her blonde head on the pillows and closing her eyes as if to enjoy in the freshness of the linen her husband's dreams.

Her husband was going away that evening, and she had come into his room to prepare his bags. When she opened the wardrobe she heard a squeak in one of the inside compartments, and started back in alarm. Gathering her skirts around her legs, she took a walking-stick with a curved handle from the corner and tried to open the door with it. When she pulled, instead of the door, a bright steel blade came out of the stick. This was so unexpected that she shuddered and let the handle of the stick fall.

Kicking aside the sword blade, she pulled out the compartment, full of old, discarded clothes of her husband. In a sudden burst of curiosity she began to arrange them and, as she replaced a faded old jacket, she felt something in the pocket which crackled like a letter. She wondered what the letter could be which had lain there forgotten for so many years. In this way Anna discovered the photograph of her husband's first wife.

Pale with excitement she ran to the window, and stood for quite a while staring at this unknown image.

The huge cape and old-fashioned clothes prevented her at first from seeing how beautiful that face was. But as soon as she realised the features, disconnecting them from the clothes of the period, she was struck by the eyes, and was filled with a feeling of jealousy and hatred; her jealousy was posthumous, but her hate was mixed with the contempt which she had felt for the other woman, when she had married her present husband. That was eleven years after the domestic tragedy which had suddenly destroyed his first household.

Anna had hated that woman, because she could not understand how she could have been unfaithful to the man whom she now adored. She also hated her because her own parents had opposed her marriage to Brivio, as if he were responsible for the disgrace and violent death of the unfaithful wife.

She knew this must be Victor's first wife; the woman who had killed herself! This was proved by the inscription on the back of the photograph, "To my darling Victor, from his Almira. November 11, 1913".

Anna's knowledge of her death was very vague. All she knew was that, when her husband discovered he was being deceived, with the impassiveness of a judge, he compelled her to take her own life.

At the moment she recalled with satisfaction her husband's condemnation, because she was exasperated by that 'darling Victor' and that 'his Almira', as if that woman had wanted to show how close were the bonds which existed between her and Victor, just simply to annoy her.

This first emotion of hate prompted by her sense of rivalry was followed by a feminine curiosity to examine the features of that face, a curiosity almost restrained by that strange consternation which one experiences on seeing something that has belonged to someone who died a tragic death, a consternation all the more profound in her case because it was bound up with her love for the husband who had once belonged to this other woman.

Looking at the face, Anna immediately noticed how unlike her own it was. And at once she wondered in her heart how on earth her husband could ever have loved this woman—though he certainly must have thought her beautiful—if he could then fall in love with a person as different as herself.

Even to her this face seemed beautiful, much more beautiful than her own, and in the picture she seemed to be a brunette, and to think that those lips had kissed her husband's! But why those sad lines around the mouth? Why the melancholy in those intense eyes? The whole face inspired deep sympathy, and Anna was almost annoyed by the gentle and real kindness which these features expressed. With a sudden movement of repulsion and disgust she seemed to see in those eyes the same expression as she noticed in her own when she looked at herself in the mirror in the morning, and thought of her husband, after they had spent the night together.

She had scarcely time to hide the photograph in her pocket when her husband appeared in the doorway and jokingly said:

"What have you been doing? As usual, you've been putting things in order, I suppose! God help me, now I'll never be able to find anything!"

Noticing the sword stick on the ground, he added:

"Aha! So you've been fencing with the clothes in the wardrobe?"

He gave one of those laughs of his which seemed to issue only from his throat, and as he laughed he looked at his wife as if he were asking her the reason for his laughter. As he looked at her, his sharp, black, restless eyes blinked rapidly.

Victor Brivio treated his wife like a child who was incapable of anything more than that ingenuous and almost infantile love with which she had surrounded him, which often bored him, and to which he had proposed to pay attention only from time to time, even then showing a certain condescension mixed with irony. It was as if he wanted to say, "Oh, very well! For the time being I'll be a child like you. A man has to do that sort of thing, but don't let us waste too much time over it!"

Anna had let the old jacket fall in which she had found the photograph. He picked it up with the point of the stick, went to the window and called to his servant in the garden. When the boy appeared in front of the window, Brivio threw the faded coat in his face saying, "This is for you."

"Now you will have less to dust," he added, turning to his wife, "and to set in order, I hope!"

Again he uttered that forced laugh of his, his eyelids blinking rapidly.

Her husband had often before left the city, and not only for a day, but also for a night, as on this occasion. Affected by the discovery of the photograph, Anna had a curious fear of being alone, as she weepingly confessed to her husband.

Victor Brivio was completely absorbed in his own affairs and was fussing about being late, so he did not receive his wife's unusual complaint very sympathetically.

"What! Why? Come, come, don't be a baby!"

He left the house in a rage without even saying good-bye.

Anna started, as the door banged behind him. There were tears in her eyes as she hastened to her room to go to bed.

"You can go," said Anna to her maid, who was waiting. "I'll undress myself. Good night."

She began to undress rapidly, staring at the floor in front of her. As her clothes slipped to the floor, she remembered that the photograph was there, and she had the feeling that those sad eyes were looking at her compassionately. She stooped resolutely to pick up her clothes, and threw them, without folding them, on a chair at the foot of the bed, as if she would thus be able to avoid the image of the dead woman, by leaving the photograph hidden.

As soon as she was in bed, she closed her eyes, and forced herself to think of the route her husband would take to the railway station. She was anxiously fighting the thoughts which had compelled her all day to observe and study her husband. She knew what obsession had caused her to do this, and she wanted to get rid of it.

She had the vague sensation that for the last three years, from the moment that she left her father's house, she had been living in a vacuum of which she was only just beginning to be conscious. She had not noticed this emptiness before, because she had filled it with her love, all unaided. Now she noticed it, because during the entire day she had held her love in abeyance, in order to see, to watch, to judge.

'He did not even say good-bye,' she thought, and again she began to cry, as if this thought were the real reason for her tears.

She sat up in bed, and suddenly reached out her hand to get her handkerchief. Now it was useless to pretend that she should not and could not look again at the photograph. She found it and turned on the light again.

How differently she had imagined this woman! Now that she looked at the real face, she had a sense of remorse for the feelings which the imaginary picture had inspired in her. She had imagined a rather stout and rubicund woman, with laughing, flashing eyes, and full of vulgar merriment. Instead, here was the picture of a young girl whose features expressed a deep and melancholy soul. A different woman from herself, it is true, but not in the worst sense, as she had previously imagined. On the contrary, this melancholy mouth looked as if it had never smiled, whereas her own had smiled so often and so happily. Certainly, as appeared from the photograph, she was a brunette, and lacked her own blonde, rosy, smiling face.

But why, why, was she so sad?

A horrible thought suddenly struck her mind and took her thoughts away from this woman. Unexpectedly she had stumbled upon a threat, not only to her peace, to her love, which had already been deeply wounded, but also to her pride as an honest woman, who had never entertained the remotest doubt concerning her husband. This other woman had had a lover, and it was because of her lover, and not because of her husband, that she was so sad!

She threw the photograph on to the night table and turned out the light, hoping to fall asleep this time without thinking of this woman, with whom she now had nothing in common. But, when she closed her eyes, she could not help seeing the eyes of the dead woman, and it was in vain that she tried to drive away the vision.

"It was not for his sake, not for him!" she murmured obstinately, as if she could get rid of this woman by insulting her.

She tried hard to recall whatever she had heard of that other man, the lover, in an effort to direct that glance and the sadness of those eyes towards the lover, and not towards herself, the lover of whom she knew nothing but the name, Arthur Valli. She knew that he had married a few years later, as if to prove that he was innocent of the crime of which Brivio accused him. He had refused emphatically to fight a duel with the latter, on the ground that he did not fight with homicidal maniacs. After that, Victor had threatened to kill him wherever he might meet him, even if in church. Then he had left the country with his wife and did not return until Victor went abroad after his second marriage.

Suddenly, Anna was completely filled with the sadness of the events she had recalled: the vileness of Valli and, after so many years, her husband's indifference, which had enabled him to remarry and start life again, as if nothing had happened; the happiness which she herself had experienced on becoming his wife, the three years which she had spent without ever thinking of that other woman. The picture came vividly before her, but as if from a great distance, and it seemed as if those eyes, full of such intense unhappiness, were saying, with a shake of the head, 'All of you people are alive, but I alone am dead!'

She felt terribly alone in the house, and she was afraid. It is true, she was alive, but for three years, ever since the day of her marriage, she had never even once seen her parents and her sister. She, who had adored them and had always been obedient and trusting, she had risen in revolt against their wishes and against their advice, because of her love for this man. For love of him she had fallen mortally ill, and she would have died, if the doctors had not induced her father to consent to the marriage. Her father did not consent, but he surrendered, swearing that, as far as he and the family were concerned, she would be as if she had never existed. There was not only the difference of age, her husband being eighteen years older than she, but the even more serious obstacle from her father's point of view, of his financial position, which was subject to rapid ups and downs, by reason of the risky undertakings in which he became involved, because of his rash faith in himself and in his luck.

In her three years of marriage, surrounded by comforts, Anna had concluded that her father's views were unjust or dictated by prejudice, so far as her husband's fortune was concerned, about which in her ignorance she entertained the same faith as he had in himself. As for the difference in their ages, there had been no disillusionment for her, so far, and no subject of surprise for other people. Victor Brivio did not feel the damage of time in his vivacious and nervous body, and even less in his mind, which was filled with indefatigable energy and eager restlessness.

Now that she was considering her life for the first time, without suspecting it, with the eyes of the dead woman, she found reason to complain of her husband. It is true that she had been wounded on several occasions by his almost contemptuous indifference towards her, but never so deeply as today. Now, for the first time, she felt desperately alone, separated from her parents, who seemed at this moment to have abandoned her, as if, by marrying Victor, she had something in common with his dead wife and was not worthy of other companionship. Her husband, who ought to have consoled her, appeared unwilling to give her any credit for the sacrifice she had made to him of her filial and family affection, as if that had cost her nothing, as if he had a right to this sacrifice, and therefore no duty on his part could compensate her for it. Perhaps he had a right, but then why did she so hopelessly fall in love with him? Surely it was then his duty to compensate her? Instead of which . . .

"That is always the way!" It seemed to Anna that these words came to her from the sad lips of the dead woman.

She turned on the light again and, as she looked at the photograph, she was struck by the expression in the eyes. So you, too, have really suffered through him? You, too, have felt that heart-

breaking emptiness, when you saw that you were no longer loved?
"Really? Really?" Anna asked the picture, choked with tears.

Then it seemed to her that those kindly eyes, filled with passion, were pitying her in their turn, sympathising with her in her abandonment, sympathising with her unrewarded sacrifice, with the love which remained locked up in her breast, like a treasure, locked in a coffer, to which he had the keys, which he never used, like a miser.

D. H. LAWRENCE

Turnabout is Fair

There is difficulty dating this story of Lawrence's, which under its original title, 'Her Turn', is mentioned in only one bibliography, *The Manuscripts of D. H. Lawrence*, compiled by L. C. Powell. From the evidence of other stories preceding it and following it in the bibliography, the best guess is that he wrote it sometime in the spring of 1912. It is possible, then, that 'Her Turn' is one of the first stories written under the influence of his wife Frieda, perhaps just after he met her, before they eloped to the Continent that year. Note the opening sentence: "She was his second wife, and so there was between them that truce which is never held between a man and his first woman."

Characteristic Lawrentian portraits are evident in the story—as in *Sons and Lovers*, Lawrence writes of his drinking coal-miner father and his strong-willed mother. One interesting touch worth pointing out is Lawrence's early use here of the tortoise as a male sex symbol. At the end of the story, the husband has smothered his rage and submitted to his wife. ". . . he dropped his fist to his side, turned, and went out, muttering. He went down to the shed that stood in the middle of the garden. There he picked up the tortoise, and stood with bent head, rubbing its horny head." Later in his life Lawrence picked up this symbol in his six 'Tortoise Poems', in which, says Harry T. Moore in *The Intelligent Heart*, "he projected the sex experience of a man in the image of a tortoise, at once delicate and blundering, viewed by Lawrence in a mood combining sympathy, amusement and participation."

SHE WAS HIS SECOND WIFE, and so there was between them that truce which is never held between a man and his first woman.

He was one for the women, and as such an exception among the colliers. In spite of their prudery, the neighbour women liked him;

he was big, naïve, and very courteous with them; he was so, even to his second wife.

Being a large man of considerable strength and perfect health, he earned good money in the pit. His natural courtesy saved him from enemies, while his fresh interest in life made his presence always agreeable. So he went his own way, had always plenty of friends, always a good job down pit.

He gave his wife thirty-five shillings a week. He had two grown-up sons at home, and they paid twelve shillings each. There was only one child by the second marriage, so Radford considered his wife did well.

Eighteen months ago, Bryan and Wentworth's men were out on strike for eleven weeks. During that time, Mrs. Radford could neither cajole nor entreat nor nag the ten shilling strike-pay from her husband. So that when the second strike came on, she was prepared for action.

Radford was going, quite inconspicuously, to the publican's wife at the 'Golden Horn'. She is a large, easy-going lady of forty, and her husband is sixty-three, moreover crippled with rheumatism. She sits in the little bar-parlour of the wayside public-house, knitting for dear life, and sipping a very moderate glass of scotch. When a decent man arrives at the three-foot width of bar, she rises, serves him, surveys him over, and, if she likes his looks, says:

"Won't you step inside, sir?"

If he steps inside, he will find not more than one or two men present. The room is warm, quite small. The landlady knits. She gives a few polite words to the stranger, then resumes her conversation with the men who interest her most. She is straight, highly-coloured, with indifferent brown eyes.

"What was that you asked me, Mr. Radford?"

"What is the difference between a donkey's tail and a rainbow?" asked Radford, who had a consuming passion for conundrums.

"All the difference in the world," replied the landlady.

"Yes, but what special difference?"

"I s'll have to give it up again. You'll think me a donkey's head, I'm afraid."

"Not likely. But just you consider now, wheer . . ."

The conundrum was still under weigh, when a girl entered. She was swarthy, a fine animal. After she had gone out:

"Do you know who that is?" asked the landlady.

"I can't say as I do," replied Radford.

"She's Frederick Pinnock's daughter, from Stony Ford. She's courting our Willy."

"And a fine lass, too."

"Yes, fine enough, as far as that goes. What sort of a wife'll she make him, think you?"

"You just let me consider a bit," said the man. He took out a pocket-book and a pencil. The landlady continued to talk to the other guests.

Radford was a big fellow, black-haired, with a brown moustache, and darkish blue eyes. His voice, naturally deep, was pitched in his throat, and had a peculiar, tenor quality, rather husky, and disturbing. He modulated it a good deal as he spoke, as men do who talk much with women. Always there was a certain indolence in his carriage.

"Our master's lazy," his wife said. "There's many a bit of a job wants doin', but get him to do it if you can."

But she knew he was merely indifferent to the little jobs, and not lazy.

He sat writing for about ten minutes, at the end of which time, he read:

"I see a fine girl full of life.

I see her just ready for wedlock,

But there's a jealousy between her eyebrows

And jealousy on her mouth.

I see trouble ahead.

Willy is delicate.

She would do him no good.

She would never see when he wasn't well,

She would only see what she wanted——"

So, in phrases, he got down his thoughts. He had to fumble for expression, and therefore anything serious he wanted to say he wrote in 'poetry', as he called it.

Presently, the landlady rose, saying:

"Well, I s'll have to be looking after our mester. I s'll be in again before we close."

Radford sat quite comfortably on. In a while, he too bade the company good night.

When he got home, at a quarter past eleven, his sons were in bed, and his wife sat awaiting him. She was a woman of medium height, fat, and sleek, a dumpling. Her black hair was parted smooth, her narrow-opened eyes were sly and satirical, she had a peculiar twang in her rather sleering voice.

"Our missis is a puss-puss," he said easily, of her. Her extraordinarily smooth, sleek face was remarkable. She was very healthy.

He never came in drunk. Having taken off his coat and his cap, he sat down to supper in his shirt-sleeves. Do as he might, she was fascinated by him. He had a strong neck, with the crisp hair growing low. Let her be angry as she would, yet she had a passion for that neck of his, particularly when she saw the great vein rib under the skin.

"I think, Missis," he said, "I'd rather ha'e a smite o' cheese than this meat."

"Well, can't you get it yourself?"

"Yi, surely I can," he said, and went out to the pantry.

"I think, if yer comin' in at this time of night, you can wait on yourself," she justified herself.

She moved uneasily in her chair. There were several jam-tarts alongside the cheese on the dish he brought.

"Yi, Missis, them tan-tafflins'll go down very nicely," he said.

"Oh, will they! Then you'd better help to pay for them," she said, amiably, but determined.

"Now what art after?"

"What am I after? Why, can't you think?" she said sarcastically.

"I'm not for thinkin', Missis."

"No, I know you're not. But wheer's my money? You've been paid the Union today. Wheer do I come in?"

"Tha's got money, an' tha mun use it."

"Thank yer. An' 'aven't you none, as well?"

"I hadna', not till we was paid, not a ha'p'ny."

"Then you ought to be ashamed of yourself to say so."

" 'Appen so."

"We'll go shares wi' th' Union money," she said. "That's nothing but what's right."

"We shonna. Tha's got plenty o' money as tha can use."

"Oh, all right," she said. "I will do."

B

She went to bed. It made her feel sharp that she could not get at him.

The next day, she was just as usual. But at eleven o'clock she took her purse and went up town. Trade was very slack. Men stood about in gangs, men were playing marbles everywhere in the streets. It was a sunny morning. Mrs. Radford went into the furnisher-and-upholsterer's shop.

"There's a few things," she said to Mr. Allcock, "as I'm wantin' for the house, and I might as well get them now, while the men's at home, and can shift me the furniture."

She put her fat purse on to the counter with a click. The man should know she was not wanting 'strap'. She bought linoleum for the kitchen, a new wringer, a breakfast-service, a spring mattress, and various other things, keeping a mere thirty shillings, which she tied in a corner of her handkerchief. In her purse was some loose silver.

Her husband was gardening in a desultory fashion when she got back home. The daffodils were out. The colts in the field at the end of the garden were tossing their velvety brown necks.

"Sithee here, Missis," called Radford, from the shed which stood halfway down the path. Two doves in a cage were cooing.

"What have you got?" asked the woman, as she approached. He held out to her in his big, earthy hand a tortoise. The reptile was very, very slowly issuing its head again to the warmth.

"He's wakkened up betimes," said Radford.

"He's like th' men, wakened up for a holiday," said the wife. Radford scratched the little beast's scaly head.

"We pleased to see him out," he said.

They had just finished dinner, when a man knocked at the door.

"From Allcock's!" he said.

The plump woman took up the clothes-basket containing the crockery she had bought.

"Whativer hast got theer?" asked her husband.

"We've been wantin' some breakfast-cups for ages, so I went up town an' got 'em this mornin'," she replied.

He watched her taking out the crockery.

"Hm!" he said. "Tha's been on th' spend, seemly."

Again there was a thud at the door. The man had put down a roll of linoleum. Mr. Radford went to look at it.

"They come rolling in?" he exclaimed.

"Who's grumbled more than you about the raggy oilcloth of this kitchen!" said the insidious, cat-like voice of the wife.

"It's all right, it's all right," said Radford.

The carter came up the entry with another roll, which he deposited with a grunt at the door.

"An' how much do you reckon this lot is?" he asked.

"Oh, they're all paid for, don't worry," replied the wife.

"Shall yer gi'e me a hand, Mester?" asked the carter.

Radford followed him down the entry, in his easy, slouching way. His wife went after. His waistcoat was hanging loose over his shirt. She watched his easy movement of well-being as she followed him, and she laughed to herself.

The carter took hold of one end of the wire mattress, dragged it forth.

"Well, this is a corker!" said Radford, as he received the burden.

"Now the mangle!" said the carter.

"What dost reckon tha's been up to, Missis?" asked the husband.

"I said to myself last wash-day, if I had to turn that mangle again, tha'd ha'e ter wash the clothes thyself."

Radford followed the carter down the entry again. In the street, women were standing watching, and dozens of men were lounging round the cart. One officiously helped with the wringer.

"Gi'e him thrippence," said Mrs. Radford.

"Gi'e 't thysen," replied her husband.

"I've no change under half-a-crown."

Radford tipped the carter, and returned indoors. He surveyed the array of crockery, linoleum, mattress, mangle, and other goods crowding the house and the yard.

"Well, this is a winder!" he repeated.

"We stood in need of 'em enough," she replied.

"I hope tha's got plenty more from wheer they came from," he replied dangerously.

"That's just what I haven't." She opened her purse. "Two half-crowns, that's every copper I've got i' th' world."

He stood very still as he looked.

"It's right," she said.

There was a certain smug sense of satisfaction about her. A wave of anger came over him, blinding him. But he waited and waited. Suddenly his arm leapt up, the fist clenched, and his eyes blazed at her. She shrank away, pale and frightened. But he dropped his fist to his side, turned, and went out, muttering. He went down to the shed that stood in the middle of the garden. There he picked up the tortoise, and stood with bent head, rubbing its horny head.

She stood hesitating, watching him. Her heart was heavy, and yet there was a curious, cat-like look of satisfaction round her eyes. Then she went indoors and gazed at her new cups admiringly.

The next week he handed her his half-sovereign without a word.

"You'll want some for yourself," she said, and she gave him a shilling. He accepted it.

CONRAD AIKEN

Fly Away Ladybird

Conrad Aiken is of course much better known for his poetry than for his prose, but the fact is that in the late 1920s and early 1930s he published three volumes of short stories—*Bring! Bring! and Other Stories* (1925), *Costumes by Eros* (1928), and *Among the Lost People* (1934). His short stories 'Mr. Arcularis' and 'Silent Snow, Secret Snow' and perhaps one or two others are well-known, but it was not until Duell, Sloan & Pearce published the collected *Short Stories of Conrad Aiken* in 1950 that his stature as a writer of short fiction was recognised.

Mr. Aiken, now sixty-nine, lives in Brewster, Mass., and *Twentieth Century Authors* points out the interesting fact that he was one of the members of the famous class of Harvard 1911, his classmates including T. S. Eliot, Van Wyck Brooks, John Reed, Heywood Broun, Robert Benchley, Alan Seeger, Robert Edmund Jones, and Walter Lippman. When we asked permission to use 'Fly Away Ladybird' Aiken was surprised that it wasn't in his collected short stories, and thought he must have just forgotten about it. It was published in *Esquire* for October 1934, and is reprinted here for the first time.

"Don't be melancholy, darling, I'm sure it will all come out all right."

"But how often have I got to tell you that I'm *not* melancholy? I'm not melancholy at all. I'm afraid you're old-fashioned. You just think I *ought* to be melancholy!"

"It's all these subterfuges, all this concealment. The way you had to go to the hospital under an assumed name. And signing a false name to the birth certificate. And now living here in this one-horse town! Good Lord."

She smiled at him, as if affectionately amused by her despair, took his arm, and they walked slowly, very slowly, up the little hill in the park. He kept his head lowered, as if thinking, and when he didn't respond to a repeated tug at his elbow, she brought her face so close to his that her forehead touched the rim of his hat.

"Besides," she said, "you're forgetting that the whole idea was mine. Wasn't it?"

"Oh, I know, but that has nothing to do with it. There's so much I want to do for you and Bibs, and can't. You oughtn't to be living here, buried away like this, and especially as I can only get here so seldom. No. And all the time I have the funniest feeling——"

"What?"

"Well, it makes me laugh sometimes. But I keep feeling that you and Bibs ought to be living with the rest of us."

"*That's* a bright idea. Your wife would be so glad, wouldn't she?"

"Gosh, yes. Just the same, if you ever saw the other kids——"

He stopped suddenly, and grinned at her.

"*That* would be all right. But suppose *she* saw *Bibs*! She'd know it in a flash."

They resumed the walk, very slowly, they passed under a maple tree, scarlet leaves had fallen on the path from the scarlet mass above them, and the sweet smoke came up to them from a smudge fire at the bottom of the hill. The delicious melancholy held them still for a moment. They stood under the tree and said nothing.

"That's for instance why it would be, I suppose, dangerous for you to live in New York. God knows New York's large enough, but if you ever *did* meet——"

"It's got to be postponed."

"And that's the sort of thing that makes me sick. This everlasting secrecy. Hole in corner."

"I told you in the beginning that I knew all about that and was prepared for it. Didn't I? And that I assumed full responsibility. It's my funeral, not yours."

"That's exactly what I'm afraid of, Enn——"

"Oh, I didn't mean *that*!"

"It's bound to be, at least in some respects. It isn't good for you. You haven't met a soul here. The minute you met people they'd begin to smell a rat. Mrs. Doane suspects already—I could see it this morning when I met her here with Bibs."

"Well, what did she do, did she bite you, or give you a dirty look?"

He didn't answer. He disengaged his arm, took out a cigarette and lit it; then flung the smoking match into a red privet bush. He was frowning. He thought how old it was that Enn could take the whole situation so calmly. He was even tempted to believe that she was somehow lacking—but lacking in what, he found it difficult to say. Morals? But there could be no question of that—the moral issue had never arisen, there was no such thing. If it was anything, it was something like delicacy. Or was it merely that she was sensible —more sensible than any woman he had ever met.

"O God, Enn, there are so many things. That awful dingy apartment of yours. And the neighbours watching you."

She took his arm again, and shook him, and laughed, her long grey eyes narrowing provocatively.

"Is that all? Is there something more?"

"Heaps. What about Bibs?"

"How do you mean, what about Bibs?"

"Well, she's four. She notices things. She knows when I spend the night there. That would be all right, if only——"

"What?"

"She knew I was her father."

She drew a deep sigh, looked away from him, said nothing. Then she pulled him closer, with her hand under his arm—so closely and so tenderly that to walk thus together, with their knees touching and disengaging, arm against arm and side against side, became difficult, and slow, and self-conscious, a delicious and awkward intimacy.

If only it could go on like this, if only it could always be like this. Their bodies seemed to be saying it, but their faces and minds were averted. He felt extraordinarily touched. It was tragic, it was beautiful.

"I sometimes wonder if you really feel it, Enn."

"Don't be a goose."

"But really, I do."

"You silly boy, we've been over it so often, haven't we? You must reconcile yourself that Bibs is mine. Not yours, mine. You agreed to that. I wanted her, not you."

"Oh, I know all that. It's a good theory."

They had come to the bench at the top of the hill. Below them the little river, with birches along the nearer margin, turned out of sight under the dilapidated wooden bridge. He remembered how they had come here before Bibs was born—he remembered the last time of all, when she had wanted to come up to see the sunset, and he had tried in vain to dissuade her, and they had climbed up so slowly, and she had turned so white. What was it she had said, something very funny. A quotation from somebody. Oh yes—"O to be oviparous, now that spring is here."

"Do you think Mrs. Doane is a good influence, Enn?"

She had sat down on the bench, her hands flat on the green wood, the fingers spread out fanwise.

"Of course. She's as good as gold. She adores Bibs."

"I know. But I don't like the slang."

"Oh, don't worry about the slang. Good heavens, if that was all!"

"What do you mean?"

"It's when I go down to New York to see you; when I'm away— all those weeks. When I come back, Bibs likes Mrs. Doane better than she does me. She always says she wants to stay with Boo. You know she calls her Boo."

He stood facing her, his head a little on one side, his cigarette lightly held between two fingers.

"And do you think that's good? Do you think it's so good?"

"Of course I don't think it's good. But what can we do? *Somebody's* got to look after her when I go away."

"But why not be sensible and give up your job, and let *me* swing it?"

Alternately, she slapped her hands on the bench, in a queer and mountingly mischievous rhythm, then clapped them together before her, wrung them at him, and laughed.

"The possessive male!"

"Possessive nonsense! It's simply a question of what's best for you and Bibs. This sort of thing is no good. It's sure to hurt you both."

She was still smiling, but as he watched her intently, her expression gradually became one of quizzical scrutiny. She looked up at him sidelong, as if making a careful appraisal.

"Are you sure you're being quite straight about this? You love Bibs and want her. You love me and want me. You don't want us to be independent. Do you?"

He turned his back and took a few steps towards the edge of the grass slope. At the bottom of the hill he could see a man emptying a basket of dead leaves on the smudge fire: the bright flames shot up for a moment into the basket as if licking away the last few morsels of the year. What Enn said was, of course, perfectly true. Or partly true. But that didn't really change it—not at all. He watched the man walk slowly along the path and drop the basket into a wheel-barrow. Yes, partly true—he did want to have them, to keep them. And why not? It seemed ridiculous that he shouldn't. They were—they ought to be—a part of his life.

Enn's voice floated towards him lightly—it gave him oddly, before he turned, the feeling that she was watching him very closely, very affectionately.

"Don't be melancholy, darling! It will all come out all right!" She was laughing at him, laughing at her use of his own words.

"Curse you, Enn—you never can be serious for five minutes on end." He said this as he walked back to the bench; he sat down beside her and dropped his hat on the grass. "What's going to happen to her when she goes to school—when she finds that other children have fathers, when they ask her who her father was? I suppose you'll have to tell her some damned fairy story about it. And then what about me? As she gets older, and sees me around—what's she going to think? She's no fool—believe me, she'll put two and two together and make it sex! And a hell of a lot of good *that* will do her. She'll end by hating me."

"Darling!"

He suddenly felt sorry for himself, he felt hurt and angry and stubborn, he wanted to be urged or comforted, and this feeling was only accentuated when she dropped her hand on his knee and lightly pinched him.

"No, Enn, it's no use."

"But darling! you forget there is such a thing as *time*. Lots can happen, lots *will* happen. All this is only a phase. When the time comes, I'll go to New York and get a job there. I'll adopt Bibs—she'll take my name, and it will be easy enough later to explain to her that I took her from an orphanage, or that nobody knew who her parents were. You'll see, it will be quite simple."

She said this unhurriedly, almost as if with no attempt to persuade —the effect upon him was to make him feel that she was, as always, overwhelmingly reasonable.

"Well, what about me—when she's older, she's sure to suspect. What about that?"

"I know, my dear. But there are other things to consider. It might be that you wouldn't any longer—be coming to see me. We might decide—for Bibs' sake—that it would be better if we separated. You might decide to give us up. Or fall in love with someone else. Or even, just decide to be a devoted father to your *own* children. After all, you *have* got them, and you do love them. It isn't as if you had nothing else. Or as if you need to begrudge me Bibs. Is it?"

"O good Lord!"

"We might as well be practical about it."

"Practical!"

He took out his leather cigarette-case, tapped a fresh cigarette repeatedly on the back of it, and lit it from the stub. Then with his forefinger he touched her hand, which still lay on his knee. She was smiling at him, but her eyes were grave, and he gave her a quick smile in answer.

"You ought to have been a lawyer, Enn. You're the most devilishly and unmitigatedly reasonable being I ever met. If I didn't know better, I'd say you had no heart."

"But you do know better, don't you . . . I'm sorry you've got to go back tonight."

"So am I."

They were both silent; a curious mutual awareness of peace came upon them, they watched the smoke from the smudge fire, which the breeze was idly sculpturing into a long blue curve over the river, over the tops of the birches. A policeman had stopped to talk to the man with the wheelbarrow. The sun was beginning to be low—he took out his watch. Four o'clock.

"Four o'clock. What time did you say——"

"I told her to bring Bibs here at half-past three. She must be late."

"She *is* late."

"Well, she probably won't be *very* late, because she has to go somewhere, she said, at half-past four. She was just to bring Bibs and go. Perhaps if we walk back—or would you rather stay here?"

"Let's walk."

They walked in silence, with linked arms, and as they turned the shoulder of the little hill, and saw the park below them, and Bibs running up the narrow path towards them, he began to feel for the first time the full force of what Enn had just been saying—(as usual) —with such extraordinary calm. Separation! Yes. It had been hanging over them for a long time, he had always known that sooner or later the shadow would begin to become substance; it was inevitable—or was it?—and now at last it had been spoken of. Very likely she had foreseen it from the outset—it was like her to foresee things, to plan things—she had known that sooner or later they must separate, and she had quite calmly decided to have Bibs, if only as an insurance against a bankruptcy which might otherwise have been complete. Yes. That was it. And now, as a consequence of the foresight itself, and as a consequence of Bibs, the separation, which she had merely foreseen as a possibility, was gradually becoming a necessity: Bibs, whom she had decided to have as a protection, must now be protected: cause had led to effect, and now effect was leading to cause. It was this—and he knew somehow that the same thoughts were in her mind, the same feelings—it was this that made her now tighten her hold on his arm, now as Bibs came running towards them, with her blue leggings and blue beret and a wilted stalk of blue chicory in her hand, tightly held. This—she was saying —is what you are losing, a part of yourself which you must lose. And Bibs, who seems to be running straight towards you, chattering and laughing to herself, making up one of her absurd and delicious stories, will not stop here, or greet you, but will pass by and go on, you will never see her again.

"And did you see the Christmas trees, all the Christmas trees, Mummy? They said how-do. I said how-do to them and they said how-do to me."

"But you haven't said how-do to Boyar."

"Will you give Boyar a big kiss?"

"No. Did you see the how-do trees, Boyar?"

"Yes, I saw the how-do trees."

When Mrs. Doane had gone, they counted the Christmas trees, and said how-do to them, and he took off his hat and shook one of them by the hand.

"And Boo says their fathers were little teeny tiny tiny *tiny* seeds, no bigger than—no bigger than a——"

"What?"

"No bigger than a *pumpkin*! An old grey pumpkin man with grey teeth and grey ears!"

"Did Boo say that?"

"Yes, Boo said that."

"And who was *your* father, Bibs? Was he a pumpkin man too?"

"Tell Boyar, blueberry."

The 'secret' expression came over her face; she stood still, she held the chicory flower before her, and gazed at it, smiling at her delicious and secret idea.

"No, he wasn't a pumpkin man. He was a—he was a—he was a——"

She began to squeal with delight, she was planning a joke, a surprise. And at once she announced triumphantly:

"He was a June-bug!"

"A June-bug! Are you sure? Why, Bibs!"

"Yes, he was a June-bug. And he flew and he flew and he flew and he flew and he flew!"

EZRA POUND

Reflexshuns on Iggurunce

'Reflexshuns on Iggurunce' was written within a few months of its publication in *Esquire* in January, 1935. It was one of a series of eight pieces Pound did for the magazine.

When he wrote this piece, Pound was living in Rapallo, on the Italian Riviera, to which he had moved from France in 1924. During the early years of the Depression he had become increasingly concerned with the evils of finance-capitalism and usury. In 'Reflexshuns on Iggurunce' Pound alludes rather murkily to these economic cure-alls. His preoccupation with usury ("Usury," he said, "and Sodomy the Church condemned as a pair, to one hell, the same for one reason— they are both against natural increases.") appears in many of his Cantos of this time:

> With usura, sin against nature,
> is thy bread ever more state rags
> is thy bread dry as paper,
> with no mountain wheat, no strong flour . . .
>
> *Canto XLV*

Finally Pound began to speak of himself as an economist rather than a poet. Then the Fascists in Italy convinced him that the Social Credit system in which he believed was not unlike their own ideas of the Corporate State, and Pound was led to support the Mussolini régime. He was arrested by American authorities on charges of treason in 1945. Later in this book Richard Rovere considers the political and historical problems in 'The Question of Ezra Pound'; and 'Reflexshuns on Iggurunce' should be read against the background of some such discussion. It is an example of the side of Pound that most interested Pound himself and most distressed his friends and countrymen.

THE REVEREND GINGRICH sez, sez he, that he can't explain why
my last piece is incomprehensible because he understands it perfectly
well.

The mind of that section of the present readers which isn't the
10,000 one hundred per cent highest possible type of reader who
understands EVERYTHING is still a dark forest to the present writer,
and E. E. Cummings tells me that when he was selling washing
machines he found the same difficulty in attaining complete com-
prehensibility.

Anybody who can understand a washing machine can understand economics by the same process; I mean so long as they keep
their eyes and minds on economics *or* the washing machine it OUGHT
to be easy, but nobody likes to do that.

I wish Mr. Hoff wd. help me. He has the pluperfect grasp on the
type of mind to which the great american public has for 40 years
entrusted its diplomacy and economics.

Take diplomacy. If ole pop gets drunk and signs a mortgage in
that condition, you think he hadn't orter have done it, but if Mr.
Woodrow Wilson was "so muzzy he couldn't find his notes", when
he was deciding the frontiers of Europe and the welfare of a few
million people, that's diplomacy.

In the old days Johnnie had to learn, sometimes, his geography.
But grown folks don't, I mean they don't if they're DIPLOMATS.

Some of the boys at Versailles saw 7 m, just like that 7 *m* on the
map. They'd heard about miles, but had never perhaps heard about
the metric decimal system. They thought the island was seven *miles*
from the shore, so there is a nice tidy little town, a nice tidy little
eyetalyan town on the other side of the Adriatic, looking like a chunk
chewed off of Venice, where they speak the venetian dialect, and a
nice bit of Jugoslav fort seven metres across the water, a channel like
a canal, boats can get through, bumping the sides now and then.

All the town is full of great grandmama's heirlooms, just as if my
Gaudiers and my Max Ernst seascape were hung up where Bugs
Moran cd. toy about with gangland vendetta. Seems the Jugoslavs
don't like any art done before the year 1500, so they occasionally
chip off a lion, with Mr. Schneider and the Baron de Wendel, and
all the blokes whom Senator Nye is lookin' into, trying like hell to
sell guns.

That's diplomacy. Some diplomatic appointments are mysterious. I mean if a man isn't sent over to represent Mr. Morgan, or
the Standard Oil or for some really normal reason, one sometimes
wonders why the government sent him. The first time I wondered
was when that flat-chested dripping slabside of codfish W. Hines
Page told me he hadn't any "instructions from Washington".
Fordie (Ford Madox Ford, Hueffer that was) had put on a high hat,
I mean a real silk-covered stove pipe, and we went down to the
Embassy, because Harry Kemp hadn't paid for his ticket. He said
he wanted some English culture and just came over to look at it.
And somebody put him in jail.

I told Page the boy had a praise-worthy curiosity and that so few
young writers wanted to learn anything, that Mr. Page better have
him let out.

Mr. Page said he represented the government and not the people,
and that he couldn't act without instructions from Washington.
The old geek had been a publisher, so this conception of im-
possibility came natural.

Ford looked at him with the sort of a look a man carrying a high
hat would use in looking at a fish that had been dead much too long.
When he got to the street he said something unfavourable to
diplomacy. He said British Diplomats sometimes weren't all that
they might be, he said that an English Ambassador mightn't have
done much, but that damn it he wd. have done more than that. So
we went to see a British Cabinet Minister and the British Home
Office let Mr. Kemp out without our having to use any more
diplomacy. I mean they grasped the idea that Kemp ought to be
allowed to look around a bit.

This may not prove anything. It merely joggled my childish impressions of a jolly old bird swinging his cane along the Quais in
Naples, or of a conversation I had heard over a partition 28 years
ago as to how the Embassy could get Mrs. Kiwogglebat into
Alfonso XIIIth's wedding ball without inviting her husband.

I 'spose they did it by the old and now ill-reputed secret diplomacy. Neither the Ambassador nor his leading attaché suggested that
it *couldn't* be done.

That's where the old diplomacy or statesmanship differed from
banking and economics.

The 10,000 readers of the highest possible type will please note that I am trying to live up to the estimate of a young Harvard man who said I was the old geezer who seemed to tell 'em what living in Yourup is like.

There was a message came into the office, were they in a position to notice it, because it was very curious that out of the Embassy window he could see three moons quite distinctly. That was a very popular Ambassador, and I never heard he signed any treaties after midnight, or by the light of three moons. This is not an 'indignation article'; I don't want to spoil any diplomat's fun. But the old world point of view is that an ambassador pulls more weight if he segregates business and booziness.

I am trying to write about iggurunce. It was suggested I write about Mr. Hemingway too, but Hem ain't nearly iggurunt enough for my purpose, not nearly as iggurunt as economics professors and delegates representing the government. It is the democratic method of getting REPRESENTED that I am trying to fathom. A lady wrote me that my economics was wrong because I disagreed with her husband and "Economics was Elmer's subject".

Being a 'subject' in that sentence meant that Elmer had been to college and his professors had TOLD him. He went on years later believing what his teachers had told him.

A professor in the London School of Economics wrote me, "It *can* but it will get into a mess." His letter is dated the 18th of September, 1934. So I suppose that's official British Economics almost up to date.

That is obscure. Hell, I admit it is obscure as it stands and I am willing to go back and explain why the prof said it.

I am an inquisitive cuss. I wanted to know, and I still want to know what a lot of self-styled and professional and very verbose blokes think about economics and money (economics is something to do with MONEY). I wanted to know what a lot of blokes thought about MONEY. What IS money?

I printed a list of questions. I asked a wop, and he printed some of my questions in Turin; the *Morning Post* took off its high hat and printed half a column in London. A bloke in Lausanne wrote down to Gino and some bloke had printed the lot in a Spanish paper, in Madrid where Hem goes to bull fights. (*El Sol.* de Madrid. 26th August.)

I said: a country can have ONE currency for internal use and another good both for internal—no, hold on, I didn't make that mistake. I was careful of my langwidg: I didn't say 'internal and external' use, like a cough lotion that's good for burns. I said "and another good both for home and foreign use". I'd have done better to say 'one good inside the country' the other 'good both inside the country and outside it'.

Anyhow the idea was clear. The prof started by sending me three funny postcards, one with a squeaker inside like a doll's.

Then he wrote me a fourteen page letter (seven sheets, long hand written on both sides, in neat highbrow professional hand writin' and containing the gem of wisdom, "It *can*, but it will get into a mess".)

He'd had his chance? When he wrote me the postcards, I wrote him patient and perlite to LOOK at the goddamn' money he was using during his vacation (he was on vacation in France). I don't know if he did it.

France has had two kinds of money for 15 years and they never confused the most dumb and damnblasted frog-eater, and of all the complainers I heard in Jimmy Charters' bar I never heard ANY of 'em complain about the coin being issued by the United French Chambers of Commerce. So I still don't see why it's a mess.

Economics was that fellow's 'subject' but he was not his nation's choice to REPRESENT 'em at the International Economic Congress. He never was, so far as I know, a delegate sent off to decide the fate of his country and her relations with other great powers. He was just another of these blokes, like Tugwell, and Moley, and Sec. Wallace. I mean economics was . . . an' so on . . . his subject.

So a DELEGATE asks me if I can ASK him "any REAL questions" and I sent him the same little slip (costs nearly ten cents a letter, with Mr. Morgenthau's new cutie dollar).

He answers me (thank god, using a typewriter):

"3. Yes, it can. And so can a man use a regular thermometer for taking his temperature, and one of his own devising for taking the temperature of a room. If he does, he creates additional complications".

That's the way a speciman delegate thinks. First he gets a fancy analogy. Second he fails to know what has been going on in the world outside his own office, and thirdly he commits what the logic teachers call a nonsequitur, or a statement of what don't *necessarily* follow.

That's why the New Deal takes so long. The last few words are a quotation. A lovely lady once said to me long ago in a very tired voice, "I have just been lunching with six generals. Now I know why the Boer War took so long."

E. E. CUMMINGS

Exit the Boob

E. E. Cummings, poet, painter, novelist, playwright, essayist, and reviewer, stated his credo early in the game:

> I would
> suggest that certain ideas gestures
> rhymes, like Gillette Razor Blades
> having been used and reused
> to the mystical moment of dullness emphatically are
> Not To Be Resharpened

Throughout his career in the world of letters Cummings has gone
his own way. Enlisting in an American ambulance corps in the First
World War, he was by mistake arrested and placed for several months
in a French prison. Out of this experience came his first book, *The
Enormous Room*. In 1931 he made a trip to Russia and subsequently
published *Eimi*, a journal of his experiences and impressions, most of
which were frankly hostile. ("I'd just as soon be imprisoned in freedom
as free in a jail.") He was labelled a Fascist by many of the literati of
the time.

Cummings' poetry, too, is a reflection of his intransigence. Adhering
to no strict typographical rules, ignoring punctuation and spelling
rules, he has continued to publish his poems in the literary magazines
for close on forty years.

In the autumn of 1952, Cummings began the first of six lectures (which
he, remaining in character, called *six nonlectures*) at Harvard as the
Charles Eliot Norton Poet in residence. In them are contained many
of the attitudes and ideas expressed eighteen years earlier in the June
1935 issue of *Esquire*: his hostility toward conformity, his thoughts on
advertising clichés, and his passionate attack on the vast conspiracy in
America to convince people to 'belong'.

MORE THAN A GREAT MANY simple folks, for some none too obscure reason, know that they know what's good for you and me. Royally basking in his painfully acquired ignorance of whatever makes life livable, this 'share the wealth' prophet butters platitudes for an invisible and immeasurable audience endowed with a simplicity so perfectly prehistoric as to be positively mythical. Quote every man a king unquote. Meanwhile a visible number of merely simplest folks surround that anonymous hater of human values who, busily raving under the peaceful stars, tells mankind just why it must come unto Doctor Marx to be goosed with a 'class struggle'. Pants-pressers of the world, unite! you have nothing to lose but your pants. Etcetera, ad infinitum: yet (oddly enough) humanity survives. Individualism flourishes. Millions upon millions of men and women have toothaches. Thousands upon thousands of authentic sadists hope that (as one of them tactlessly assured myself) "some day I'll be in the mouths of the best people".

What ample zest! What copious verve! What abundant enthusiasm! What boundless bonhommerie! It's actually hard to imagine that there really was a time when everything wasn't known to be known and everybody didn't know that they knew it. But science says that a time there was; and science is an honourable man. A time there was when even the most omnipotent emperor didn't know that he knew and he never could know that he had B. O.— and can't you imagine his ill-starred consort, mounting her dazzling throne with a hideous case of Morning Mouth? Sure an' 'tis a merciful miracle our mysterious mothers and fabulous fathers got themselves born at all at all. Hail, hail, the civilisation's all here . . . although one rather suspects that something must be not far from wrong when every punk can't automatically become Albert Lincoln or Abraham Einstein, merely by letting a button press itself or (if there must be such a thing as imperfection) by throwing a switch: am I right? Wouldn't a ducky invention like that simplify the whole horrid complicated unemployment problem rather nicely? Answer me, you twenty-five hundred dollar a week apotheosis of cinematographic idiocy. Or (if you prefer) just try to lift those already lifted eyebrows. Hoot, lass, 'tis not a Nude Eel in my sporran either way.

Note that the stalwart champion of Civilisation, the dulcet handmaid of Progress, the omnipotent Genie of the uncorked Unknown—science—has succeeded in shrinking our so-called world until it doesn't fit anybody. But there's something stranger still: the fact that any number of simple folks, no matter how mutually antagonistic they may seem to you and me, can (and do) inhabit one and the same microscopic blunder—the blunder of 'thinking' that 'people' can be 'improved'. Believe it or not, each of these cranks knows that each of them knows that he, she or it has the absolutely only authentic dope on how to better its, her or his so-called neighbour. Well and bad: but as long as that neighbour equals X, Y probably doesn't mind; and as long as it doesn't equal X, X possibly doesn't mind. Nobody really minds perhaps, until that neighbour becomes XY——

Did you ever share an otherwise palatial dungheap with much too many other vividly stinking human beings? Did you ever (attired in all the majesty of a wilted monkey, with sixty-odd pounds of erroneously distributed junk banging your coccyx) go foolishly limping and funnily hobbling up and down a river of feebly melting tar entitled 'company street'? Did you, accidentally, ever exchange your hard-earned right to visit freedom for the doubtful privilege of policing latrines; just because you'd failed—as a warrior can't and mayn't—to grunt loudly at the exact moment when those real hands of yours stuck that real bayonet of Uncle Sam's into an imaginary fellowman? Ah, the ecstasy of it all! And the rapturous ritual of standing in line (here, by the by, we can use what writers who know that they know call 'a blazing sun') waiting and waiting and waiting and waiting to partially submerge one slipperiest plate in one stickiest kettle of lukewarm once upon a time water, through which meander lazily something like two hundred remains of something which somebody said was supposed to have once upon a time been tapioca pudding . . .

Well, anyhow—the so-called fascist styles for a not too distant future look simply fascinating. Off with your earmuffs, ladies fair, and hear what your well-dressed man will wear. And you, upstanding nonpareil of American masculinity, lend me your auditory appendages. You will wear (sic) mud and you will wear gas and at least three kinds of lice and you will wear terror and agony and hatred and digust and shrapnel and (without knowing it) a funny

little foolish little feeble little fairylike grinless grin. Yes indeedy.
Big though you be, big boy, you'll carry that tiny faggoty feeble
foolish funny thingless thing wherever you go—all the while
never so much as suspecting you've quietly turned into somebody
else.

"Who in hell is this s. o. b. to tell me what I'll do?" an outraged
sample of the more widely circulated brand of intellectual snob
cordially inquires.

Now let said outraged sample keep his shirt on; if he thinks we
despise fighting, he's agreeably mistaken. We don't. But neither do
we ignore the obvious and incredible fact that, if individuals are
organisms, multitudes are mechanisms. Courage we consider
whatever is most important on earth; and multitudes do not have
courage. A 'soldier' who prefers going over the top to being shot in
the back by his superior officer is not a man. A man is an entirety,
not a fraction of something. A man has courage.

As for who ourselves are: we honestly feel that they couldn't be
trusted to furnish the outraged sample with a correct answer—not
that he wants a correct answer; far from it. What he wants is a
simpler answer, which happens to be completely different. The
business of a correct answer is to ask a question. The business of a
simple answer is the business of a machine-gun bullet: to know that
it knows.

I do not know that I know—I merely feel deeply—that your
correspondent is no mechanism. He is not a 'nasty' and he is not a
'red' and he is not a 'jingo' and he is not a 'pacifist' and he is not a
'solar engine' and he is not any other form of simple answer. He is
alive. What is more, he enjoys nothing so much as being alive. What
is most, he would not (so far as an ignorant bloke like him can guess)
willingly exchange the worst spontaneous complexity of life for the
best premeditated simplicity of something else. Artists are odd, that
way. In the immortal words of no less modest a specimen of complexity than the Polish artist Marcoussis "we are living in an
Apocalypse. It is necessary to be very intelligent". Certainly not
quite oddly enough, a very great many prophets, cranks, busy-
bodies, snobs, opportunists, simple folks (and other nonartists) do
not know that they do not know precisely what the word Apocalypse
means.

By God, a good dictionary ought to get up on its hind legs and tell them, sometime.

Just a moment (interrupts somebody whom, for the sake of brevity, we'll call Z). I heartily disapprove of cranks (Z comfortingly continues) but there's something of which I disapprove even more heartily; and that's a supercrank. What do I mean by a super-crank? I mean the world's only extant Total Loss: The Art For Art's Sake guy. At least cranks care enough about their fellow men to try to influence them. Not so your Artist With A Capital A. O no: He lives in an Ivory Tower; and He sings hymns to Abstract Beauty; and He doesn't give a hoot in Hell if the whole human race goes to the dogs. He expects mere human beings to appreciate His 'genius'. Absolutely: and He wonders why out-and-out honest-to-God Flesh-and-blood men and women, who don't shirk their responsibilities to the community and who'd rather drop dead than lead the parasitic existence which He idolises, somehow can't afford to waste their meagre leisure pulling three or four stale ideas out of several tons of affected gibberish which He, forsooth, calls His 'work'! See what I'm driving at? Huh? Get the illusion? Speak up!

I think you mean 'allusion', my friend; but let that pass. You apparently dislike snobs; so do I. And of snobs there are many varieties.

Only the other day, for instance, I was talking to a variety of snob which might fairly be called the supersnob. Listen (I said to this supersnob) here's a coin, called a 'nickel'; it has two sides, 'heads' and 'tails'. And if I did flip it, the question would be: 'heads' or 'tails'? If, on the other hand, I felt like taking the El to 125th Street, the question would be, not 'heads' or 'tails', but is it a 'nickel' or isn't it? Very well. Now for a metaphor: there is a coin called 'dictatorship'; it has two sides, 'fascism' and 'communism'. If you're a guy who thinks he's lucky, you get all excited over the question: which side up will 'dictatorship' land—shall we have 'communism' or 'fascism'? If, however, you're a man who wants to get somewhere—and if 'dictatorship' is your last coin—and if you find that 'dictatorship' fails to produce the desired result, that it hasn't the value it claims to have, that it simply doesn't turn the trick, that (in short) it's a dud—then what do you do? You grin, baby, and you walk. That's what I said to the supersnob. And he answered: but it might rain.

Fortunately, there still exist persons for whom living means something more complex than keeping out of the rain. Some of these backward, unscientific, possibly even idiotic, persons are artists; the vast majority are not. None of these insufficiently mechanised monsters can possibly be called snobs or supersnobs or Ivory Tower lads. Maybe these pitifully outmoded reactionaries, who haven't forgotten what feet are for, constitute 'forgotten men'; I wouldn't know that I knew. One of them, in Biblical parlance, is my neighbour. He resides near me, in a town called Silver Lake, in the state of New Hampshire; and his incomparable name is actually Mike Frost.

Now, ladies and gents, having handed the so-called institution of modern warfare some dirty cracks, I shall (with your permission) allow Mike Frost to lay a sweet bouquet upon the so-called altar of freedom. Listen——

Mike Frost is no slouch. By which I mean that, if he fought the recent war (alias the great war, alias the war to end wars) on his so-called native heath, it was Uncle Sam's fault for not getting Mike Frost any farther away from Silver Lake, New Hampshire, than Portsmouth, New Hampshire—which was nevertheless a Big Change. Mike Frost, alias my neighbour, was grateful to Uncle Sam for the Big Change. What is more, Mike Frost enjoyed every inch of the War With A Capital A. What is most, that well nigh fatal crusade to end all attempts to make this so-called world safe for anything whatever—by furnishing my neighbour, Mike Frost, with such otherwise unattainable complexities as Travel and Irresponsibility—equals unto this very hour the biggest, if not the only, so-called thing in the so-called life of a so-called human being.

Verbum sap.

THOMAS WOLFE

<hr>

Arnold Pentland

When Thomas Wolfe died in September 1938, he had published two major novels, *Look Homeward, Angel* and *Of Time and the River*. Out of the chest-high pile of manuscript left, his final editor, Edward C. Aswell, carved two more big novels, *The Web and the Rock* and *You Can't Go Home Again*. Wolfe's short story, 'The Hollow Men' (*Esquire*, October 1940), was part of that material; it is the major part of Chapter 29 of *You Can't Go Home Again*.

In 1943 Aswell published *The Hills Beyond*, a final posthumous collection of Wolfe's stories and sketches. 'Arnold Pentland' was included, under the title 'A Kinsman of His Blood'. Aswell said it was "written in 1934 or 1935. It fits, obviously, into *Of Time and the River*. It was either cut from that manuscript or is an example of something Tom had to go back and write when he realised too late that he had left it out of the book in which it belonged." *Esquire* had published the story in June 1935, introducing Arnold Pentland as a hitherto unknown member of Eugene Gant's family, Wolfe's own family, whose story he had told in his first two novels.

Much later, Aswell released for publication Wolfe's early, full-length play, *Welcome to Our City*, which appeared in *Esquire* in October 1957.

<hr>

FROM TIME TO TIME, during his Sunday visits to his Uncle Bascom's house, Eugene would meet his cousin, Arnold Pentland. Arnold was the only one of Bascom's children who ever visited his father's house: the rest were studiously absent, saw their father only at Christmas or Thanksgiving, and then like soldiers who will make a kind of truce upon the morning of the Lord's nativity. And certainly the only reason that poor tormented Arnold ever came to Bascom's house was not for any love he bore him—for their relation to each other was savage and hostile as it had been since Arnold's childhood —but rather, he came through loneliness and terror, as a child comes home, to see his mother, to try to find some comfort with her if he could.

Even in the frequency of these visits, the dissonant quality of his life was evident. After months of absence he would appear suddenly, morosely, without a word of explanation, and then he would come back every Sunday for several weeks. Then he would disappear again, as suddenly as he came: for several months, sometimes for a year or more, none of them would see him. The dense and ancient web of Boston would repossess him—he would be engulfed in oblivion as completely as if the earth had swallowed him. Then after months of silence, he would again be heard from: his family would begin to receive postal cards from him, of which the meaning was often so confused that nothing was plain save that the furious resentment that sweltered in him against them was again at work. Thus, in the same day, Bascom, his daughters, and his other son might all receive cards bearing a few splintered words that read somewhat as follows:

"Have changed my name to Arthur Penn. *Do not try to find me, it is useless!* You have made an outcast out of me—now I only want to forget that I ever knew you, have the same blood in my veins. *You have brought this on yourselves—I hope I shall never see your faces again!* Arthur Penn."

After this explosion they would hear nothing from him for months. Then one day he would reappear without a word of explanation, and for several weeks would put in a morose appearance every Sunday.

Eugene had met him first one Sunday afternoon in February at his uncle's house; Arnold was sprawled out on a sofa as he entered, and his mother approaching him, spoke to him in the tender, almost pleading tone of a woman who is conscious of some past negligence in her treatment of her child and who is now, pitiably too late, trying to remedy it.

"Arnold," she said coaxingly, "Arnold—will you get up now, please, dear—this is your cousin—won't you say hello to him?"

The great fat obscenity of belly on the sofa stirred, the man got up abruptly and blurting out something desperate and incoherent, thrust out a soft, grimy hand and turned away. Arnold Pentland was a man of thirty-six. He could have been rather small of limb and figure had it not been for his great soft shapeless fatness—a fatness pale and grimy that suggested animal surfeits of unwholesome food. He had lank, greasy hair of black, carelessly parted in the middle, his face, like all the rest of him, was pale and soft, the features blurred by fatness and further disfigured by a greasy smudge of beard. And from this fat, pale face his eyes, brown and weak, looked out on the world with a hysterical shyness of retreat, his mouth trembled uncertainly with a movement that seemed always on the verge of laughter or hysteria, and his voice gagged, worked, stuttered incoherently, or wrenched out desperate shocking phrases with an effort that was almost as painful as the speech of a paralytic.

His clothing was indescribably dirty. He wore a suit of old blue serge, completely shapeless, and shiny with the use of years, and spotted with the droppings of a thousand meals. Half the buttons were burst off the vest, and between vest and trousers there was a six inch hiatus of dirty shirt and mountainous fat belly. His shoes were so worn that his naked toes showed through, and his socks were barely more than rags, exposing his dirty heels every time he took a step. The whole creature was as grievously broken, dissonant, and exploded as it is possible for a human life to be, and all the time his soft brown eyes looked out with the startled, pleading look of a stricken animal.

It was impossible to remain with him without a painful feeling of embarrassment—a desire to turn away from this pitiable exposure of disintegration. Everyone felt this but his father; as for Bascom, he just dismissed the conduct of his son impatiently, snorting down his nose derisively, or turning away as one would turn away from the gibberings of an idiot.

Dinner that day—the Sunday of Eugene's first meeting with his cousin—was an agonising experience for everyone save Bascom. Arnold's conduct of his food was a bestial performance; he fell upon it ravenously, tearing at it, drawing it in with a slobbering suction, panting, grunting over it like an animal until layers of perspiration stood out on his pale wide forehead. Meanwhile, his mother was making a pitiable effort to distract attention from this painful performance; with a mask of attempted gaiety she tried to talk to her nephew about a dozen things—the news of the day, the latest researches in 'psychology', the base conduct of the Senate 'unreconcilables', or the researches of Professor Einstein, the wonder-working miracle of the human mind. At which Arnold, looking up and glaring defiantly at both of them, would suddenly explode into a jargon of startling noises that was even more shocking than his bestial ruminations over food:

"M-m-m-man at Harvard . . . fourteen languages . . . A guh-guh-guh-guh——" he paused and glared at his mother with a look of desperate defiance while she smiled pitiable encouragement at him—"A gorilla," he marched it out at last triumphantly. "Can't speak one!" and he paused again, his mouth trembling, his throat working convulsively, and then burst out again—"put gorilla cage with man . . . all over! . . . done for! . . . half a minute!" He snapped his fingers. "Gorilla make mince meat of him . . . Homer . . . Dante . . . Milton . . . Newton . . . Laws of Gravity. . . . Muh-muh-muh-muh——" again he gagged, craned his fat neck desperately along the edges of his dirty collar and burst out— "Mind of man! . . . Yet when dead—nothing! . . . No good! . . . Seven ten-penny nails worth more!" He paused, glaring, his throat working desperately again, and at length barked forth with triumphant concision, "Brisbane!" and was still.

"Ah-h!" Bascom muttered at this point, and, his features contorted in an expression of disgust, he pushed his chair back, and turned half away—"What is he talk-ing about, anyway! . . . Gorillas—Harvard—Fourteen languages." Here he laughed sneeringly down his nose. "Phuh! Phuh! Phuh! Phuh! Phuh! . . . Homer—Dante—Newton—seven ten-penny nails—Brisbane! . . . Phuh! Phug! Phuh! Phuh! Phuh! . . . Did anyone ever hear such stuff since time began!" And contorting his powerful features he laughed sneeringly down his nose again.

"Yes!" cried Arnold angrily, throwing down his napkin and glaring at his father with wild resentful eyes, shot suddenly with tears—"And you, too! . . . No match for guh-guh-guh-guh-*gorilla!*" he yelled. "Think you are! . . . Egotist! . . . Muh-muh-

muh——" he paused, gagging, worked his neck along his greasy collar and burst out—"Megalomaniac! . . . Always were! . . . But no match gorilla . . . get you!"

"Ah-h!" Bascom muttered, confiding his eloquent features into vacancy with an expression of powerful disgust—"You don't know what you're talk-ing about! . . . He has no conception—oh, not the slightest!—not the faintest!—none whatever!" he howled, waving his great hand through the air with a gesture of scornful dismissal——

The next Sunday, when Eugene had gone to Bascom's house, he was surprised when the old man himself came to the door and opened it. In response to the boy's quick inquiry about his aunt, Bascom, puckering his face in a gesture of disgust, and jerking his head towards the kitchen, muttered:

"Ah-h! She's in there talking to that—fool! . . . But come in, my boy!" he howled, with an instant change to cordiality. "Come in, come in, come in!" he yelled enthusiastically. "We've been expecting you."

From the kitchen came the sound of voices—a woman's and a man's at first low, urgent, blurred, then growing louder; and suddenly he could hear Arnold's voice, the wrenched-out, desperate speech now passionately excited:

"Got to! . . . I tell you, mother, I've got to! . . . She needs me . . . and I've got to go!"

"But, Arnold, Arnold!" his mother's voice was tenderly persuasive and entreating. "Now quiet, dear, quiet! Can't you quiet yourself a moment while we talk about it?"

"Nothing to talk about!" his voice wrenched the words out desperately. "You've seen the letters, mother. . . . You see what she says, don't you?" his voice rose to a hysterical scream.

"Yes, dear, but——"

"Then what is there to talk about?" he cried frantically. . . . "Don't you see she wants me? . . . Don't you see she's in some terrible trouble with that—that brute . . . that she's begging me to come and take her away from him?"

"Oh, Arnold, Arnold!" his mother's voice was filled with pitiable entreaty, hushed with an infinite regret. "My poor boy, can't you see that all she says is that if you ever go out there she would be glad to see you." He made some blurted out reply that was indecipherable and then, speaking gently but incisively, she continued, "Arnold:— listen to me, my dear. This woman is a married woman, twenty years older than yourself, with grown children of her own. . . . Don't you understand, my dear, that those letters are just the friendly letters that a woman would write to a boy she once taught in school? Don't you see how much these letters you have written her have frightened her—how she is trying in a kind way to let you know——"

"It's a lie!" he said in a choking tone—"a dirty lie! You're against me like all the rest of them! I'll not listen to you any longer! I'll go and get her—I'll bring her back with me, no matter what you say— and to hell with you!" he yelled. "To hell with all of you!"

There was a sound of scrambling confusion, and then he came flying through the swinging door that led into the kitchen, jamming his battered hat down on his head, his eyes wild with grief and anger, his lips trembling and convulsed, murmuring soundless imprecations as he fled. And his mother followed him, a small wren-like figure of a woman, her face haggard, stamped with grief and pity, calling, "Arnold! Arnold!" desperately to that fat untidy figure that went past like a creature whipped with furies, never pausing to look or speak or say good-bye to anyone, as he ran across the room, and left the house, slamming the door behind him.

The story, with its wretched delusion, was pitiable enough. Since his second year at high school, Arnold had cherished a deep affection for a woman who had taught him at that time. She was one of the few women who had ever shown a scrap of understanding for him, and her interest had been just the kindly interest that a warm-hearted and intelligent woman might feel for a wretched little boy. To her, as to everyone else, he had been an ugly duckling, but this had wakened her protective instinct, and actually made him dearer to her than the more attractive children. And because of this she had taught him more—done more for him—than any other person he had even known, and he had never forgotten her.

When Arnold had left school, this woman had married and moved to California with her husband. But in the twenty years that had elapsed since then her old friendship with the boy—for 'boy' he still was to her—had never been broken. During all that time Arnold had written her several times a year—long rambling letters filled with his plans, despairs, ambitions, hopes and failures; the incoherent record of an incoherent personality—and the woman had always answered him with short, brisk, friendly letters of her own.

And during all these years, while he remained to her the 'boy' that she had taught, her own personality was undergoing a fantastic transformation in his memory. Although she had been a mature and rather spinsterly female when he had known her, and was now a grey-haired woman in the upper fifties, it seemed to him now that she had never been anything but young and beautiful and fair.

And as that picture developed in his mind it seemed to him that he had always loved her—as a man would love a woman—and that the only possible meaning in these casual and friendly letters that she wrote to him, lay in the love she bore for him.

Nothing could be done to stop him. For months now he had come to his mother with trembling haste each time that he received one of the letters. He would read them in a trembly voice, finding in the most casual phrases the declarations of a buried love. And his own replies to these friendly notes had become steadily more ardent and intimate until, at last, they had become the passionate and hysterical professions of a man in love. The effect of this correspondence on the woman was evident—evident to everyone but Arnold himself. At first, her replies had been written in the same friendly tone that had always characterised her notes to him, but a growing uneasiness was apparent. It was evident that in a kindly way she was trying to check this rising tide of passion, divert his emotion into the old channel of fellowship. Then, as his letters increased in the urgent ardour of their profession, her own had grown steadily more impersonal; the last, in answer to his declaration that he "must see her and would come at once", was decidedly curt. It expressed her cold regret that such a visit as he proposed would be impossible—that she and her family would be "away for the summer"—told him that the journey to California would be long, costly, and unpleasant, and advised him to seek his summer's recreation in some more agreeable and less expensive way.

Even the chilling tenor of this letter failed to quench him. Instead, he 'read between the lines', he insisted on finding in these curt phrases the silent eloquence of love, and though months had passed since this last letter, and he had written many ardent times since then, he was even convinced that her protracted silence was just another sign of her love—that she was being suppressed through fear, that she was held in bitter constraint by that tyrannical 'brute', her husband—a man of whom he knew nothing, but for whom he had conceived a murderous hatred.

Thus, against all the persuasions of his mother he had decided to go. And that day when he had fled out of his father's house with bitter imprecations on his lips had marked the final moment of decision. Nothing could be done to stop him, and he went.

He was gone perhaps a month; no one knew exactly how long he was away, for none of his family saw him for about a year. And what the result of that strange meeting may have been, they never heard—and yet never needed to be told.

From that moment on he was completely lost to them; the legend of that last defeat, the ruin of that final and impossible hope was written on him, inscribed on his heart and living in his eyes in letters of unspeakable terror, madness, and despair.

One night in April when Eugene had been prowling around the dark and grimy streets of the South Boston slums he saw a familiar figure in lower Washington Street. It was his cousin, Arnold Pentland. A fine spring rain had been falling all night long, and below the elevated structure the pavements were wet and glistening. Arnold was standing at a corner, looking around with a quick distracted glance, clutching a tattered bundle of old newspapers under one arm.

Eugene ran across the street, calling to him, "Arnold! Arnold!" The man did not seem to hear at first, then looked around him in a startled way and at last, as Eugene approached him, calling him by name again, he shrank together and drew back, clutching his bundle of old papers before him with both hands and looking at his cousin with the terror-stricken eyes of a child who has suddenly been attacked.

"Arnold!" the other cried again. "*Arnold!* Don't you know me? . . . I'm your cousin—Eugene!" And as he made another step towards the man, his hand outstretched in greeting. Arnold scrambled back with such violent terror that he almost fell and then, still holding the bundle of old papers before him protectively, stammered:

"Duh—duh—duh—don't know you. . . . Some mistake!"

"Oh, there's no mistake!" the boy cried impatiently. "You know me! . . . I've met you a dozen times at Uncle Bascom's house. . . . Look here, Arnold——" he took off his own hat so that the man could better see his face—"You know me now, don't you?"

"No!—no!" Arnold gasped, moving away all the time. "Wrong man. . . . Name's not Arnold!"

The other stared at him a moment in blank astonishment and then exploded:

"Not Arnold! Of course, it's Arnold! Your name's Arnold Pentland, and you're my first cousin. Look here, Arnold, what the hell is this anyway? What are you trying to do?"

"No! . . . No! . . . Mistake, I tell you. . . . Don't know you! Name's not Arnold. . . . Name's Arthur Penn."

"I don't give a damn what you call yourself!" Eugene now cried angrily. "You're Arnold Pentland just the same, and you're not going to get away from me until you admit it! Look here! What kind of trick is this anyway? What are you trying to pull on me?"— and in his excitement he took the man by his arm and shook him.

Arnold uttered a long wailing cry of terror and wrenching free struggled backward crying:

"You leave me alone now! . . . All of you leave me alone! . . . I never want to see any of you again!"

And turning he began to run blindly and heavily away, a grotesque and pitiable figure, clutching his bundle of sodden newspapers, bent over toward the rain.

Eugene watched him go with a feeling of nameless pity, loneliness, and loss—the feeling of a man who for a moment in the huge un-numbered wilderness of life, the roaring jungle of America, sees a face he knows, a kinsman of his blood, and says farewell to him for ever. For that moment's vision of that fat, stumbling figure running blindly away from him down a dark wet street was the last he would ever have. He never saw the man again.

JOHN DOS PASSOS

The Celebrity

Esquire was originally started as a quarterly, but the first issue was such a success that it was immediately changed to a monthly. Along with Ernest Hemingway, Nicholas Murray Butler, Gilbert Seldes, Ring Lardner, Jr., William McFee, Erskine Caldwell, George Ade, and a swarm of other celebrated names, John Dos Passos contributed to this first issue, Autumn 1933. Under the title, 'Back Home in 1919', he published the first Charley Anderson section from *The Big Money*, the last novel in his trilogy, *U.S.A.* It was the first of many portions of this book that would see advance publication in the magazine.

Charley Anderson appears at the end of *The 42nd Parallel*, the first volume of *U.S.A.*, as a Swedish boy who drifts from job to job and girl to girl until the time he finally sails for France as a mechanic in an ambulance section. Anderson does not appear in *1919*, the second volume, but in the third novel of the trilogy, *The Big Money*, he is the principal character. Anderson returns from France as an heroic air ace who, after a series of women, business ventures and alcoholic quarrels, finally kills himself driving drunkenly into an express train.

'The Celebrity' takes place soon after Charley Anderson's return from the war. It appeared in *Esquire* in August 1935, one year before publication of *The Big Money*, in which it appears as an incident in the fourth Charley Anderson section. In the *Esquire* story, Charley Anderson is not called by name, he is "the young man from the sticks"; Paul and Eveline Johnson, named in the novel, are here "the couple he'd met on the French Line boat"; and Al Johnson becomes "the man who never forgot a face".

Between 1933 and 1936 *Esquire* continued to present numerous sections of *The Big Money*—specifically, the short biographies of F. W. Taylor, Thorstein Veblen, and Isadora Duncan; several of the Margaret Dowling episodes; and fragments which Dos Passos later worked into the book as parts of THE CAMERA EYE and NEWSREEL. A year and a half later, in October of 1937, Dos Passos began writing once again for

Esquire: this time a series of articles covering the Spanish Civil War. They, too, were later to appear in book form as *Journey Between Wars* (1938).

THE YOUNG MAN FROM THE STICKS got into the Grand Central Station too late in the day to start attending to the business he'd come for. He stood swinging his suitcase in the middle of the glowing pavement near the information booth. It was a rainy day. The station looked huge and lonely in spite of the late afternoon crowd. Then he suddenly remembered the phone number of the couple he'd met on the French Line boat. He went over to a phone booth and called. She answered. He recognised her voice at once. She said why didn't he come down and have a sandwich with them, she had some interesting people coming for cocktails. He said he'd be tickled to death, hung up, went and checked his bag, and took the subway downtown. When he got out at Astor Place he had to ask the newsvendor which way was west. He found the house and the right name over a bell. Then he suddenly felt very shy.

After all he didn't know them very well, he didn't know how well he'd be able to keep up with interesting people. He got up his nerve and gave the bell a jab. The latch on the door buzzed. He went up a flight of creaky stairs and there she was, holding open a tall white door.

"I hope you're not dreadfully hungry," she said. "Charles Edward Holden is coming and he's always late."

"Not at all . . . Why that's fine," said the young man from the sticks.

He followed her into a long tall room full of people and cigarette smoke. The husband came up and pressed a pink cocktail into his hand. "He said maybe he'd come," said the husband. "Well here's how."

"Here's how," said the young man from the sticks, blinking a little round the room.

"Mr. Zbsssk . . . Meet Miss Mmmmtbx . . . I'm sure you know Ttm Krmmt."

The couple he'd met on the French Line boat had vanished. The young man from the sticks held tight to his cocktail glass and moistened his lips with his tongue. He looked around at the men's faces and the women's faces and the cocktail glasses and women's hats round about him. Everybody was talking at once.

He approached a long-nosed lanky man who stood by himself with his back to the wall.

"Nasty day," he said.

"In what way?" said the lanky man without looking at him.

"I mean the rain."

"So it's raining is it?" The lanky man took a cigarette out of a fresh package, looked for a moment as if he was going to offer one but thought better of it and put them back in his pocket. The young man from the sticks brought out a cigarette of his own. The lanky man had just blown out his match and stood staring at the ceiling, letting the blue smoke pour out of his large nostrils. The young man began to stammer. He stuck the cigarette unlighted in the corner of his mouth and managed to get the words out "MMM mister Holder . . . what line . . . er . . . is he in?" "Holdy," said the lanky man turning his back and walking away. "He's shot his bolt."

At that minute a man grabbed the young man from the sticks by the buttons of his vest. "Where was it we met? . . . you tell me . . . I bet you don't remember."

The young man from the sticks shook his head. Then he smiled and held out his hand. "Maybe it was over on the other side," he said.

"No it was somewhere uptown . . . I never forget a face." The man who never forgot a face had a very pink face with circular lines on it. He was pretty well tanked. It looked as if some of the pink from the cocktails had got into his face.

"Very interesting people here . . ." the young man began timidly.

"Why kid ourselves?" the man who never forgot a face broke in. He rolled his boiled codfish eyes. "You know and I know that it's not like the old days. . . . Don't you, old timer?"

The young man nodded and blushed. "But this feller who's coming . . . Mr. Holdy?"

"Nothing but a clique . . . a collection of logrollers . . ." The man who never forgot a face winked. "After all us old newspaper men understand these things."

"Oh I see," said the young man.

The man who never forgot a face took him by the sleeve and led him through the crowd into the back room. "Scotch in here," he whispered mysteriously over his shoulder.

"Oh I see," said the young man.

It was quieter in the back room. It was possible to hear what people said. The couple he'd met on the boat were sitting quietly eating chicken salad with a few friends with whiskies and sodas beside them. "Oh here you are," they cried out with forced brightness.

"I was telling this young man . . . it turns out we're old friends . . . that it's not like the old days at 63 . . . you remember?"

"Or 321," said a sallow woman with a veil on her nose.

"Or at Marian's," sighed the couple he'd met on the French Line boat.

He was settled on the couch beside them with a plate of chicken salad on his knees. He wasn't following the conversation so well. So he spent his time with the supper and the whisky and soda. The man who never forgot a face was arguing with a haggard faced man with black eyebrows as to whether Charles Edward Holden was a communist. One man said he was a communist, the other said he was a paid agent of Wall Street. Every now and then the woman the young man had met on the French Line boat leaned forward and said smiling, "But you're both too silly." The haggard faced man with the black eyebrows finally got to his feet and said Charles Edward Holden ought to be shot against a white wall.

That broke up the group. The young man from the sticks found that he was getting sleepy what with the heat of the room and the scotch on top of the pink cocktail. He got to his feet. The woman he'd met on the French Line boat looked up at him with her handsome tired long-lidded eyes. "You don't think so do you?"

"No indeed," said the young man. He roamed around looking for the bathroom and instead got into the kitchenette where the husband was washing glasses.

"Lemme help you wipe," he said.

"No. I've got a system," said the husband.

"Say won't those birds get into trouble if they talk like that?" The young man jerked his thumb over his shoulder.

"This is a free country."

"I don't mean they're wrong . . . But I've got my living to make," said the young man from the sticks.

"A man's got a right to his opinions," said the husband pouring out the soapy water into the sink.

"Where I come from," said the young man from the sticks, "the Declaration of Independence stirs up a hornet's nest."

When the glasses were washed they went out through the hall to the front room. People had thinned out a little. The man who was talking about shooting them against a white wall strode up to them as they came in waving a crooked forefinger. "Now you're both office workers . . . You tell us what the white-collar classes think about it. Are they coming round to the side of the working class?"

"It takes plenty work to stay in the working class, these days," said the young man from the sticks.

"Do you mean to tell me . . ." the haggard faced man began.

There were three long rings on the doorbell. Everybody quieted down. "There he is," said somebody.

"Sounds like his ring," said the husband.

The couple the young man had met on the French Line boat went to the door. A small nattily dressed young man came in. "Oh we thought you were Charles Edward Holden," said a girl.

"Well maybe I am," said the new young man. "I've felt funny all day." The remark didn't go so well. You could feel the silence freezing around people's mouths.

"Well I think I'd better be getting along," said the young man from the sticks. He said good-bye to the husband and added, "And thank our charming hostess for me."

In the hall he found his charming hostess and the new young man talking profoundly together. They didn't notice him. Downstairs on the stoop he found the man who never forgot a face. "So it got a bit too dense for you too? . . . When the dear lady has more than three of her beaux present at one time it becomes positively stifling . . . I suppose you know that Holden is the real number one."

"You don't say," said the young man from the sticks, yanking up the collar of his overcoat because it was still drizzling.

"Better come and have a bite to eat. I know a wonderful place . . . almost like the old days. Those stand-up suppers get you in the long run."

"They sure do," said the young man from the sticks.

They went in by a black door through a corridor that smelt of toilets into a stuffy bar-room that had a few tables with dirty table-cloths in a row at the end. They sat down at a table and ordered two ryes.

"I know where it was we met . . . It was years ago at Little Hungary."

"But I've never been to Hungary," said the young man from the sticks.

"Sure . . . Here's how . . . I never forget a face . . . Now I sometimes get confused on names."

On the strength of that they had several more ryes with beer chasers. The man who never forgot a face kept seeing people he knew at the bar. They got up and went over to the bar to join the crowd. A stubby girl in a Bulgarian blouse who had come in with two ash-coloured young men was warmly greeted as Darling. He put his arm around her neck and started to introduce her all around. When he came to the young man from the sticks he hesitated. "Oh you're getting old," she sing-songed. "Can't remember names any more."

"Sure I can, Darling, meet . . . My very dear friend . . . Meet Colonel . . ." The young man from the sticks had put out his hand and was just going to say his name when the man who never forgot a face came out with "Charles Edward Holden."

The girl had a turned-up nose and blue eyes with dark rings under them. The eyes looked up at the young man from the sticks while she shook his hand. "Not really . . . Oh I've so wanted to meet you, Mr. Holden . . . I've read every word you ever wrote."

"But I'm not really . . ." he stammered.

"Not really a colonel," said the girl with her voice full of honest understanding.

"Just a colonel for a night," said the man who never forgot a face, with a wave of a hand, and ordered up a round of whiskies.

They went on drinking.

"Oh Mr. Holden," said the girl, who put her whiskies away without water like a trouper, "isn't it wonderful that we should meet like this. I thought you were much older and not nearly so good looking. Now Mr. Holden, I want you to tell me all about everything."

"Better call me Charley."

"My name's Bobbie . . . you'll call me Bobbie won't you?"

She drew him away down towards the empty end of the bar a little. "I was having a rotten time. . . . They are dear boys, but they won't talk about anything except how Phyllis drank iodine because Edward doesn't love her any more . . . I hate personalities, don't you? I like to talk about problems and things that count, don't you? I like the kind of people who do things. I mean world conditions, Marxism, books and things like that, don't you? Did you ever read the first chapter of *Capital* out loud?"

"Well maybe," began the young man from the sticks.

The girl was plucking at his sleeve.

"Suppose we go somewhere quiet and talk. I can't hear myself think in here."

"Do you know some place we can dance?" he asked. The girl nodded.

On the street she took his arm. The wind had gone into the north, cold and gusty. They walked east and down a street full of tenements and crowded little Italian stores. The girl rang at a basement door. While they were waiting she put her hand on his arm. "I got some money. . . . Let this be my party."

"But I wouldn't like that."

"All right. We'll make it fifty-fifty . . . I believe in sex equality, don't you?"

While they were waiting for the door to open he leaned over and kissed her. Her lips were there all ready. "Oh this is a wonderful evening for me," she said snuggling up to him. "You are the nicest celebrity I ever met . . . Most of them are pretty stuffy, don't you think so? No joy de vivre . . . When we have time I want you to explain me your theory of the effect of the commodity dollar on working-class consumption." "But," he stammered, "I'm not . . ."

The door opened. "Hello, Jimmy," said the girl to a slick looking young man in a brown suit as they brushed past him into the narrow passage. "Meet the boy friend . . . Mr. Grady, Mr. Holden." The young man's eyes flashed. "Not Charles Edward . . ." The girl nodded her head excitedly so that a big lock of her hair flopped over one eye. "Well sir, I'm surely happy to meet you . . . I'm a constant reader, sir."

The girl mussed up Jimmy's hair. "He's one of the toughest mugs in Manhattan, but he's very nice to his friends."

Bowing and blushing, Jimmy found them a table next to the dance floor in the stuffy little pale pink cabaret hot from the spotlights and the cigarette smoke and the sweat of people dancing. Then she grabbed his hand and pulled him to his feet. They danced. The girl rubbed close to him till he could feel her little round breasts through the Bulgarian blouse. "My, the boy can dance," she whispered. "Let's forget everything. . . . Who we are . . . the day of the week."

"Me . . . I forgot two hours ago," he said giving her a squeeze.

"You're just a plain farmer lad and I'm a bashful barefoot girl."

"More truth than poetry to that," he said through his teeth.

"Poetry . . . I love poetry, don't you . . . I like to go up to the roof and read it in the rain . . . I'm a pagan child at heart, aren't you? . . . And then you'll tell me all about your work."

They danced until the place closed up. They were staggering when they got out on the black empty streets. They stumbled past garbage pails. Cats ran out from under their feet. They stopped at a corner to talk about unemployment with a cop. In every dark doorway they stopped and kissed. The milkman with his frame of empties was just coming out of the door of the house where she lived. Overhead the sky was getting haggard. As she was looking for her latchkey in her purse, she whispered thoughtfully, "People who really do things make the most beautiful lovers, don't you think so?"

It was the young man from the sticks who woke up first. Sunlight was pressing in through the uncurtained window. The girl was asleep, her face crushed into the pillow. Her mouth was open and with the deep rings under her eyes she looked considerably older than she had the night before. Her skin was pasty and green and she had stringy hair. He grabbed his clothes and dressed as quietly as he could. His watch had stopped. Must be late as hell. On a big table deep in dust and littered with drawings of funny looking nudes, he found a sheet of yellow paper that had half a poem on the back of it. He scribbled on it: Good-bye good luck Chas. Ed. Holden, and tiptoed out the door with his shoes in his hand. He was so afraid she'd wake up that he didn't put on his shoes until he'd gone down three flights to the street door.

THOMAS MANN

The Godly Warrior

'The Godly Warrior' was written in 1902 and was later reprinted in
Stories of Three Decades (1936) under the title 'Gladius Dei'. Mann was
twenty-seven when the story first appeared, and his long major novel,
Buddenbrooks, published a year earlier, was just beginning to attract
attention. Many of Mann's early short stories deal with "the marked
man", literally or symbolically the artist in his relation to life, the individual, isolated, alienated from the *status quo*. Like the young hero in
'Gladius Dei' he is, inevitably, psychologically disrupted.

When the story appeared in *Esquire* (in April of 1936) it ran with the
subtitle: 'A Symbolic Portrayal of the Intolerant Puritanism that is
an Early Augur of Fascism'. Subtitling is a difficult art, too, and it may
be that Mann's paradoxical commitment to (and identification of the
sick maladjusted *artist* with) the Savonarola figure of Hieronymus was
overlooked. Certainly a writer of subtitles in 1936 might have the evils
of Fascism more immediately in his mind than Thomas Mann did in
1902; but it is a further testimony to the complexity of Mann's stories
that even such a purely political interpretation could be made.

MUNICH was radiant. Above the gay squares and white columned
temples, the classicistic monuments and the baroque churches, the
leaping fountains, the palaces and parks of the Residence there
stretched a sky of luminous blue silk. Well-arranged leafy vistas
laced with sun and shade lay basking in the sunshine of a beautiful
day in early June.

There was a twittering of birds and a blithe holiday spirit in all the
little streets. And in the squares and past the rows of villas there
swelled, rolled and hummed the leisurely and entertaining traffic of

that easy-going charming town. Travellers of all nationalities drove about in the slow little droschkies looking right and left in aimless curiosity at the house-fronts; they climbed and descended museum stairs. Many windows stood open and music was heard from within: practising on piano, cello or violin—earnest and well-meant amateur efforts; while from the Odeon came the sound of serious work on several grand pianos.

Young people, the kind that can whistle the Nothung motif, and fill the pit of the Schauspielhaus every evening, wandered in and out of the University and Library with literary magazines in their coat pockets. A court carriage stood before the Academy, the home of the plastic arts, which spreads its white wings between the Turken-strasse and the Siegestor. And colourful groups of models, pictures-que old men, women and children in Albanian costume, stood or lounged at the top of the balustrade.

Indolent, unhurried sauntering was the mode in all the long streets of the northern quarter. There life is lived for pleasanter ends than the driving greed of gain. Young artists with little round hats on the backs of their heads, flowing cravats and no canes—carefree bachelors who paid for their lodgings with colour-sketches—were strolling up and down to let the clear blue morning play upon their mood, also to look at the little girls, the pretty, rather plump type, with the brunette bandeaux, the too large feet and the unobjection-able morals. Every fifth house had studio windows blinking in the sun. Sometimes a fine piece of architecture stood out from a middle-class row, the work of some imaginative young architect; a wide front with shallow bays and decorations in a bizarre style very expressive and full of invention. Or the door to some monotonous façade would be framed in a bold improvisation of flowing lines and sunny colours, with bacchantes, naiads and rosy-skinned nudes.

It was always a joy to linger before the windows of the cabinet-makers and the shops for modern articles-de-luxe. What a sense for luxurious amusing nothings, and significant line is displayed in the shape of everything! Little shops that sell picture-frames, sculptures and antiques there were in endless number; in their windows you might see those busts of Florentine women of the Renaissance, so full of noble poise and poignant charm. And the owners of the smallest and meanest of these shops spoke to you of Mino da Fiesole and

Donatello as though he had received the rights of reproduction from them personally.

But on the Odeonsplatz, in view of the mighty loggia with the spacious mosaic pavement before it, diagonally opposite to the Regent's palace, people were crowding round the large windows and glass show-cases of the big art shop owned by M. Bluthenzweig. What a glorious display! There were reproductions of the master-pieces of all the galleries in the world, in costly decorated and tinted frames, the good taste of which was precious in its very simplicity. There were copies of modern paintings, works of a joyously sensuous fantasy, in which the antique seemed born again in humorous and realistic guise; bronze nudes and fragile ornamental glassware; tall, thin earthenware vases with an iridescent glaze produced by a bath in metal steam; editions de luxe which were triumphs of modern binding and presswork, containing the works of the most modish poets, set out with every possible advantage of sumptuous elegance. Cheek by jowl with these, the portraits of artists, musicians, philosophers, actors, writers, displayed to gratify the public taste for personalities. In the first window, next the book-shop, a large picture stood on an easel, with a crowd of people in front of it, a fine sepia photograph in a wide old-gold frame, a very striking reproduction of the sensation at this year's great international exhibition, to which public attention is always invited by means of effective and artistic posters stuck up everywhere on hoardings among concert programmes and clever advertisements of toilet preparations.

If you looked into the windows of the book-shop your eye met such titles as *Interior Decoration Since the Renaissance*, *The Renaissance in Modern Decorative Art*, *The Book as Work of Art*, *The Decorative Arts*, *Hunger for Art*, and many more. And you would remember that these thought-provoking pamphlets were sold and read by the thousand and that discussions on these subjects were the preoccupation of all the salons.

You might be lucky enough to meet in person one of the famous fair ones whom less fortunate folk knew only through the medium of art; one of those rich and beautiful women whose Titian-blonde colouring Nature's most sweet and cunning hand did not lay on, but whose diamond parures and beguiling charms had received immortality from the hand of some portrait-painter of genius and whose love-affairs were the talk of the town. These were the queens of the artist balls at carnival-time. They were a little painted, a little made up, full of haughty caprices, worthy of adoration, avid of praise. You might see a carriage rolling up the Ludwigstrasse, with such a great painter and his mistress inside. People would be pointing out the sight, standing still to gaze after the pair. Some of them would curtsey. A little more and the very policemen would stand at attention.

Art flourished, art swayed the destinies of the town, art stretched above it her rose-bound sceptre and smiled. On every hand obsequious interest was displayed in her prosperity, on every hand she was served with industry and devotion. There was a downright cult of line, decoration, form, significance, beauty. Munich was radiant.

A youth was coming down the Schellingstrasse. With the bells of cyclists ringing about him he strode across the wooden pavement towards the broad façade of the Ludwigskirche. Looking at him it was as though a shadow passed across the sky, or cast over the spirit some memory of melancholy hours. Did he not love the sun which bathed the lovely city in its festal light? Why did he walk wrapped in his own thoughts, his eyes directed on the ground? No one in that tolerant and variety-loving town would have taken offence at his wearing no hat; but why need the hood of his ample black cloak have been drawn over his head, shadowing his low, prominent and peaked forehead, covering his ears and framing his haggard cheeks?

What pangs of conscience, what scruples and self-tortures had so availed to hollow out these cheeks? It is frightful, on a sunny day, to see care sitting in the hollows of the human face. His dark brows thickened at the narrow base of his hooked and prominent nose. His lips were unpleasantly full, his eyes brown and close-lying. When he lifted them, diagonal folds appeared on the peaked brow. His gaze expressed knowledge, limitation and suffering. Seen in profile his face was strikingly like an old painting preserved at Florence in a narrow cloister cell, whence once a frightful and shattering protest issued against life and her triumphs.

Hieronymus walked along the Schellingstrasse with a slow, firm stride, holding his wide cloak together with both hands from inside.

Two little girls, two of those pretty, plump little creatures with the bandeaux, the big feet and the unobjectionable morals, strolled towards him arm in arm, on pleasure bent. They poked each other and laughed, they bent over with laughter. They even broke into a run and ran away still laughing, at his hood and his face. But he paid them no heed. With bent head, looking neither to the right nor to the left, he crossed the Ludwigstrasse and mounted the church steps.

The great wings of the middle portal stood wide open. From somewhere within the consecrated twilight, cool, dank, incense-laden, there came a pale red glow. An old woman with inflamed eyes rose from a prayer stool and slipped on crutches through the columns. Otherwise the church was empty.

Hieronymus sprinkled brow and breast at the stoup, bent the knee before the high altar and then paused in the centre nave. Here in the church his stature seemed to have grown. He stood upright and immovable, his head was flung up and his great hooked nose jutted domineeringly above the thick lips. His eyes no longer sought the ground but looked straight and boldly into the distance, at the crucifix on the high altar. Thus he stood a while, then retreating he bent the knee again and left the church.

He strode up the Ludwigstrasse, slowly, firmly, with bent head in the centre of the wide unpaven road, towards the mighty loggia with its statues. But arrived at the Odeonsplatz he looked up, so that the folds came out on his peaked forehead, and checked his step, his attention being called to the crowd at the windows of the big art shop of M. Bluthenzweig.

People moved from window to window, pointing out to each other the treasures displayed and exchanging views as they looked over one another's shoulders. Hieronymus mingled among them and did as they did, taking in all these things with his eyes, one by one.

He saw the reproductions of masterpieces from all the galleries in the world, the priceless frames so precious in their simplicity, the Renaissance sculpture, the bronze nudes, the exquisitely bound volumes, the iridescent vases, the portraits of artists, musicians, philosophers, actors, writers; he looked at everything and turned a moment of his scrutiny upon every object. Holding his mantle closely together with both hands from inside, he moved his hood-covered head in short turns from one thing to the next, gazing at each a while with a dull, inimical and remotely surprised air, lifting the dark brows which grew so thick at the base of the nose. At length he stood in front of the last window, which contained the startling picture. For a while he looked over the shoulders of people before him and then in his turn reached a position directly in front of the window.

The large red-brown photograph in the choice old-gold frame stood on an easel in the centre. It was a Madonna, but an utterly unconventional one, a work of entirely modern feeling. The figure of the Holy Mother was revealed as enchantingly feminine and beautiful. Her great smouldering eyes were rimmed with darkness and her delicate and strangely smiling lips were half parted. Her slender fingers held in a somewhat nervous grasp the hips of the Child, a nude boy of pronounced, almost primitive leanness. He was playing with her breast and glancing aside at the beholder with a wise look in his eyes.

Two other youths stood near Hieronymus, talking about the picture. They were two young men with books under their arms, which they had fetched from the library or were taking thither. Humanistically educated people, that is, equipped with science and with art.

"The little chap is in luck, devil take me!" said one.

"He seems to be trying to make one envious," replied the other. "A bewildering female!"

"A female to drive a man crazy! Gives you funny ideas about the Immaculate Conception."

"No, she doesn't look exactly immaculate. Have you seen the original?"

"Of course; I was quite bowled over. She makes an even more aphrodisiac impression in colour. Especially the eyes."

"The likeness is pretty plain."

"How so?"

"Don't you know the model? Of course he used his little dressmaker. It is almost a portrait, only with a lot more emphasis on the corruptible. The girl is more innocent."

"I hope so. Life would be altogether too much of a strain, if there were many like this *mater amata*."

"The Pinakothek has bought it."

"Really? Well, well! They knew what they were doing, anyhow. The treatment of the flesh and the flow of the linen garment are really first-class."

"Yes, an incredibly gifted chap."

"Do you know him?"

"A little. He will have a career, that is certain. He has been invited twice by the Prince-Regent."

This last was said as they were taking leave of each other.

"Shall I see you this evening at the theatre?" asked the first. "The Dramatic Club is giving Machiavelli's *Mandragala*."

"Oh, bravo! That will be great, of course. I had meant to go to the Varieté but I shall probably choose our stout Niccolo after all. Good-bye."

They parted, going off to right and left. New people took their places and looked at the famous picture. But Hieronymus stood where he was, motionless, with his head thrust out; his hands clutched convulsively at the mantle as they held it together from inside. His brows were no longer lifted with that cool and unpleasantly surprised expression; they were drawn and darkened; his cheeks, half shrouded in the black hood, seemed more sunken than ever and his thick lips had gone pale. Slowly his head dropped lower and lower, so that finally his eyes stared upwards at the work of art, while the nostrils of his great nose quivered.

Thus he remained, for perhaps a quarter of an hour. The crowd about him melted away but he did not stir. At last he turned slowly on the balls of his feet and went hence.

But the picture of the Madonna went with him. Always and ever, whether in his hard and narrow little room or kneeling in the cool church, it stood before his outraged soul, with its smouldering dark-rimmed eyes, its riddlingly smiling lips—stark and beautiful. And no prayer availed to exorcise it.

But the third night it happened that a command and summons from on High came to Hieronymus, to intercede and lift his voice against the frivolity, blasphemy and arrogance of beauty. In vain like Moses he protested that he had not the gift of tongues. God's will remained unshaken: in a loud voice He demanded that the faint-hearted Hieronymus go forth to sacrifice amid the jeers of the foe.

And as God would have it so, he set forth one morning and wended his way to the great art shop of M. Bluthenzweig. He wore his hood over his head and held his mantle together in front from inside with both hands as he went.

The air had grown heavy, the sky was livid and thunder threatened. Once more crowds were besieging the show-cases at the art shop and especially the window where the photograph of the Madonna stood. Hieronymus cast one brief glance thither; then he pushed up the latch of the glass door hung with placards and art magazines. "As God wills," said he and entered the shop.

A young girl was somewhere at a desk writing in a big book. She was a pretty brunette thing with bandeaux of hair and big feet. She came up to him and asked pleasantly what he would like.

"Thank you," said Hieronymus in a low voice and looked her earnestly in the face, with diagonal wrinkles in his peaked brow. "I would speak not to you but to the owner of this shop, Herr Bluthenzweig."

She hesitated a little, turned away and took up her work once more. He stood there in the middle of the shop.

Instead of the single specimens in the show-windows there was here a riot and a heaping-up of luxury, a fulness of colour, line, form, style, invention, good taste and beauty. Hieronymus looked slowly round him, drawing his mantle close with both hands.

There were several people besides him. At one of the broad tables running across the room sat a man in a yellow suit, with a black goat's-beard, looking at a portfolio of French drawings, over which he now and then emitted a bleating laugh. He was being waited on by an under-nourished and vegetarian young man, who kept on dragging up fresh portfolios. Diagonally opposite the bleating man sat an elegant old dame, examining art embroideries with a pattern of fabulous flowers in pale tones standing together on tall perpendicular stalks. An attendant hovered about her too. A leisurely Englishman in a travelling cap with his pipe in his mouth sat at another table. Cold and smooth-shaven, of indefinite age, in his good English clothes, he sat examining bronzes brought to him by M. Bluthenzweig in person. He was holding up by the head the dainty figure of a nude girl, immature and delicately articulated, her hands crossed in coquettish innocence upon her breast. He studied her thoroughly, turning her slowly about. M. Bluthenzweig, a man

with a short, heavy brown beard and bright brown eyes of exactly
the same colour, moved in a semicircle around him, rubbing his
hands, praising the statuette with all the terms his vocabulary
possessed.

"A hundred and fifty marks, Sir," he said in English. "Munich
art—very charming, in fact. Simply full of charm, you know. Grace
itself. Really extremely pretty, good, admirable, in fact." Then he
thought of some more and went on, "Highly attractive, fascinating."
Then he began again from the beginning. His nose lay a little flat on
his upper lip, so that he breathed constantly with a slight sniff into
his moustache. Sometimes he did this as he approached a customer,
stooping over as though he were smelling at him. When Hieronymus entered, M. Bluthenzweig examined him cursorily in this way,
then devoted himself again to his Englishman.

The elegant old dame made her selection and left the shop. A
man entered. M. Bluthenzweig sniffed briefly his capacity to buy
and left him to the young bookkeeper. The man purchased a faïence
bust of young Pietro de' Medici, son of Lorenzo, and went out
again. The Englishman began to depart. He had acquired the
statuette of the little girl and left amid bowings from M. Bluthenzweig. Then the art dealer turned to Hieronymus and came
forward.

"You wanted something?" he said, without any particular
courtesy. Hieronymus held his cloak together with both hands and
looked the other in the face almost without winking an eyelash. He
parted his big lips slowly and said:

"I have come to you on account of the picture in the window
there, the big photograph, the Madonna." His voice was thick and
without modulation.

"Yes, quite right," said M. Bluthenzweig briskly and began
rubbing his hands. "Seventy marks in the frame. It is unfadable—a
first-class reproduction. Highly attractive and full of charm."

Hieronymus was silent. He nodded his head in the hood and
shrank a little into himself, as the dealer spoke. Then he drew
himself up again and spoke:

"I would remark to you first of all that I am not in the position to
purchase anything, nor have I the desire. I am sorry to have to dis-
appoint your expectations. I regret if it upsets you. But in the first

place I am poor and in the second I do not love the things you sell. No, I cannot buy anything."

"No? Well, then?" asked Bluthenzweig, sniffing a good deal. "Then may I ask——"

"I suppose," Hieronymus went on, "that being what you are you look down on me because I am not in a position to buy."

"Oh—er—not at all," said M. Bluthenzweig. "Not at all. Only——"

"And yet I beg you to hear me and give some consideration to my words."

"Consideration to your words. H'm—may I ask——"

"You may ask," said Hieronymus, "and I will answer you. I have come to get you to remove that picture, the big photograph, the Madonna, out of your window and never display it again."

M. Bluthenzweig looked a while dumbly into Hieronymus' face— as though he expected him to be abashed at the words he had just uttered. But as this did not happen he gave a violent sniff and spoke himself:

"Will you be so good as to tell me whether you are here in any official capacity which authorises you to dictate to me, or what does bring you here?"

"Oh, no," replied Hieronymus, "I have neither office nor dignity from the state. I have no power on my side, Sir. What brings me hither is my conscience alone."

M. Bluthenzweig, searching for words, snorted violently into his moustache. At length he said:

"Your conscience . . . well, you will kindly understand that I take not the faintest interest in your conscience." With which he turned round and moved quickly to his desk at the back of the shop, where he began to write. Both attendants laughed heartily. The pretty Fraulein giggled over her account-book. As for the yellow gentleman with the goat's-beard, he was evidently a foreigner, for he gave no sign of comprehension but went on studying the French drawings and emitting from time to time his bleating laugh.

"Just get rid of the man for me," said M. Bluthenzweig shortly over his shoulder to his assistant. He went on writing. The poorly paid vegetarian approached Hieronymus smothering his laughter, and the other salesman came up too.

"May we be of service to you in any other way?" the first asked mildly. Hieronymus fixed him with his glazed and suffering eyes.

"No," he said, "you cannot. I beg you to take the Madonna picture out of the window, at once and for ever."

"But—why?"

"It is the Holy Mother of God," said Hieronymus in a subdued voice.

"Quite. But you have heard that Herr Bluthenzweig is not inclined to accede to your request."

"We must bear in mind that it is the Holy Mother of God," said Hieronymus again and his head trembled on his neck.

"So we must. . . . But should we not be allowed to exhibit any Madonnas—or paint any?"

"It is not that," said Hieronymus, almost whispering. He drew himself up and shook his head violently several times. His peaked brow under the hood was entirely furrowed with long deep crossfolds. "You know very well that it is vice itself that is painted there —naked sensuality. I was standing near two simple young people and overheard with my own ears that it led them astray upon the doctrine of the Immaculate Conception."

"Oh, permit me—that is not the point," said the young salesman smiling. In his leisure hours he was writing a brochure on the modern movement in art and was well qualified to conduct a cultured conversation. "The picture is a work of art," he went on, "and one must measure it by the appropriate standards as such. It has been very highly praised on all hands. The state has purchased it."

"I know that the state has purchased it," said Hieronymus. "I also know that the artist has twice dined with the Prince-Regent. It is common talk—and God knows how people interpret the fact that a man can become famous by such work as this. What does such a fact bear witness to? To the blindness of the world, a blindness inconceivable, if not indeed shamelessly hypocritical. This picture has its origin in sensual lust and is enjoyed in the same—is that true or not? Answer me! And you too answer me, Herr Bluthenzweig!"

A pause ensued. Hieronymus seemed in all seriousness to demand an answer to his question, looking by turns at the staring attendants

and the rock back M. Bluthenzweig turned upon him, with his own
piercing and anguishing brown eyes. Silence reigned. Only the
yellow man with the goat's-beard, bending over the French drawings, broke it with his bleating laugh.

"It is true," Hieronymus went on in a hoarse voice that shook
with his profound indignation. "You do not dare deny it. How then
can honour be done to its creator, as though he had endowed mankind with a new ideal possession? How can one stand before it and
surrender unthinkingly to the base enjoyment which it purveys,
persuading oneself in all seriousness that one is yielding to a noble
and elevated sentiment, highly creditable to the human race? Is
this reckless ignorance or abandoned hypocrisy? My understanding
falters, it is completely at a loss when confronted by the absurd fact
that a man can achieve renown on this earth by the stupid and
shameless exploitation of the animal instincts. Beauty? What is
beauty? What forces are they which use beauty as their tool today—
and upon what does it work? No one can fail to know this, Herr
Bluthenzweig. But who, understanding it clearly, can fail to feel
disgust and pain? It is criminal to play upon the ignorance of the
immature, the lewd, the brazen and the unscrupulous by elevating
beauty into an idol to be worshipped, to give it even more power
over those who know not affliction and have no knowledge of
redemption. You are unknown to me, and you look at me with
black looks—yet answer me! Knowledge, I tell you, is the pro-
foundest torture in the world; but it is the purgatory without whose
purifying pangs no soul can reach salvation. It is not infantile,
blasphemous shallowness that can save us, Herr Bluthenzweig; only
knowledge can avail, knowledge in which the passions of our loath-
some flesh die away and are quenched."

Silence.—The yellow man with the goat's-beard gave a sudden
little bleat.

"I think you really must go now," said the underpaid assistant
mildly.

But Hieronymus made no move to do so. Drawn up in his hooded
cape he stood with blazing eyes in the centre of the shop and his
thick lips poured out condemnation in a voice that was harsh and
rusty and clanking.

"Art, you cry; enjoyment, beauty! Enfold the world in beauty and endow all things with the noble grace of style—Profligate, away! Do you think to wash over with lurid colours the misery of the world? Do you think with the sounds of feasting and music to drown out the voice of the tortured earth? Shameless one, you err! God lets not Himself be mocked, and your impudent deification of the glistening surface of things is an abomination in His eyes. You tell me that I blaspheme art. I say to you that you lie. I do not blaspheme art. Art is no conscienceless delusion, lending itself to reinforce the allurements of the fleshly. Art is the holy torch which turns its light upon all the frightful depths, all the shameful and woeful abysses of life; art is the godly fire laid to the world that being redeemed by pity it may flame up and dissolve altogether with its shames and torments. Take it out, Herr Bluthenzweig, take away the work of that famous painter out of your window—you would do well to burn it with a hot fire and strew its ashes to the four winds— yes, to all the four winds——"

His harsh voice broke off. He had taken a violent backwards step, snatched one arm from his black wrappings and stretched it passionately forth, gesturing towards the window with a hand that shook as though palsied. And in this commanding attitude he paused. His great hooked nose seemed to jut more than ever, his dark brows were gathered so thick and high that folds crowded upon the peaked forehead shaded by the hood; a hectic flush mantled his hollow cheeks.

But at this point M. Bluthenzweig turned round. Perhaps he was outraged by the idea of burning his seventy-mark reproduction; perhaps Hieronymus' speech had completely exhausted his patience. In any case he was a picture of stern and righteous anger. He pointed with his pen to the door of the shop, gave several short, excited snorts into his moustache, struggled for words and uttered with the maximum of energy those which he found:

"My fine fellow, if you don't get out at once I will have my packer help you—do you understand?"

"Oh, you cannot intimidate me, you cannot drive me away, you cannot silence my voice," cried Hieronymus as he clutched his cloak over his chest with his fists and shook his head doughtily. "I know that I am single-handed and powerless, but yet I will not cease until you hear me, Herr Bluthenzweig! Take the picture out of your window and burn it even today! And burn not it alone! Burn all these statues and busts, the sight of which plunges the beholder into sin, burn these vases and ornaments, these shameless revivals of paganism, these elegantly bound volumes of erotic verse! Burn everything in your shop, Herr Bluthenzweig, for it is a filthiness in God's sight. Burn it, burn it!" he shrieked, beside himself, describing a wild, all-embracing circle with his arm. "The harvest is ripe for the reaper, the measure of the age's shamelessness is full—but I say unto you——"

"Krauthuber!" Herr Bluthenzweig raised his voice and shouted towards a door at the back of the shop. "Come in here at once!"

And in answer to the summons there appeared upon the scene a massive and overpowering presence, a vast and awe-inspiring, swollen human bulk, whose limbs merged into each other like links of sausage—a gigantic son of the people, malt-nourished and immoderate, who weighed in, with puffings, bursting with energy, from the packing-room. His appearance in the upper reaches of his form was notable for a fringe of walrus beard; a hide apron fouled with paste covered his body from the waist down, and his yellow shirt-sleeves were rolled back from his heroic arms.

"Will you open the door for this gentleman, Krauthuber?" said M. Bluthenzweig, "and if he should not find the way to it, just help him into the street."

"Huh," said the man, looking from his enraged employer to Hieronymus and back, with his little elephant eyes. It was a heavy monosyllable, suggesting reserve force restrained with difficulty. The floor shook with his tread as he went to the door and opened it.

Hieronymus had grown very pale. "Burn——" he shouted once more. He was about to go on when he felt himself turned round by an irresistible power, by a physical preponderance to which no resistance was even thinkable. Slowly an inexorably he was propelled towards the door.

"I am weak," he managed to ejaculate. "My flesh cannot bear the force . . . it cannot hold its ground . . . no . . . but what does that prove? Burn——"

He stopped. He found himself outside the art shop. M. Bluthenzweig's giant packer had let him go with one final shove, which set him down on the stone threshold of the shop, supporting himself with one hand. Behind him the door closed with a rattle of glass.

He picked himself up. He stood erect, breathing heavily, and pulled his cloak together with one fist over his breast, letting the other hang down inside. His hollow cheeks had a grey pallor; the nostrils of his great hooked nose opened and closed; his ugly lips were writhen in an expression of hatred and despair and his red-rimmed eyes wandered like those of a man in a frenzy over the beautiful square.

He did not see that people were looking at him with amusement and curiosity. For what he beheld upon the mosaic pavement before the great loggia were all the vanities of this world: the masked costumes of the artist balls, the decorations, vases and art objects, the nude statues, the femal busts, the pictureque rebirths of the pagan age; the portraits of famous beauties by masterly hands, the elegantly bound erotic verse, the art brochures—all these he saw heaped in a pyramid and going up in crackling flames amid exultant cries from the people enthralled by his own frightful words. The yellow background of cloud had drawn up over the Theatinerstrasse and from it issued wild rumblings; but what he saw was a burning fiery sword, towering in sulphurous light above the joyous city.

"*Gladius dei super terram* . . ." his thick lips whispered; and drawing himself still higher in his hooded cloak while the hand hanging down inside it twitched convulsively he murmured quaking, "*cito et velociter!*"

F. SCOTT FITZGERALD

Three Acts of Music

F. Scott Fitzgerald wrote, in seven years, forty-five pieces for *Esquire*. Among them were some of his finest short stories and his most famous essay, 'The Crack-Up' (his title wryly continued, 'or The Best Laid Plans'), which, more than any other of his non-fiction work, has led to an understanding of the continuity of Fitzgerald's private, public and literary self.

In one of the three instalments he observed, "There are always those to whom all self-revelation is contemptible". And many of Fitzgerald's friends were, indeed, at least alarmed for him by the utter directness with which he confessed to despair and took stock of his personal history in print. In an affectionate and uneasy letter, Dos Passos (whose novel, *The Big Money*, had just been published) inquired how he found time to worry about his inner situation at such a moment in history (1936) and further suggested that if he wanted to crack up he at least ought to write serious fiction about it instead of giving it in pieces to Arnold Gingrich. But, like one of his own mythically aristocratic heroes, Fitzgerald remained superior to feelings of shame; and certainly such authentic personal candour has seldom emerged from between the covers of a slick magazine.

'Three Acts of Music' was published in May 1936, directly after the Crack-up series, and it is here reprinted for the first time. Arnold Gingrich tells how it came to be written:

"Zelda was in an expensive private sanitarium. Scott was too proud to let her be put anywhere else and had overextended his credit in all directions. We had kept making advances, sometimes by day to banks and sometimes by night to hotels, to cover cheques that Scott would write as soon as he had sent us a wire asking for the advances, and finally our auditors began asking about this non-writing writer who was getting more frequent advances than anybody else.

"I went down to Baltimore to see what I could do about it.

"Scott said, '*The Saturday Evening Post* won't give me any more money until I deliver a manuscript, and I can't write the only kind of thing they'll take. They want stories of young love. Ober [Fitzgerald's literary agent] has the patience of a saint, but his resources aren't endless, and he can't advance me any more money out of his own pocket, and now if you and your auditors fail me, I've nowhere left to turn.'

"I said that just to satisfy the auditors, and to be able to say that a script—perhaps needing some revision—had been received on such and such a date so the account wouldn't look like all going out and nothing coming in, Scott should write three purported articles simply saying why he couldn't write. I suggested that he put down anything that came into his head, as automatic writing in the Gertrude Stein manner, or that, if even that were beyond his powers of concentration, he simply copy out the same couple of sentences over and over, often enough to fill eight or ten pages, if only to say I can't write stories about young love for *The Saturday Evening Post*.

"I also hoped that there might be a therapeutic value in writing these three non-articles, in that the mere writing about why he couldn't write might in itself prime the pump enough to get him started writing again. Actually that's what happened. The first three articles were: 'The Crack-Up,' 'Pasting It Together,' and 'Handle It With Care'; and then along came a fourth, although the series as such was finished, called 'Three Acts of Music.' "

I

THEY COULD HARDLY HEAR IT for a while. It was a slow gleam of pale blue and creamy pink. Then there was a tall room where there were many young people and finally they began to feel it and hear it.

What were they—no. This is about music.

He went to the band-stand; the piano player let him lean over his shoulder to read:

"From *No, No, Nanette* by Vincent Youmans."

"Thank you," he said, "I'd like to drop something in the horn but when an interne has a dollar bill and two coins in the world he might get married instead."

"Never mind, doctor. That's about what I had when I got married last winter."

When he came back to the table she said:

"Did you find out who wrote that thing?"

"*No!* When do we go from here?"

"When they stop playing 'Tea for Two'."

Later as she came out of the women's dressing-room, she asked the man, "Who played it?"

"My God, how do I know. The band played it."

It dripped out the door now:

Tea . . .

. . . two

Two . . .

. . . tea

"We can never get married. I'm not even a nurse yet."

"Well, let's kill the idea—let's spend the rest of our lives going around and listening to tunes. What did you say that writer's name was?"

"What did *you* say? You went over and looked, dint you?"

"*Didn't* you," he corrected her.

"You're so swell all the time."

"Well, at least I found out who wrote it."

"Who?"

"Somebody named Vincent Youmans."

She hummed it over:

"And you . . .

. . . for me

And me . . .

. . . for you

Al—

o—

o—

n-n . . ."

Their arms went about each other for a moment in the corridor outside the red room.

"If you lost the dollar bill and the other nickel I'd still marry you," she said.

II

This is now years later but there was still music. There was 'All Alone' and 'Remember' and 'Always' and 'Blue Skies' and 'How About Me'. He was back from Vienna but it didn't seem to matter so much as it had before.

"Wait in here a moment," she said outside the operating room.
"Turn on the radio if you want to."

"You've got mighty important, haven't you?"

He turned on:

> Re-mem-ber
> the night
> the night
> you said—

"Are you high-hatting me?" she inquired, "or did medicine
begin and end in Vienna?"

"No, it didn't," he said humbly. "I'm impressed—evidently you
can supervise the resident or the surgeons——"

"I've got an operation of Doctor Menafee's coming in and there's
a tonsilectomy that's got to be postponed. I'm a working girl. I'm
supervising the operating room."

"But you'll go out with me tonight—won't you? We'll get them
to play 'All Alone'."

She paused, regarding him.

"Yes, I've been all alone for a lot of time now. I'm somebody—
you don't seem to realise it. Say who is this Berlin anyhow? He was
a singer in a dive, wasn't he? My brother ran a roadhouse and he
gave me money to get started with. But I thought I was away from
all that. Who is this Irving Berlin? I hear he's just married a
society girl——"

"He's just married——"

She had to go. "Excuse me. I've got to fire an interne before this
gets going."

"I was an interne once. I understand."

They were out at last. She was making three thousand a
year now and he was still being of a conservative old Vermont
family.

"This Irving Berlin now. Is he happy with this Mackay girl?
Those songs don't sound——"

"I guess he is. The point is how happy are you?"

"Oh, we discussed that so long ago. What do I matter? I matter
in a big way—but when I was a little country girl your fambly
decided——

"Not *you*," she said at the alarm in his eyes. "I know *you* never did."

"I knew something else about you. I knew three things—that you were a Yonkers girl—and didn't pronounce the language like I did——"

"And that I wanted to marry you. Let's forget it. Your friend Mr. Berlin can talk better than we can. Listen to him."

"I'm listening."

"No. But *lis*den, I mean."

Not for just a year but—

"Why do you say my friend Mr. Berlin? I never saw the guy."

"I thought maybe you'd met him in Vienna in all these years."

"I never saw him."

"He married the girl—didn't he?"

"What are you crying about?"

"I'm not crying. I just said he married the girl—didn't he? Isn't that all right to say? When you've come so far—when——"

"You are crying," he said.

"No, I'm not. Honest. It's this work. It wears down your eyes. Let's dance."

—o
—ver
—head

They were playing.

Blue
skies
o
ver
head

She looked up out of his arms suddenly.

"Do you suppose they're happy?"

"Who?"

"Irving Berlin and the Mackay girl?"

"How should I know whether they're happy? I tell you I never knew them—never saw them."

A moment later she whispered:

"We all knew them."

III

This story is about tunes. Perhaps the tunes swing the people or the people the tunes. Anyhow:

"We'll never do it," he remarked with some finality.

Smoke gets in your eyes said the music.

"Why?"

"Because we're too old. You wouldn't want to anyhow—you've got that job at Duke's Hospital."

"I just got it."

"Well, you've just got it. And it's going to pay you four thousand."

"That's probably half what you make."

"You mean you want to try it anyhow?"

When your heart's on fire

"No. I guess you're right. It's too late."

"—Too late for what?"

"Just too late—like you told me."

"But I didn't mean it."

"You were right though. . . . Be quiet:

> *Lovely*
> > *to look at*
> *Romantic*
> > *to know*

"You're all those things in the song," he said passionately.

"What? Lovely to look at and all that? You should have told me that fifteen years ago. Now I'm superintendent of a woman's hospital." She added, "And I'm still a womam." Then she added, "But I'm not the woman you knew any more. I'm another woman."

> *—lovely to look at* the orchestra repeated.

"Yes, I was lovely to look at when I was nothing—when I couldn't even talk plain——"

"I never knew——"

"Oh, let's not go over it. Listen to what they're playing."

"It's called 'Lovely to Look At'."

"Who's it by?"

"A man named Jerome Kern."

"Did you meet *him* when you went back to Europe the second time? Is he a friend of yours?"

"I never saw him. What gives you the impression I met all these big shots? I'm a doctor. Not a musician."

She wondered about her own bitterness.

"I suppose because all those years I met nobody," she said finally. "Sure, I once saw Doctor Kelly at a distance. But here I am—because I got good at my job."

"And here I am, because——"

"You'll always be wonderful to me. What did you say this man's name was?"

"Kern. And I didn't say it *was*. I said it *is*."

"That's the way you used to talk to me. And now both of us are fat and—sort of middle-aged. We never had much. Did we?"

"It wasn't my fault."

"It wasn't anybody's fault. It was just meant to be like that. Let's dance. That's a good tune. What did you say was this man's name?"

"Kern."

> *They*
> > *asked me how I*
> > > *knew—ew—ew—*

"We've had all that anyhow, haven't we?" she asked him. "All those people—that Youmans, that Berlin, that Kern. They must have been through hell to be able to write like that. And we sort of listened to them, didn't we?"

"But my God, that's so little——" he began but her mood changed and she said:

"Let's not say anything about it. It was all we had—everything we'll ever know about life. What were their names—you knew their names."

"Their names were——"

"Didn't you ever know *any* of them in that fifteen years around Europe?"

"I never saw one of them."

"Well, I never will." She hesitated before the wide horizon of how she might have lived. How she might have married this man, borne him children, died for him—of how she had lived out of sordid poverty and education—into power—and spinsterhood. And she cared not a damn for her man any more because he had never gone off with her. But she wondered how these composers had lived. Youmans and Irving Berlin and Jerome Kern and she thought that if any of their wives turned up in this hospital she would try to make them happy.

MAXIM GORKI

Life in a Prison Cell

Alexei Maximovich Pyeshkoff coined his pen name, Maxim Gorki (Maxim 'the Bitter'), when his first story was published in 1892. Six years later his *Sketches and Stories* appeared, and from junk gatherer in the city dumps, dish washer on a Volga steamer, floor scrubber, diaper washer, stevedore, janitor-gardener and general holder of odd jobs, Gorki became the most famous proletarian writer in Russia. His picture appeared on postcards and cigarette boxes; tramps and rebels adopted him as their patron; and he was introduced to Chekhov and Tolstoi. Lenin called him the foremost representative of proletarian art and sought his writings for Bolshevik publications.

More than any other writer, Gorki bridges the gap between pre- and post-revolutionary Russian literature. He was the first in Russian literature to write about the proletariat, and this was one of the reasons his writing created such an immediate sensation. From the turn of the century his activities and his writing were tied up with the struggles of the Bolshevik party. Even his death, in 1936, is supposed to have been caused by an anti-Stalinist physician.

Gorki was imprisoned four times in his life: in 1890 the charge was lodging with political suspects; in 1898 he was jailed in Metekh Castle for 'revolutionary activities'; in 1901, accused of sedition, he was confined for five months (in spite of his ill health: he suffered from T.B.) in the Nizhni-Novgorod prison; and in 1905, for his fierce denunciation of the slaughter by Czarist forces of 500 workers, he was imprisoned for six weeks in St. Petersburg's Fortress of St. Peter and St. Paul, the prison for high treason. 'Life in a Prison Cell' reflects these experiences. The story lights up again the paradoxical way in which Gorki can indicate his opposition to passivity and non-resistance to evil with a grim setting and plot. The nameless protagonist continues rebellious to the end and, phoenix-like, emerges in his own grim triumph (the smoke escaping through the window; the spots on the wall trembling 'joyously'). With remarkable psychological insight Gorki

D

makes his character intensely individual at the same time as he uses him
as representative of a whole social group.

'Life in a Prison Cell' appeared in *Esquire* for April 1937.   It is not
mentioned in the Library of Congress Bibliography of Gorki in English,
and is reprinted here for the first time.

THE EVENING CHECK-UP had just ended.   Standing in the middle
of his cell the prisoner listened to the last sounds from the prison yard
dying out.

The bolt creaked noisily; the air shook as though from the sharp
report of a gun; this was followed by a heavy sound of iron bars, a
firm and even step, and then nothing more.   You would have
thought that the prison had suddenly been plunged into a substance
that was impervious and sealed not only to sounds, but even to the
air.

For another two minutes, without moving from the spot, the
prisoner listens: nothing more comes to shatter the overwhelming
silence.   Then he lightly sighs with relief, contracts his eyebrows,
casting a mistrusting glance at the dark corners of the cell, and
slowly approaches the window with silent steps.

He is a man still quite young, with an unhealthy-looking face, and
with large eyes.   They are opened wide, and an expression of fearful
expectation never leaves them.   An imprint of terror and amazement
hangs about his whole person; this impression is accentuated still
further by his tapering shoulders, which are raised as if to conceal his
head.   It is two months now since he has been arrested, but he hasn't
been questioned yet, and he doesn't know for what reason they have
locked him up in this frightful room with its yellow doors and iron-
barred window.   He has waited a long time to learn what he was
guilty of; at first he had been indignant, and had protested; he
pictured the frantic alarm of his poor old parents, and this idea
plunged him now into fits of tears, and now into outbursts of pent-up
rage.

But days after days had passed, and the silent walls had gradually
worn away the fiery strength of his body, replacing it with a perpetual state of fear, and his being was filled with an eternal wait for
something terrible to happen.

Standing near the window, he presses his face against the iron bars, without winking an eye, and desperately looks out into the night. And the night is so laden with darkness, that it seems that if you could pass your arm outside, it would be enveloped by a black and moist substance, like soot. Somewhere, far away, a tiny light glitters wretchedly and, completely surrounded by the darkness, it also seems to be imprisoned. From behind his iron bars the man has become accustomed to look towards this unknown little light each night, and he realises that it is just as weak as he, and therefore resembles him. And each night, after the check-up, surrounded by silence and darkness, the man feels fear ascending and growing in him.

He would like to turn around and examine his cell, but he doesn't dare. He knows that the cell gets its light from a lamp hanging from the casing above the door, and that shadows lie hidden in the corners; he knows that besides these shadows, the bed, the table, and the chair, the cell contains absolutely nothing else, for it is impossible for anything else to be there. He is convinced of it, he knows it; but still he doesn't quite believe it, and even though he has a very clear notion of his isolation, he feels nevertheless as if he weren't alone.

For a long time he has known by heart the location of the smallest spots and cracks in the paint on the walls and, even while continuing to stare into the night, he seeks to picture them to himself in order to calm himself and subdue his fear. Above the bed someone before him had covered the wall with huge columns of figures, having probably applied himself to long, studied calculations in order to beguile the emptiness of the days and to fight against his loneliness. On the wall opposite were sprawled wide green spots of dampness, and in one of them a hand had scratched in large type:

> Over hill and dale we marched, yo, ho!
> Two highwaymen of Koussovo,
> Without any ambition and just rags on our back,
> Then we spent the night at a girl friend's shack,
> Where we had plenty to drink and plenty of snack.
> . . . . Hah!

He had thought about this 'hah' for a long time, asking himself

what meaning it could have had as to the state of mind of the two
highwaymen. . . . A shout of joy? Of cruelty? And he had
decided that this interjection probably expressed the appetite, the
pleasure of eating and drinking like gluttons, yes, precisely, greedily
chewing away . . . he pictured that very easily. Those two highwaymen must have been well-known jolly blades, cut-throats,
ragged and happy, and certainly incapable of feeling the slightest
fear. But, on the other hand, he had no success in imagining how the
man must have felt who in a corner beside the door had scribbled,
"Here tarried Jacob Ignatier Orissof for murdering his wife and
Sacha Grizlof on account of their filthy carrying-on. It was in
January, 1897, that I cut out their insides." Lower down was represented a foul oath, and a cottage with three windows and above
the roof something like a jumble of hair, probably standing for trees
or smoke coming out of the chimney.

In the opposite corner, near the window, a piece of torn away
plaster makes one think of an animal whose skin one was trying to
tear off. The door is constructed of heavy timber and rimmed with
iron. A square opening cut into the thickness of the wood is con-
cealed on the outside by the addition of a little metal cross which
does not stuff it up completely, and makes this gap, through which
the light from the corridor steals in, seem like a misshapen eye,
always watching.

The prisoner knows his cell even in its most minute details, and
yet the more he knows it, the more he can feel the presence there of
something which he doesn't see, but which he can almost touch.
This something returns each night to fill his heart with terror, and
each night it becomes bolder and bolder. It always stands behind
him, and even when he presses his back against the wall it still
remains behind him, invincible, silent, and triumphant, and blowing cold chills down to his marrowbones. You could call it a monster,
incessantly brooding over him with lust, which suddenly, in the
nakedness of all its horror, will sink its slimy paws into his heart, and
will begin to squeeze, squeeze. . . . It is gigantic, heavy, greenish
as the mud in a marsh, and coated over with a stinking secretion.
The prisoner feels it, clearly, and his whole body trembles; he
continues to look through the irons of the window, for he does not
dare to turn around. His eyes pain him, as if the darkness of the

night had come and touched them, and was weighing down upon them; his legs shake with fatigue, but he cannot tear himself away from the spot where he is standing, for fear that in turning round he may discover this 'thing' that terrorises him.

And all this while, on the outside, the silence and the darkness merge into one single mass, and it seems that everything on the earth has been stifled by this cataclysm, that everything is dead, and that nothing is left in the world but just one man, locked up in this cell, and condemned to eternal waiting—the most frightful of punishments.

He will be waiting for the rest of eternity: years, centuries—and this night is going to be indefinitely prolonged; there will no longer be any day, and the sun will never rise again! And this 'thing' will always be there behind him, and will continue to watch him, in silence. . . .

Heavy footsteps have re-echoed behind the window. The prisoner jumps up with joy, but then he hastily draws back, becomes motionless, and listens.

"Halt!" commands a hollow and sluggish voice; there is the sound of the butt-ends of guns hitting the ground. The sentry counts rapidly and in a low voice:

"Twelve windows. . . . Two watch-towers." . . .

"Now, you, Finn, if you should see a head moving near one of the windows, that's no reason for shooting. Get it?"

"I get it."

"Explain that to him, adjutant."

In the silence each word rings out sharp and clear, like the brightness of a flash of fire in the dark.

"And if you see anyone looking out through the window, you don't have to shoot. Do you understand?"

"Perfectly, adjutant."

The voice of the one answering thus is timid and sad, and you can feel that the words he pronounces are strange to him, while the other one's voice is low, rough, and authoritative.

"But if someone should pass through the window, and should begin to flee either this way or that way—well, you see, don't you?"

"Perfectly, adjutant."

"Then immediately you are to cry out, 'Who goes there?' Once, twice, and the third time you are to shoot in the air, to give the alarm . . . but you also are to fire at the one escaping, or else you're to strike him from above with your butt-end or bayonet . . . if that's any better, understand?"

"Perfectly, adjutant."

"And so, look, you pace to and fro, from here . . . to here, and you watch the windows. And you must take great care not even to close your eyes for a second."

"No, no, adjutant."

"All right, now repeat. Under what conditions are you to fire?"

"If he comes towards me . . ."

"And if he should simply leap over the wall?"

A long silence. You could hear someone breathing with difficulty, and you could also hear a rumbling and impatient moving about.

"Well, damn you . . . ?"

"Then . . . you must hit . . ."

"And if you should see a head by the window?"

Again, silence. The sound of the butt-ends. Someone spits.

"Well, blockhead! Shake the cobwebs out of your brains, damn you!"

"Then, nothing."

"Why no! No, imbecile! Then you must say, 'Pull in your head!' Do you understand all that? All right, that's good. Now, beat it! March!"

The prisoner has again leaned over by the window to try to make out who this sentry is with this sorry voice. But the narrow alley between the prison wall and the high outside slope is veiled in darkness. A dim outline moves around slowly there, and almost noiselessly, and only the bayonet gleams sometimes in the dark, like a fish reflected in the water.

"Pull in your head . . . !" resounds the timid voice of the soldier.

The prisoner draws a step back, turns round abruptly towards the door, and takes a look all around in his cell. Then he goes towards his bed, sits down, and leaning forward, supporting himself on his hands, he steadily looks at the wall facing him.

A little mouse jumps out from behind the plinth and softly rolls along the floor, just as a ball of wool would roll. Clever and graceful, it runs to and fro, lifting up its little nose and smelling the air. Its little ears wriggle. While following it with his eyes, the prisoner never stops listening to the restless and rapid beating of his heart.

"If it is already ten o'clock, then there are still six or seven hours left to wait before dawn comes . . ."

And at this thought anguish overwhelms him. Its sensations are so bitter that it seems that every bone in his body is being pounded, that his muscles are tearing, and that his skin is shrinking just as if it is wasting away.

He lets his head droop even more, he clenches his teeth, and thus he remains motionless for a long time, a long time.

"Ah—ah—ah . . . oh—oh—oo—oo!"

He leaps up with a shock. For a second he thought that it was from his heart that this long and sorrowful wailing had escaped, without his having been conscious of it. But no, that comes from the window; it is on the outside that someone is groaning, and the sound, hardly audible, empties itself like a long thin string into the cell through the iron bars.

"Oh—oh—oh!" weeps and groans the voice in the night.

It is the sentry singing. He listens, and his lips tremble a little. The melody is not very familiar to his ear, and it sounds like a distant song, far away from this country, sung in days of old, else-where, very far from this prison and this night. It is not a captivating tune and the voice singing it also lacks charm, but you would call it the slow destruction of a broken tree. At the side of a precipice, below the muddy waves of a powerful current of water, a whining tree; its bare exposed roots are struck by the water, which pulls and tears them; the breaking up of the ice after the snowstorms has broken its branches one by one, and the poor tree, hanging over the abyss, swings back and forth, and sadly groans . . . and soon it will be hurled with just one stroke into the river.

"What can really be the words of that song?" the prisoner asks himself. And the dream goes away, while the song continues, sweet and humble.

The singer doesn't dare sing any louder; he must be afraid of something. And the prisoner penetrates still more and more into the song and it seems to him now that it is in him, in his heart, that the weeping is his distress moaning out loud, his grief, his fear of loneli-ness, his uneasiness about the future.

Enthralled by the song, he falls powerless upon his bed, his face buried in the blanket. It is only when one remembers one's mother that one can sing like that, when one thinks about the sufferings of a mother's heart from whom her son has been taken, and when one thinks about the sorrow of a son who has lost his mother.

Tearlessly and quietly a sobbing in spasms shakes his whole body, and, stretched out on his bed, he gives voice to his suffering in the strange melody which another is singing.

"Mother, my mother . . . I have done nothing . . . I am innocent! They have taken and imprisoned me here . . . mother, save me! I am afraid . . . mother . . . my mother . . . mother . . ."

And now he calls upon them, both of them. She, his mother, full of love for him; her face is wet with tears, and he clearly sees anguish in her eyes. He, his father, wasted away and ill, powerless to console his mother, for his heart is growing weaker, torn by unrest and the fear of the fate that awaits his child.

In the darkness the father's and mother's gazes are fiery, they search, they look, their fire becomes stronger and then gradually dies out. . . . And this song is like the echo of the moaning of these old people over their son.

He jumps down from the bed, rushes towards the door, and with his closed fists he begins banging on it, crying and begging:

"Open up! Release me! . . . I can't stand it any longer! . . . Have pity! . . . Open! . . . please!"

At the iron bars appears a face with a heavy moustache, which moves as a harsh voice begins scolding:

"Well? You're beginning to make a rumpus again, are you? Tut, tut . . . that's not nice. Moreover you're a boy that's had some learning and education, and you should understand. It is forbidden to make any noise . . ."

"Listen to me, I beg of you . . . my mother, you must understand! I have a mother . . . tell that to them over there . . . let me go! I'll return . . ."

"Heavens, it is forbidden to make any noise at night! Why don't you understand that? People are sleeping—everything's asleep. . . . And you begin to knock and disturb the quiet. It's not allowed . . ."

"But listen! I beg you . . ."

"And after that they'll put you in the dungeon."

"But please, tell them . . ."

"That won't be of any use; this isn't the first time. You know that they've already answered several times: 'Don't listen to him.' I'm therefore asking you here and now not to make any more noise. It is forbidden to make any noise here."

And the moustache disappears.

"Listen!" the prisoner whispers again, beseechingly pressing his cheek against the bars in order to see in the direction of the steps that are moving away.

All that he gets for an answer is the even sound of boots on the flagstones.

"Listen! Come back!" whispers the prisoner. "Come back, I beg you . . . stay near the door so that I'll be able to see you. . . ."

Everything is quiet. You can no longer hear the mournful song through the window.

A knee on the floor, the prisoner presses his head against the door, his fingers clinging to the thick knob. His forehead is glued to the iron framework, and the metallic cold spreading through his whole body gives him shivers.

Now, after this outburst, he feels that in his heart has burst a huge abscess and that into his blood vessels is being poured a thick, sticky poison which is robbing him of the last of his strength.

Silence. Only his heart is beating rapidly enough to burst.

But now a new noise is suddenly born. It re-echoes from behind the wall on the left. In the next cell someone is walking back and forth feverishly, like a beast in a cage whose claws are creeping over the floor. And even the sound of these steps is like the panting of an angry deer. The prisoner raises himself, and with his face white with pallor, his eyes alight with great suffering, staggering, he approaches the table near the bed. On the table is a jug of water and a vial containing some drops of ether prescribed yesterday by the doctor. There are still many of them. The young man seizes the vial with his trembling fingers . . . then, putting it down again, he sinks down on his bed. He feels empty now, and the frenzy of a little while ago already seems to him so remote, although only a few

minutes have elapsed from the time he was making his fists black and
blue against the door.

And again anguish envelops his body and soul, and it seems to
him that his life is melting away in him.

The lamp above the door lights up the bed, the table, and all the
space separating the door from the window. But opposite the bed,
near the wall, and in the corners darkness reigns, and this darkness
makes the spots of dampness spread out on the wall appear to be
living. They seem to be moving. In the daytime they only resemble
a geography map, but in the night, when you look steadily at them,
they recall human faces, perhaps the faces of all those who have been
imprisoned in this cell.

That could be possible. A man remains imprisoned within four
walls for many long days, and the walls soak-in his smell; so why
wouldn't they also soak-in his thoughts? And why couldn't they
reflect his soul?

The soul of man is something which is volatile. With a free man
the soul spreads out around on the whole of life . . . while in prison
the walls absorb the soul of the imprisoned man . . . certainly! And
why couldn't these dark spots in the plaster be the reflection of the
souls of the two highwaymen of Koussovo and of all the other
humans who were imprisoned here?

These spots have nothing terrible about them, although they may
become animated with a silent life. There they are moving, changing form. If they could speak, they could whisper, not very distinctly,
human words. . . . But how frightful is the darkness beside them!
That also is living, and imperceptible and deceitful at the same
time! In it is hidden the power that dominates over the human soul,
a cruel power. One breathes it with the air. It creeps into the soul
like rust, and slowly, implacably, it rends it asunder. It absorbs the
thoughts of man, and one's entire being is diluted in it; and although
it hasn't any visible and finite form, at any moment it can suddenly
blossom forth into something horrible, which has never been seen
and which it is impossible to foresee.

Without removing his eyes from the spots on the wall, the prisoner
stretches out his hand towards the table, finds the jug of water after
groping, and with an abrupt gesture empties it on the wall. And,
in being poured out, the water gives the noise of fleeing, as if

someone, frightened, were running away, with an angry hissing.

The prisoner draws back, and stretches out his arms before him, as if he is protecting himself against an attack. The water flows down the length of the wall, making the spots disappear, and drop by drop it softly trickles down to the floor.

"God," the man whispers, holding his head in the palms of his hand, "God . . . I think . . . I believe I'm becoming . . ."

He doesn't dare pronounce that awful word.

His exhausted arms have been battered down; powerless, they rest on his knees. In the grips of terror his head bubbles, violently, with all kinds of shapeless ideas. He is seated on his bed, and he swings his body more and more, to and fro, from right to left; but his eyes seem to be riveted to the darkness in which they are plunged. And he feels that his whole body is sinking, that he is being swallowed up into an abyss which is bottomless, that he is slowly falling, and that there is nothing to which he can hang on.

"God"—and his lips move incessantly.

But suddenly conscience, with a start, gets the upper hand again. A vivid and piercing feeling of shame holds him back, and someone in his inner conscience whispers to him:

"It is a crime to die like this, a shame, a shame! Death is not more horrible, not more terrible than the agony of fear . . ."

He gets up again, looks towards the table, seizes the vial of ether with a trembling hand; but it slips through his fingers, and breaks in the basin with a noise as sharp and as harsh as a cutting laugh. The smell of ether permeates the cell.

The man bends over the basin and frantically picks up the broken pieces of glass. He looks at them lying in the palm of his hand. His breathing is choking, his head is whirling, and an unknown force wants to close his eyes. This sensation increases his fear, and it seems to him that invisible and powerful arms are gradually encompassing him. His whole body quivers, and he walks backwards from the table to the door. Something icy is pursuing him, and is breathing right into his face.

"No. . . . No . . . !" he repeats, with a mad look.

And suddenly, bringing his hand to his mouth, he abruptly snaps up the pieces enclosed in his palm, and begins grinding them with his teeth. They rip and cut away his gums, his lips, his tongue. Very soon his face is contracted with pain, and his mouth fills with warm blood and with a salty taste. He leans his head forward, and spits everything out together . . . blood, and pieces of glass. He can feel it oozing out from where his lips meet, and he watches the horrible designs being formed on the floor by the tears which are burning his eyes, tears of bitterness, for he realises that he is absolutely helpless.

"I can't . . . I can't . . ." there is a humming in his head. "I can't die. . . . God help me!"

And this taste of warm, salty blood in his mouth is mixing with the taste of acute sorrow, which is gnawing at his heart.

But suddenly, his conscience remembers something.

That girl, that young heroine who had purified herself by fire! . . . This time he rocks with joy, and challenges the darkness with a bitter ecstasy. He suddenly feels as if he has been regenerated, and his whole body and gestures have regained a strange assurance.

A sunny smile spreads over his whole face, and without hurrying he approaches the table, even though he is continually spitting out glass and blood; he takes the basin in which the ether has spilled, places the footstool right against the door, and then climbs up on it, all the while pouring the contents of the basin drop by drop over his head. Then he carefully takes down the cell lamp, takes off with a sharp little blow the glass case, which quietly falls on the bed, jumps down happily from the stool, and standing up in the middle of the room, facing the spots on the wall, facing the darkness, he says in a very low voice:

"Forgive me . . ." Then, lifting the lamp right over his head, and with a voice that is stronger and more assured, he says, "They will forgive!"

The fire falls on his head as from heaven, and instantaneously envelops him completely. For a second the man hesitates in the midst of the flames, but then, beating the air with his two arms, he lets loose a shout of triumph. The blue strips of fire caress him on all sides, flashing through him like serpents, and the cell is as bright as if it were daylight—while the spots on the wall tremble joyously.

On the outside the iron bars on the door give way . . .

But when the people penetrated into the cell, there was no longer anything on the ground but a mass of something black and burned, which hardly resembled a human body—though it still moved, and groaned softly, softly.

Thin bits of smoke ascended spirally up to the ceiling, where there was a thick and suffocating mist gathered together in heavy volutes; then the smoke escaped through the window from the prison, as if it didn't want to conceal from the light of dawn either the crime or the victim.

FERENC MOLNAR

Heavenly and Earthly Love

The atmosphere in Budapest around the turn of the century (the place and time in which Ferenc Molnar grew to maturity) was one of perpetual gaiety and high life. Like Vienna, Budapest during the last phase of the tottering Austro-Hungarian Empire was an extremely hospitable place to a young man of means, especially if he possessed, as did Molnar, wit, sophistication, and charm. Born in 1878 and educated for the law (which he never practised), Molnar became a journalist, meanwhile enjoying all the advantages to be derived from wealth and social position. His personal life was spiced with numerous romantic affairs, which, along with his pranks and sparkling conversattion, fed Budapest gossip for over two decades.

Writing on a marble-topped café table, drinking and talking while he worked, Molnar penned short stories, novels, brief dialogues, and over forty stage plays. Many of his works treat affairs of the heart in a graceful, rarefied way; some of them, such as the short dialogue 'Heavenly and Earthly Love', could be called *objets d'art*, characterised by a certain charm, polish, frivolity, and cleverness, and finished off with an ironic twist.

Molnar's fame rests on his longer dramatic writings: he is the author, for instance, of *Liliom*, familiar to American and British audiences as the Rodgers and Hammerstein musical, *Carousel*. Molnar also wrote a full-length play with the title *Heavenly and Earthly Love*, which has no relation to the story here. Acts 1, 3, 4, and 5 of the play are in the Theatre Collection of the New York Public Library in typescript. The short dialogue below appeared in *Esquire* for April 1938.

Fleeing the Nazis, Molnar crossed to the United States in 1940, and settled in New York's Plaza Hotel, where, until his death in 1952, he played host to a select group of Hungarian and international literati. A zestful, white-haired gentleman, he could often be seen strolling in the environs of Central Park South.

EVENING. A soft foggy vapour slowly descends upon the Stephanie-strasse, while the lights from the distant street lanterns glimmer from out of the distance. From the city the muffled clatter of wagons sounds as though coming from a heavily carpeted room. Two gentlemen promenade upon the Stephaniestrasse in the middle of the carriage road, where the *fiacres* hastily roll along on a happy, dusty Sunday afternoon.

The First (giving himself credit for being about to say something exceptionally clever): "I am inclined to believe that sensual and spiritual love among women is never equally distributed. Titian is right."

The Second: "Why is Titian right?"

The First: "Because he painted the lovely picture *Heavenly and Earthly Love*. It shows two women. The one is nothing but heavenly joy and peace. The second is nothing but fleshly sensuality. It is thus also in life."

(He puffs deeply upon his cigar as one who has solved a problem. He is proud and happy.)

The Second: "You believe that, really?"

The First: "Yes. I cannot help it. I am a simple fellow and I love luxuriant women. The soulful life is beautiful, as are the pangs of love; yet as far as I am concerned all such folly evaporates from my head when my lips glide over the lips of a woman. Delicately and hot, over a woman's lovely red mouth. At such times I feel as if tiny sparks of electricity were flying from one hot, dry pair of lips to the other."

The Second: "Women train one."

The First: "How so?"

The Second: "A man may be trained for all things. It seems . . . this lady . . . don't be afraid, I'm not the least inquisitive . . . that your lady is a sensuous being. And so you also dream of kisses. My lady . . . don't be afraid, I shall not be indiscreet . . . is very different. I really don't know. Perhaps it is because she is thin; but she somehow managed to train me her way. To recognise spiritual tenderness and joy-bringing friendship as the real basis and meaning of even such sinful relationships."

The First: "Perhaps; yes. A thin woman."

(He resumes smoking, since once more he feels that he has solved the problem upon the basis of natural science. He is well satisfied with himself.)

The Second: "She is refined and timid in love. She has beautiful thoughts. In love, the kiss serves her only as a background for her lovely, delicate thoughts. You will probably think I am just stupid. However, I feel that it is possible to part as brother and sister even after an afternoon spent in the sweetest kind of intimacy. Suffused with a glowing, happy peace and the quiet of an unclouded memory in our hearts."

The First: "There are so many varieties of women! When I leave my lady, I feel like a wild male that goes stalking and bellowing through the forest because someone has torn him from the side of his mate. And she also leaves me as a proper female should. With bleeding lips, a wild longing, an amative hatred and a certain revengeful feeling in her heart. For sensuous love can never be completely satisfied."

(He smokes again for obvious reasons.)

The Second: "My lady could never understand such love-making. She would learn to hate and despise me were I to talk in this fashion."

The First: "Mine would laugh at you were she to hear you talk. You know that when you set out to court a woman you try anything. And so I also tried some of those soulful jests. But she stopped with such vehemence that I lost all pleasure in that sort of thing for all time to come. Between us two there is never such talk. Kisses, kisses, embraces, burning, seething. To be aroused. To be insatiable! That's it!" (He smokes.)

The Second: "It is astonishing that we two should have met!"

The First: "How so?"

The Second: "Well, because we personify the two extremes. You live the love of the blood while I live the feelings of the soul. Yours is the voluptuous, aroused woman; while mine is the slender, pale woman."

The First: "Well, actually my lady really is not so voluptuous."

The Second: "And mine is not so very slender."

The First: "Mine is rather medium. Not too fat nor too thin. She just appears voluptuous."

The Second: "My lady leans towards the medium. She appears rather slender. Also, she is not pale, but rosy pale."

The First: "Mine also is not exactly chubby-faced. She is rosy. But fiery rosy."

The Second: "It would be great fun to bring these two women together. How would they converse with one another? I have heard of something written by a French dramatist. To go out in a quartet. To dine together!"

The First: "That wouldn't be possible. They may be acquainted already."

The Second: "You. . . . The Devil! How strange! Perhaps they really know one another?"

The First: "Perhaps they are actually friends."

The Second (with excitement): "I say . . ."

The First (already half guessing what the other would say): "Well?"

The Second: ". . . if you tell me the name of your lady, I'll tell you the name of mine."

(They walk wordlessly alongside of each other for a while and the idea seems to please them both exceedingly. They are at present contemplating whether to reveal the name of the woman in question would be harmless business or base roguery.)

The First (after a long pause): "Give me your hand."

(The Second stretches out his hand.)

(They exchange a long manly handclasp, hard and firm, as their eyes meet in a strange look.)

The First: "Frau Katharine Szabo."

The Second: "What?"

(His eyes stare like those of a madman.)

The First: "Now it's your turn."

The Second: "Who? What? What did you say? What . . . did you say?"

The First: "Frau . . . Katharine Szabo."

The Second (grasps him by the arm): "You . . ."

The First: "Well? Well? What's the matter?"

The Second: "That is also the name of my lady!"

(A horrible silence.)

The First: "Tuesday, Thursday and Saturday."

The Second: "Monday, Wednesday and Friday."

(Another pause.)

The First: "And . . . Sunday?"

The Second (with tears in his eyes): "Who knows?"

The First: "And that is your spiritual lady?"

The Second: "Yes. The slender, pale and soulful lady. The heavenly love. The timid virgin."

The First: "And that is the voluptuous, aroused, sensuous lady. The earthly love. The feminine fire. The wild female."

The Second: "I could weep."

The First: "You feel like weeping because you have loved her as a spiritual woman. I could laugh because she has trained me the other way."

(The one who wanted to weep smiles bitterly. The one who wanted to laugh makes a tragic face.)

The Second: "What is to become of us?"

The First: "You ask me that? We are wise, modern people and so we shall not kill each other. I don't know what you spiritual people think. We sensual men become stunned at the thought of another man having anything to do with our women. The matter is very simple. I don't need her any more." (They shake hands.)

The Second: "We spiritual people . . . we spiritual people . . . I also don't need her any more."

The First: "I have an idea."

The Second: "Well?"

The First: "My idea is excellent. In fact I feel as though during the course of my entire life I have not had such a good idea. Listen here. This woman has so skilfully managed to make two distinctly different women of herself that it seems no more than decent and proper to reward her."

The Second: "Reward her? With what? And how can we——?"

The First: "By both . . . as it seems proper for real gentlemen to do . . . accepting her conception of living. If she therefore desires to be two distinctly different women, let's accept her as two distinctly different personalities. Let's simply believe her. And . . ."

The Second: "And . . . ?"

The First: "And all remains as before."

The Second (without reflection): "Good!"

The First: "Are we agreed?"

The Second: "Yes."

The First: "And never . . . never . . . let's mention this affair between us again. In fact let's never speak of any love affair of any sort that concerns ourselves, after this. And she will also notice no difference in our conduct towards her. I will continue to be sensuous and you will lay particular stress upon the spiritual, as before. And we shall both live happily and contentedly. Farewell."

The Second: "Farewell."

(A short, rapid handclasp and they depart to the left and right. Both resolve within themselves to change their conduct and policy with the woman in order to squeeze out the other. Both hearts burn and on the morrow both will make a scene before the woman. And tomorrow the woman will throw them both out and look about for two others to take their place. And the woman will be in the right!)

THEODORE DREISER

***

The Tithe of the Lord

The favourite joke about Theodore Dreiser is that he had no talent—
only genius. Certainly his ponderous style has produced some of the
most notoriously graceless sentences in American classic literature (for
instance, notice the dangling participle in the first sentence of the story
below); and his ideas, which shifted between determinism, communism and mysticism, were often philosophically inconsistent to the point
of incongruity. Yet in novels such as *An American Tragedy*, *Sister Carrie*,
and *Gennie Gerhardt*, Dreiser succeeded through the intensity of his pity
in creating characters which now seem more acutely central to American
life than those of any other author of the first half-century with the
exception of F. Scott Fitzgerald.

'The Tithe of the Lord' was one of sixteen Dreiser pieces first published in *Esquire*. He wrote it somewhere between 1933 and 1936—
roughly a decade after *An American Tragedy*, To the typical Dreiser
trap of instinctive necessity *versus* social pressures is here added a less
typical dimension, arrived at through the mysticism of this later period
—that of the demands of conscience in relation to God.

'The Tithe of the Lord' appeared in the July 1938 issue, and is here
reprinted for the first time.

***

SITTING THERE, cold and helpless, on a park bench, the thought
intrigued Benziger. "Suppose I do just that . . . make a bargain
with the Lord? Supposing, here and now, I should try to make such
a contract? Would it work?" Would the Lord, for instance,
prosper him as He had prospered his father, he who was now so
miserable, so at odds with the world? Assuming there was a Lord,
and that He really acted in behalf of those who, like him, had

sinned, would He forgive him his early errors? Restore him to a decent social position; make him as well off as he was before? Would He?

Then and there he decided he was going to try it. He was going to make a deal with God, or whoever it was that ran the world, just as he would make a deal with anyone in the business world. If God would help him to get over this despair so that he could get work and get on his feet again, he would, from then on until his death, *devote ten per cent of everything he should gain to helping those who needed help worse than he did.* Furthermore, he would leave women alone. Or better yet, get married, and be helpful—and faithful—to one woman.

When I first met Benziger, which was some years subsequent to this bargain with the Lord, I knew he was the type who would fit this story I had heard about him, exactly. He was a little under the medium height and weight, dark, rather brown skin, with healthy, cheerful, genial eyes, good nose and attractive mouth, a most enticing and reassuring smile. His forehead was low and wide, and over it fell curly brown-black hair. At this time he was thirty-eight years of age, neat, agreeable, assured, and very successful—the head of an important manufacturing unit of the American Wicker Furniture Trust or Combine.

But Benziger, as anyone could see, was considerably more than a manufacturer of wicker furniture. Frank Kelcey, the architect, a close friend to both of us, who was building gay summer homes for a score of people on Long Island—among them Benziger, told me that Benziger was that rare thing, a character, a man of the world in business, almost an artist. Since Kelcey was sure I would like him, he had introduced us.

Just the same, at first, I took his statements in regard to Benziger with a grain of salt. He was from Rock Island and Chicago. The group he represented—manufacturers, bankers, etc.—were, here in the East at least, considered pretty raw socially. Yet—Benziger was different. He swept me with an engaging, hearty smile. We entered into a conversation and I found he possessed imagination and charm as well as business ability. He appeared to have travelled a good deal—to China and India and the Malay Peninsula. Unlike most business-bound men, he talked almost romantically of bars and cafés and out-of-the-way amusements in all of these lands. Before we parted, he invited me to see his new summer home on the North Shore of Long Island when it was completed.

But I will not go into that. It was all pleasant—although unimportant, and afterwards I invited him and his wife to my place at Shell Cove once or twice.

What was more important, though, was what Kelcey told me after Benziger was gone—that is, a month or so later. According to Kelcey, Benziger had had a most amazing youth. His father, a conventional, religious, rich man of Rock Island, Illinois, had been in the furniture business before him, and while Benziger was a boy had tried to interest him in the very successful plant he had there. But Benziger, who at that time was obviously of a playful, restless and somewhat erratic nature, was not interested in what he considered such a prosaic enterprise. So, without consulting his father, he finally left home for Chicago—a move which caused considerable feeling between them He did well enough, and presently got a position with a broker on the Chicago Board of Trade. Pretty soon he joined several clubs—also became acquainted with a young North Side social group.

Inside of two years, and without much, if any, exchange of letters or visits between him and his father, he married a girl of considerable means and social position and thereafter appeared to be established and as devoted to her as she was to him. According to things which Kelcey had learned, the wife, Rhoda, was not as clever as Benziger, but truly beautiful, slight, blonde, witty and affectionate. They had numerous friends and were considered to be substantial members of their community and gay as well as smart.

Then, at the end of the third year of Benziger's marriage, his young wife committed suicide!

"Would you think," Kelcey asked of me, "after visiting and talking with Benziger, that he was the sole surviving remnant of a marriage tragedy?"

"I would not," I replied.

"Just the same," said Kelcey, "he is."

And then, because I was really interested, he furnished the following details of the tragedy which astonished me as it startled Chicago, and more so the Benziger social set, because there was no evidence that such a thing was likely to occur.

Not more than six months before his wife's death, the Benzigers had been introduced to a young, well-to-do and clever married couple named Ellis, from Wisconsin. The husband, Calvin Ellis, was a young eingineer connected with a Chicago construction company. His wife's name was Olive.

The four of them became fast friends and went about everywhere together.

Olive, while more sensual than Rhoda, and perhaps a little more attractive, was not younger or gayer. She was different, dark and a little sly perhaps—whereas Mrs. Benziger, Rhoda, was open and confiding, and terribly, yet by no means selfishly, devoted to Benziger. In fact, she made it a point not to keep any strings or tabs on him— merely to love him, as he insisted always that he loved her.

Olive Ellis had a strong magnetism or hypnotism, and yet, according to all reports, she was anything but the brash forward type. Instead, she was rather aloof and evasive. But there was that compelling allure of her temperament—all the more so because she appeared not to follow anyone. In fact, until she met Benziger, she was apparently devoted to her husband—wholly so.

Then the tragedy, of which Kelcey had heard so much!

"I don't know how you size him up, Mr. Lamborn," he said to me, "but Benziger appears to be a fine and able man. He loves pleasure, of course, but he is a good business man too, and treats his employees well—he even has a profit-sharing system and of course you have met his present wife?"

"She seems to be a very sensible as well as a beautiful young woman," I interpolated.

"And I suppose you know about the baby boy they've adopted?"

"Yes. He talked to him over the Long Distance while I was visiting him."

"He is genuinely devoted to the child and to his wife also," said Kelcey.

"Rose, this time," I commented.

"Yes, Rose, that's her name. The daughter of a wealthy Chicago grain merchant. Really nice woman, isn't she?"

"Very," I said. "I imagine he must have thought, after that first affair of his, that a healthy, sober, home-loving and not too romantic girl was the best for him."

"I guess that's right too," agreed Kelcey. "Only, in connection with that Rhoda-Olive affair, it appears that Olive fell in love with Benziger first—not he with her. She was one of those complicated beauties from whom you never know what to expect. At least so the papers indicated. At any rate, she either secretly or openly enticed Benziger. According to his confession at the trial, he was an easy victim. What he said he felt at that time (it was in all the Chicago papers when I lived there) was that love to him was not the intense thing which his wife Rhoda took it to be. He loved her, of course, but not the life-and-death way that gripped her.

"Besides, as he said, Rhoda was too sweet and liberal and gay to check him up enough. The thing in particular that deceived him in connection with his wife was that she never appeared to be jealous. As he mournfully confessed to the world, she was probably so infatuated with him that she was anxious to appear to agree with his light variable views on life and love without actually doing so. She did not want to appear to hold him and still she did want to be exclusively happy with him. And that was why he grieved so much afterwards as he says. At any rate, neither he nor she anticipated any such dread disaster as that which followed Olive's arrival on the scene.

"According to Benziger," went on Kelcey, who largely talked this story to me as I am telling it, "Olive was not essentially cruel either. She had some fantastic notion, based on her conception of her own beauty and charm I suppose, that she could conquer Benziger and continue to live with Ellis. Ellis cared for her very much, so much indeed that he was willing to make allowances, as he actually stated to the newspaper reporters at the time. He was, as he publicly declared, no narrow-moralist. People were people and couldn't always be good—particularly women. Anyhow, he loved Olive, admired Benziger and Rhoda immensely and felt sure that Benziger and Olive contemplated no enduring change. He added, he felt sufficiently sure of Olive and her affection for him to feel that she would come back to him, just as Benziger would go back to Rhoda. And should Olive come back (as she did of course) he would forgive her as he actually did.

"In the case of Benziger, before the tragedy, he had even gone so far as to say, jestingly, to Ellis that if he did not look out he would take his wife away from him, and Ellis had answered, 'Well, I doubt it. I would have to see it first to believe it.' They were as good friends as that."

"Pretty up-to-date friends," I commented.

"I'll say," went on Kelcey. "Anyhow, what really happened was that when Rhoda came home to their apartment from some affair one afternoon, she found Benziger and Olive in a semi-compromising position. According to the newspapers at the time, all Rhoda said on seeing them was 'Oh', and then, 'I believe I had better go.' At that she turned and left the room. Of course Olive went at once and Benziger started to look for his wife. When he reached her room, however, it was locked. By the time he got in she had already taken poison and was dying. She was dead before any doctor could reach her."

"So he's the man," I said, remembering reading about the affair at the time.

"Yes, he's the man. But what I am getting to in connection with him, Mr. Lamborn, is something very different. He may tell you this himself some day when you come to know him better, because I think he likes to talk about it. It's the finer side of him.

"But quite naturally, right after the suicide of his wife he was all broken up. His business and social friends avoided him and he resigned from all his clubs. His father, instead of coming to his aid, wrote him a condemnatory letter and deplored his career.

"As for himself, as he told me, he was all shot to pieces, hardly knew which way to turn, because, while still loving Rhoda, he felt that he had committed an enormous, and of course irreparable, wrong, which was certain to follow and wreck him everywhere. Chicago was through with him, his father, father-in-law—all who had known him in the past; so instead of pulling himself together and going to work, he went drifting about the country, drinking and gambling, until he was broke and became sick. Finally he got so low that he was sleeping in the parks, bumming his way on trains— anything to get rid of brooding over what had befallen Rhoda, Olive, Ellis and himself."

"I can understand it," I agreed sympathetically.

"And I!" emphasised Kelcey. "But what interests me still more is his comeback."

"Let's have that," I said.

"Well, here it is," said Kelcey. "As he was sitting in a park one winter morning in Detroit, without a job and hungry, cold, he started to reflect on his life so far. Up to that time, he said (and this was all of two years later after his wife's suicide), he had never troubled to think of himself as a failure who might come back—but rather as a failure who couldn't. He was down. He was through—and that was the end of it.

"However, at that time, one night when he was lying in a ten-cent flop house, a crazy religionist invaded the place and began distributing a tract or leaflet. Benziger said he was half drunk and half sleeping at that time, but just the same he could see the religionist—tall and thin and angular and consumptive, with long dirty hair and hands, stopping about and handing out those leaflets, or laying them on the cots or bodies of those sleeping. Finally he handed Benziger one, and the next morning Benziger noted that it read 'Turn Ye—Repent'. According to him, he was not much interested, because the man who had distributed the tract was a bum himself. But, just before crumpling the leaflet up and throwing it away Benziger re-read that one line at the top, 'Turn Ye—Repent'.

"Then two days later when he was much more sober and colder, and about at the end of his tether, and sitting in this park, having no money to get a cot or anything to eat, Benziger had begun thinking of this man and then, because his father had always been extremely religious—of him. His father was a hard-boiled Calvinist and believed in predestination. But also, and in spite of his belief in predestination, in free will. That is, he argued that although a man was predestined to do evil, still in some strange way, which he never troubled to explain, he could and should do good, too: a paradox which had always made Benziger laugh.

"At any rate, since he found the tract in his pocket and was so low in his mind, he turned the thing over and studied it. Then because his father had once used the words 'Turn Ye—Repent' in connection with something, he quite suddenly began to think of another phase or peculiarity of his father, whose custom it had been for years to devote ten per cent of all that he earned to the furtherance of what he called the Lord's work.

"According to Benziger, his father called this *The Tithe of the Lord*, and maintained that anyone who made such an agreement with God, and thereafter faithfully fulfilled it, and also led a decent moral life, would most certainly prosper as he himself had prospered. God would make him prosper.

"Strangely enough, Benziger himself had never coupled 'sinning with women' as anything but natural. But now that he was so low he began to think of his illicit relationship with Olive Ellis, since with her he had brought about Rhoda's death. Perhaps after all there was evil in it. Maybe his father was right.

"Anyway, sitting there shivering and hungering in the park that cold morning, this thought led him to go over his own life to see whether he had really committed a great evil, or whether he had just been young and foolish and unintentionally bad. And eventually he decided that he had not been so much evil as just foolish. For instance, he said to himself, if he had really known how deeply Rhoda cared for him, how much he really meant to her, and that the sight of him in another woman's arms could have proved so fateful, he would not have so lightly and foolishly betrayed her in their own apartment.

"His mind having gone this far, he next turned not only to the line, 'Turn Ye—Repent' but to that contract which his father insisted that he had made with the Lord. And then he said to himself, 'Supposing here and now I should try to make such a contract? Would it really work?' Sitting there cold and hopeless on a park bench the thought intrigued him. 'Might it not be so? Who could say?' His father was successful and scornful of such a life as his. 'Turn Ye—Repent . . . Turn Ye—Repent'. The words, he said, rang in his ears, just as though someone were talking to him— nudging at his elbow—'Turn Ye—Repent'. Even the bum who had handed him the tract began to take on the look of an emissary.

"But supposing, he asked himself, he did just that—made a bargain with the Lord—his father's God—not his really up to now—then what? Would He help him now at this particular point in his life when he was so miserable? So at odds with the world? Would the Lord, for instance, prosper him as He had prospered his father, he who was now so miserable, so at odds with the world? Assuming there was a Lord and that He really acted in the behalf of those who, like him, had sinned, would He, for instance, forgive him his early error? Restore him to a decent social position, and make him as well off as he was before? Would He?

"'Well,' he said to himself, 'I might try it.'

"So, there and then, this he swore to do. Having done so, he got up and was about to go somewhere to see if he could wash his hands and face and beg a little money in order to get breakfast, and then look for work, when just as he started there came through the misty, cold Detroit morning, a man with a basket in which were sandwiches and coffee.

"This was as early as five o'clock in the morning, and when the man, a rather clean youngish type, of about thirty-five, dressed in a good suit and overcoat, reached Benziger, he stopped and said, 'Brother, will you have some coffee and a sandwich? It must be cold out here. It won't cost you a cent. You are welcome to it in the name of the Lord.'

"Benziger told me, he was so astonished and taken aback by this sudden appearance, a man speaking in the name of the Lord he had just agreed to deal with, that he could scarcely speak. He took the sandwich and the coffee, thanked the man and started eating and drinking. Meantime the man disappeared. Yet, once the man was gone, Benziger was not so much convinced of a miracle of any kind as he was puzzled and perhaps a little superstitious, at least superstitious enough to believe that his oath might have had something to do with it. Perhaps—who could say? Was this really the first move or gesture on the part of the Lord in connection with that offer he had made? A sign, for instance, that the Lord had heard and was making the first move?

"Having consumed the food, he did as he planned before—got up, walked to some part of the city where he could clean himself as much as possible. He then went to look for work, deciding to take anything—dish-washing, cleaning, ditch-digging, just so long as it was work, and got a little money. It meant food, a bed, a shave, a better suit of clothes. Since he understood bookkeeping and clerking he might find some work in this field later. Once he got really started on a comeback he might look into the wicker furniture business and maybe get interested in that as his father had wanted him to. And might not the great business his father had built now prove a door through which he could return and succeed? He might even go back to his father and confess everything, and work hard for him, and so bring about a reconciliation between them. However, he never did that. Rather he decided to wait until he himself was thoroughly successful.

"He did get work, almost immediately, as a dish-washer, later as a waiter and then as a clerk in a brokerage house. Shortly afterwards he secured a minor position with a Detroit wickerware furniture company. Here he set out to study the business and advance himself. After two years he became superintendent of a department and later assistant to the general manager. It was not till then that he returned to his father and made peace with him, although he did not go into the business there with his father. Instead, he waited until he was very successful in the wickerware trust or combine before he persuaded his father—who was quite old then—to join up with it.

"Then after he had made his peace with his father, he said that he was seized with the desire to return to Chicago and there restore himself to a real position in the city from which some twelve years before he had been so summarily dismissed. And so it was that he joined and later bought into the Chicago General Wickerware Manufacturing Company, eventually to become one of the principal units of the American Wickerware Company. In Chicago he also met his present wife—Rose—after eight years of individual struggle—and married her."

"So that's his story, is it?" I said.

"Yes, that's the story," said Kelcey. "She was the daughter of a grain merchant in Chicago, a member of an excellent family. After two or three years of marriage it turned out that she could not have a child so they agreed to adopt a son—the one you heard him calling up when you were out at his place."

"In short—a modern version of the prodigal son," I said.

"Something like it," said Kelcey.

Despite my cynical doubts about this so called 'bargain' I took a real liking to Benziger and we became fairly close friends. So perhaps it was natural that after a while he should himself tell me about the same story Kelcey had. But he told it less dramatically, much more conservatively, than had Kelcey, and with not the least trace of vanity, nor yet of false modesty.

He was now a man of real power in the Wickerware Trust—one of the truly dynamic figures in it. Not only that, but he travelled a great deal. So much so that I saw very little of him. For one thing, the shipping interests with which I was identified required my removal to London, and later, for a period of at least three years, to Calcutta. It was only after some ten years of moving about that my wife and I finally settled down again in our home at Shell Cove. In the meantime, as I had read in our American papers, there had developed some trouble between the American Wickerware Trust and the Government.

Still later, I read that the Wickerware Trust had been ordered to dissolve and that each manufacturing unit must be conducted independently of the others. Benziger's unit, I gathered, was his old Chicago unit, and I assumed that he would live there. Then after that I read of some financial difficulties which appeared to involve Benziger's Chicago business and that it was placed in the hands of a receiver.

Some two years later I heard that Benziger was dead, but just what it was that had brought all this about I could not guess. Yet I was stirred by the recollection of his contract with the Lord and wondered how it had all worked out—whether he had faithfully lived up to it.

It was not until a year or two after that, when I met Winston Henneberry, a Chicago banker, who had known Benziger for years, that I learned what had really happened in those later years of Benziger's strange life.

"Oh, so you knew him?" commented Henneberry.

"Well, by no means intimately," I explained, and recited my contacts with Benziger and a mere suggestion of Kelcey's story.

"One of the strangest and yet really able and charming men I have ever known out here. As big a success and failure as we have ever had here," said Henneberry.

"Indeed?"

"Yes," said Henneberry, who in the main was your typical conservative, cautious, semi-religious banker. Obviously, as I could see, he had liked Benziger very much personally, and yet was troubled by nearly all that he knew of him. "I'm still puzzled about that pact of his with the Lord," he said.

"Myself also," I said. "That is really what I wanted to talk to you about. What happened to him in connection with that, if anything?"

"Well, *there is a story*. At least there's something about the whole thing that puzzles me to this day. You know, he died quite as broke as he was that first time he left Chicago after his first wife killed herself."

"No!"

"And not only that, but under almost the same circumstances. That is, he dropped everything, his wife, that adopted boy of his, Chicago, his friends, his business, and apparently he began drinking and tramping. He was broke when he left here—in trouble with his old friends and business associates. And all on account of a woman —or maybe two women or more. But the general impression out here is that it was a girl he kept in the background here for a long time."

"A sort of Rhoda and Olive complex," I ventured.

"Possibly. I'm not sure. The thing that has always interested me though is that his second success in life should have ended as the first one did."

"In *precisely* the same way, you say?"

"Well, not exactly, of course, no. The second Mrs. Benziger is still here, but pretty much depressed, for she cared for him quite as much as did his first wife, I am sure.

"As I look at it, while unquestionably he was a good business man and primarily desirous of being one, he was also something of a romanticist, a fellow who didn't really care for hard and fast business at all. He was very vivid and attractive. Young and attractive women were always drawn to him. He had what my wife calls a winsome smile, and he and his wife were invited everywhere. And always, until the last four or five years of his life anyway, he appeared with his wife.

"After that it was different. He began to neglect her. Before that, though, he had begun to take 'solitary' business trips or vacations, some of them lasting several months. But that wasn't good for his commercial affairs. His business associates didn't like it. Incidentally, a friend of mine in Chicago saw Benziger on a boat running between Marseilles and Singapore, at a time when Benziger was supposedly alone on some business matters. With Benziger was a very attractive young woman. Insofar as this friend could see, outside of frequent walks around the decks or dining at her table there was nothing wrong. However, the two disappeared at Singapore, and not so long after that Benziger was back in Chicago."

"One swallow doesn't make a summer," I said.

"No, but there was still something more," went on Henneberry. Like Kelcey before him, he seemed to me to be talking in order to solve something for himself. "Because of that pact with the Lord, Benziger always appeared to me to be more than anxious to share what he made with a lot of people, his employees, the poor, the charities, and new and different kinds of relief organisations, which he either devised or sponsored.

"And these charities were different: much more personal to him. For one thing, not long after he was fairly successful again, he set up an early morning coffee and sandwich relief tour of all Chicago Parks and loafing places of the down-and-outs. But there was never any public ostentation in connection with it. He never spoke of it, and it wasn't written up in the newspapers, nor any mention made of it except in private among his personal friends. Some West Side restaurant man with whom he dealt conducted the whole thing for him and at the end of the year Benziger footed the bill. I know because our bank handled the cheques.

"Furthermore, without using his own name in any way, he built, about fifteen years before he died, a bum's roost or lodging house in the poorest district of the West Side, yet really a very fine one, the best I have ever seen anywhere. That cost him to my positive knowledge, over $300,000. It was equipped with everything that could reasonably contribute to the comfort and sanitation of the men who roosted there. It could house nearly three hundred men a night and the price per night was only fifteen cents. For that, they got a good clean bed, a shower, with clean towels, a nightshirt that was washed every day, and a morning paper in the morning so that they could look over the want ads. Not only that but a breakfast could be got for ten cents and a dinner for fifteen cents, and even as little as a dime.

"I went over the place with him after it was completed and must say that I never saw a more handsome, cleanly, or conveniently arranged building. At that time, as I recall it, he said to me that he knew what it was to be without a place to sleep or something to eat, and he wanted others in that condition to get a better deal than he had had. It was that sort of thing that made him very popular around Chicago with a lot of people."

"That agreement of his with the Lord," I said.

"Oh yes, I suppose so," replied Henneberry. "Only, and now I don't know whether there is anything to what I am going to say or not, but it is a little curious to me that not so long after I began, among others, to notice those trips of his (perhaps a year or so after I heard the story about the girl on the Marseilles-Singapore boat) that the troubles of the Wickerware Trust with the Government began.

"Now, don't think I'm superstitious—I'm just commenting on it as a fact—nothing more. As you may recall, it was charged at that time that the Trust was indulging in unfair competition, wrecking rival firms and the like. And while Benziger was not the head of the Trust, still he was a dominant figure in the directorate. Naturally, I wondered about these charges in connection with his pact, and in the midst of it all he came and talked to me about it. He said, as I recall, that while they were ugly charges and were a reflection on him and looked serious, nevertheless if there had been any unfair competition thus far, he personally had had nothing to do with it; also that he was going to look into the matter, and if there were things which he could control, he was going to put a stop to them or get out.

"Just the same, some bad practices were actually proved and the Trust dissolved, and he didn't get out. Just why, I don't know. I think his excuse was that he had to stay to straighten things out—or that he couldn't get out without a great loss to himself and others, which may have been true enough. At any rate, he didn't.

"But there was that other thing, his running around with those women, at that very time. His wife told me so afterwards."

"Odd," I said.

"But by then," went on Henneberry very solemnly as I thought—almost religiously even, "he was not the same man he had been before he began to neglect his wife. He looked older and was less

E

enthusiastic, often talked and acted as though life wasn't as interesting to him any longer. Also there seemed a very large amount of personal expenses which Benziger had to foot and some commercial disarrangements which seemed to affect his personal interests. I know for one thing that at about that time he had to borrow a lot of money, six hundred thousand dollars. Also that not only fully three-quarters of his trust certificates, but most of his private property, were already hypothecated.

"Then worst of all, towards the last, he had even to cut out his contributions to those various Chicago charities, excluding of course those two I have mentioned as being his own.

"At any rate, just at the time of the proposed indictment, and with his wife still here with his adopted son, he left Chicago. It was whispered by some that he had gone to some island in the South Seas with a girl, but whether that is so or not I can't say. Fortunately his wife had some property of her own, her father's, and that couldn't be touched. So she and the boy moved into her father's old house on the North Side. Then two years later she got a wire from a hospital in Denver. Benziger was there sick and he died only a few days after she got there. But there were some things he wanted to tell her. He told her he had deceived her long before she knew it, but that he had cared for her and was sorry, only that he hadn't been able to live up to the pact the way he hoped he could, and so——"

"Not really?"

"Yes."

"He admitted that himself?"

"His wife said so to me."

I paused to think about it and, as I did so, Henneberry went on with this:

"Alonzo Carlson, one of our Vice-Presidents, used to argue in connection with Benziger, after his death of course, that it was the early influence of his father, together with his memory of him, which over-emphasised for him that first great social smash of his. Also that being over-kindhearted and playful, the suicide of his young wife pulled him down more than it should have; caused him to feel guilty and regretful and so to react toward this severe commercial life, which, after all, he did not like. Also that finally it proved too much for him—a strain—and so he broke again. At any rate, there was that agreement *with God*, which, according to his own confession, hung over him."

"He made it when he was down and out, you see," I interrupted, "and the subsequent success which came to him he probably identified with that. Also he probably hooked his success up with the necessity of making good in the way that he had agreed to make good—that is, not only by giving ten per cent of all he earned, but by leading the better kind of life which made such a success as his possible. And when he didn't succeed in keeping it up he broke."

"Precisely, but it is a fact that somehow all of these things seemed to come rather quickly together—his going away on those trips, the Trust's policies towards others, and his big losses generally."

"In other words, the Lord struck quick, eh?"

"Well," said Henneberry, "it is true that when he returned from that Singapore trip, which was the first one I heard of, he looked different—acted that way, and I'm satisfied that he was unhappy within himself. In fact, whether anybody knew anything or not, he may have felt that his moral derelictions were being charged up to him. I don't know of course, but it was about that time that those several things in connection with his business troubles started."

"You seem to make out a pretty fair case," I said.

"Not me, I'm merely telling you what I know. Only there is one other interesting thing. After his death his wife wired me and I had the body brought back to Chicago, where it was placed in her family plot, alongside of her father. Then I went over everything that had to be gone over, and among the different things was that lodging house, which she couldn't carry any more, and that coffee and sandwich charity. It was only then that I discovered that for over a year after his disappearance and three years before his death, he had neglected financing not only the lodging house which he prized so highly, but also that sandwich and coffee service. Only Rose, knowing how close that had been to his heart, and caring for him so much, had supported both from money left her by her father, until after his death she couldn't do it any longer.

"Beautiful," I said.

"The Tithe of the Lord," added Henneberry.

"His wife firmly believed that his failure to keep that agreement was at the bottom of all his troubles. She said she first began to fear for him in connection with that when she realised how seriously he took his pact during the first years of their marriage. Afterwards, she said, particularly when they grew so successful, he began to become more worldly again. He liked to drink, gamble, club about a good deal. Then, of course, there were those trips, principally at first with men, she was sure, officials of the Trust. Afterwards some woman or women, and then——"

"Wifely interest, I fear," I said.

"Possibly—and yet Rose is certainly a very kind and generous person and loved him very much."

"All the more reason," I said.

"—at any rate," he went on, "while I am not a member of any faith, I do believe in a God and in His control in some mysterious way of the affairs of this world. While I cannot personally say whether Benziger deliberately broke this agreement or whether the breaking of it was, as you seem to think, forced upon him, I still believe if he did break it and did believe deeply in the significance of it, it is probable that it might have affected him in some way."

"Benziger was not a religious man," I interpolated, "but when he was down and out and suddenly thought of his religious father, he thought he would investigate this mysterious Thing and give it a trial and then and there made that agreement. When things began to happen coincidentally with the agreement, of course, he did not know what to make of it, but he couldn't help having a superstitious feeling that the agreement he made had something to do with it.

"Naturally when a person makes such an agreement he is sceptical and yet does not know what will happen if it is broken. He cannot help but feel afraid and perhaps become haunted by his own conscience. For, in a way, an agreement like this is really an agreement with your conscience. When he found that he could not live up to this pact, his mind was troubled with it, for his conscience must have always been whispering to him about it, and this, after a slip or two on his part, due to an overwhelming desire for another type of life, led no doubt to his drinking and slipping further."

"You may be right," said Henneberry.

"While he did not very much believe there was a God," I added, "he kept fulfilling his agreement, just in the event there should be one, and of course his conscience was clear as long as he did.

But not being sure of this mysterious Thing, as soon as he stopped fulfilling the agreement he was haunted by the whispering of his conscience."

"In other words," said Henneberry, "you are not a religious man."

"Not in the accepted sense of the words, no."

"Well, I am," he said. "You call it conscience but to me conscience is God, or the only thing we know of as God, our guide. And when we go against that, we go against Him."

"So be it," I said. "And it may be that both of us are talking of one and the same power."

"I think we are," he said.

ERNEST HEMINGWAY

The Butterfly and the Tank

Beginning in the first issue—Autumn 1933—Ernest Hemingway was a regular contributor to *Esquire*. In all, he contributed some 34 pieces. Most of these are his regular monthly 'letters'—from Cuba, Spain, Tanganyika, Key West, Paris, Bimini and New York. Many of these letters contain material which he later re-worked in books and novels. The famous essay 'On the Blue Water: A Gulf Stream Letter' (April 1936), for instance, contains a 178-word anecdote which was the 'germ' of *The Old Man and the Sea*.

Many of Hemingway's most anthologised stories appeared first in *Esquire*: 'The Snows of Kilimanjaro' (with Scott Fitzgerald named instead of 'Julian') and 'The Capital of the World' (which appeared in the magazine as 'The Horns of the Bull').

During the Spanish Civil War, Ernest Hemingway raised $40,000 on his personal notes to buy ambulances for the Loyalists in Madrid. To pay off this debt he made several trips to Spain as a correspondent for the North American Newspaper Alliance. He was there throughout most of the year 1937, writing and reporting, and also working on the film *The Spanish Earth*. He did not contribute to *Esquire* during 1937 (his last contribution had been 'Snows'—in August 1936), but, beginning in November of 1938, there appeared the first of three stories about Chicote's bar in Madrid (still a flourishing café there, attracting artists and theatre people) during the siege of Madrid. The first of these, 'The Denunciation', appeared in November 1938; the second, 'The Butterfly and the Tank', in December. There was then a lapse of a month before the longest and most fully sustained, 'Night Before Battle,' appeared in February of 1939. On August 23, Arnold Gingrich had wired Hemingway at the L Bar T Ranch in Cody, Wyoming: *Sending cheque for $1800 Barclay today. Would like third Chicotes story by all means. Hate to be insistent, but spot for this issue has been held open and hope you can fill it. Feel grand—got stories again.*

'The Butterfly and the Tank' is reprinted here for the first time.

ON THIS EVENING I was walking home from the censorship office to the Florida Hotel and it was raining. So about halfway home I got sick of the rain and stopped into Chicote's for a quick one. It was the second winter of shelling in the siege of Madrid and everything was short including tobacco and people's tempers and you were a little hungry all the time and would become suddenly and unreasonably irritated at things you could do nothing about such as the weather. I should have gone on home. It was only five blocks more, but when I saw Chicote's doorway I thought I would get a quick one and then do those six blocks up the Gran Via through the mud and rubble of the streets broken by the bombardment.

The place was crowded. You couldn't get near the bar and all the tables were full. It was full of smoke, singing, men in uniform, and the smell of wet leather coats, and they were handing drinks over a crowd that was three deep at the bar.

A waiter I knew found a chair from another table and I sat down with a thin, white-faced, Adam's-appled German I knew who was working at the censorship and two other people I did not know. The table was in the middle of the room a little on your right as you go in.

You could't hear yourself talk for the singing and I ordered a gin and angostura and put it down against the rain. The place was really packed and everybody was very jolly; maybe getting just a little bit too jolly from the newly made Catalan liquor most of them were drinking. A couple of people I did not know slapped me on the back and when the girl at our table said something to me, I couldn't hear it and said, "Sure."

She was pretty terrible looking now I had stopped looking around and was looking at our table; really pretty terrible. But it turned out, when the waiter came, that what she had asked me was to have a drink. The fellow with her was not very forceful looking but she was forceful enough for both of them. She had one of those strong, semi-classical faces and was built like a lion tamer; and the boy with her looked as though he ought to be wearing an old school tie. He wasn't though. He was wearing a leather coat just like all the rest of us. Only it wasn't wet because they had been there since before the rain started. She had on a leather coat too and it was becoming to the sort of face she had.

By this time I was wishing I had not stopped into Chicote's but had gone straight on home where you could change your clothes and be dry and have a drink in comfort on the bed with your feet up, and I was tired of looking at both of these young people. Life is very short and ugly women are very long and sitting there at the table I decided that even though I was a writer and supposed to have an insatiable curiosity about all sorts of people, I did not really care to know whether these two were married, or what they saw in each other, or what their politics were, or whether he had a little money, or she had a little money, or anything about them. I decided they must be in the radio. Any time you saw really strange looking civilians in Madrid they were always in the radio. So to say something I raised my voice above the noise and asked, "You in the radio?"

"We are," the girl said. So that was that. They were in the radio.

"How are you, Comrade?" I said to the German.

"Fine. And you?"

"Wet," I said, and he laughed with his head on one side.

"You haven't got a cigarette?" he asked. I handed him my next to the last pack of cigarettes and he took two. The forceful girl took two and the young man with the old school tie face took one.

"Take another," I shouted.

"No thanks," he answered and the German took it instead.

"Do you mind?" he smiled.

"Of course not," I said. I really minded and he knew it. But he wanted the cigarettes so badly that it did not matter. The singing had died down momentarily, or there was a break in it as there is sometimes in a storm, and we could all hear what we said.

"You been here long?" the forceful girl asked me. She pronounced it bean as in bean soup.

"Off and on," I said.

"We must have a serious talk," the German said. "I want to have a talk with you. When can we have it?"

"I'll call you up," I said. This German was a very strange German indeed and none of the good Germans liked him. He lived under the delusion that he could play the piano, but if you kept him away from pianos he was all right unless he was exposed to liquor, or the opportunity to gossip, and nobody had ever been able to keep him away from those two things yet.

Gossip was the best thing he did and he always knew something new and highly discreditable about anyone you could mention in Madrid, Valencia, Barcelona, and other political centres.

Just then the singing really started in again, and you cannot gossip very well shouting, so it looked like a dull afternoon at Chicote's and I decided to leave as soon as I should have bought a round myself.

Just then it started. A civilian in a brown suit, a white shirt, black tie, his hair brushed straight back from a rather high forehead, who had been clowning around from table to table, squirted one of the waiters with a flit gun. Everybody laughed except the waiter, who was carrying a tray full of drinks at the time. He was indignant.

"*No hay derecho*," the waiter said. This means, "You have no right to do that," and is the simplest and the strongest protest in Spain.

The flit gun man, delighted with his success, and not seeming to give any importance to the fact that it was well into the second year of the war, that he was in a city under siege where everyone was under a strain, and that he was one of only four men in civilian clothes in the place, now squirted another waiter.

I looked around for a place to duck to. This waiter, also, was indignant and the flit gun man squirted him twice more, light-heartedly. Some people still thought it was funny, including the forceful girl. But the waiter stood, shaking his head. His lips were trembling. He was an old man and he had worked in Chicote's for ten years that I knew of.

"*No hay derecho*," he said with dignity.

People had laughed, however, and the flit gun man, not noticing how the singing had fallen off, squirted his flit gun at the back of a waiter's neck. The waiter turned, holding his tray.

"*No hay derecho*," he said. This time it was no protest. It was an indictment and I saw three men in uniform start from a table for the flit gun man and the next thing all four of them were going out the revolving door in a rush and you heard a smack when someone hit the flit gun man on the mouth. Somebody else picked up the flit gun and threw it out the door after him.

The three men came back in looking serious, tough and very righteous. Then the door revolved and in came the flit gun man. His hair was down in his eyes, there was blood on his face, his necktie was pulled to one side and his shirt was torn open. He had the flit gun again and as he pushed, wild-eyed and white-faced, into the room he made one general, unaimed, challenging squirt with it, holding it towards the whole company.

I saw one of the three men start for him and I saw this man's face. There were more men with him now and they forced the flit gun man back between two tables on the left of the room as you go in, the flit gun man struggling wildly now, and when the shot went off I grabbed the forceful girl by the arm and dived for the kitchen door.

The kitchen door was shut and when I put my shoulder against it it did not give.

"Get down here behind the angle of the bar," I said. She knelt there.

"Flat," I said and pushed her down. She was furious.

Every man in the room except the German, who lay behind a table, and the public-school-looking boy, who stood in a corner drawn up against the wall, had a gun out. On a bench along the wall three over-blonde girls, their hair dark at the roots, were standing on tiptoe to see and screaming steadily.

"I'm not afraid," the forceful one said. "This is ridiculous."

"You don't want to get shot in a café brawl," I said. "If that flit king has any friends here this can be very bad."

But he had no friends, evidently, because people began putting their pistols away and somebody lifted down the blonde screamers and everyone who had started over there when the shot came, drew back away from the flit man, who lay, quietly, on his back on the floor.

"No one is to leave until the police come," someone shouted from the door.

Two policemen with rifles, who had come in off the street patrol, were standing by the door and at this announcement I saw six men form up just like the line-up of a football team coming out of a huddle and head out through the door. Three of them were the men who had first thrown the flit king out. One of them was the man who shot him. They went right through the policemen with the rifles like good interference taking out an end and a tackle. And as they went out one of the policemen got his rifle across the door and shouted, "No one can leave. Absolutely no one."

"Why did those men go? Why hold us if anyone's gone?"

"They were mechanics who had to return to their airfield," someone said.

"But if anyone's gone it's silly to hold the others."

"Everyone must wait for the Seguridad. Things must be done legally and in order."

"But don't you see that if any person has gone it is silly to hold the others?"

"No one can leave. Everyone must wait."

"It's comic," I said to the forceful girl.

"No it's not. It's simply horrible."

We were standing up now and she was staring indignantly at where the flit king was lying. His arms were spread wide and he had one leg drawn up.

"I'm going over to help that poor wounded man. Why has no one helped him or done anything for him?"

"I'd leave him alone," I said. "You want to keep out of this."

"But it's simply inhuman. I've nurse's training and I'm going to give him first aid."

"I wouldn't," I said. "Don't go near him."

"Why not?" She was very upset and almost hysterical.

"Because he's dead," I said.

When the police came they held everybody there for three hours. They commenced by smelling of all the pistols. In this manner they would detect one which had been fired recently. After about forty pistols they seemed to get bored with this and anyway all you could smell was wet leather coats. Then they sat at a table placed directly behind the late flit king, who lay on the floor looking like a grey wax caricature of himself, with grey wax hands and a grey wax face, and examined people's papers.

With his shirt ripped open you could see the flit king had no undershirt and the soles of his shoes were worn through. He looked very small and pitiful lying there on the floor. You had to step over him to get to the table where two plain-clothes policemen sat and examined everyone's identification papers. The husband lost and found his papers several times with nervousness. He had a safe conduct pass somewhere but he had mislaid it in a pocket, but he kept on searching and perspiring until he found it. Then he would put it in a different pocket and have to go searching again. He perspired heavily while doing this and it made his hair very curly and his face red. He now looked as though he should have not only an old school tie but one of those little caps boys in the lower forms wear. You have heard how events age people. Well this shooting had made him look about ten years younger.

While we were waiting around I told the forceful girl I thought the whole thing was a pretty good story and that I would write it sometime. The way the six had lined up in single file and rushed that door was very impressive. She was shocked and said that I could not write it because it would be prejudicial to the cause of the Spanish Republic. I said that I had been in Spain for a long time and that they used to have a phenomenal number of shootings in the old days around Valencia under the monarchy, and that for hundreds of years before the Republic people had been cutting each other with large knives called Navajas in Andalucia, and that if I saw a comic shooting in Chicote's during the war I could write about it just as though it had been in New York, Chicago, Key West or Marseilles. It did not have anything to do with politics. She said I shouldn't. Probably a lot of other people will say I shouldn't too. The German seemed to think it was a pretty good story however, and I gave him the last of the Camels. Well, anyway, finally, after about three hours the police said we could go.

They were sort of worried about me at the Florida because in those days, with the shelling, if you started for home on foot and didn't get there after the bars were closed at seven-thirty, people worried. I was glad to get home and I told the story while we were cooking supper on an electric stove and it had quite a success.

Well, it stopped raining during the night, and the next morning it was a fine, bright, cold early winter day and at twelve forty-five I pushed open the revolving doors at Chicote's to try a little gin and tonic before lunch. There were very few people there at that hour and two waiters and the manager came over to the table. They were all smiling.

"Did they catch the murderer?" I asked.

"Don't make jokes so early in the day," the manager said. "Did *you* see him shot?"

"Yes," I told him.

"Me too," he said. "I was just here when it happened." He

pointed to a corner table. "He placed the pistol right against the man's chest when he fired."

"How late did they hold people?"

"Oh, until past two this morning."

"They only came for the *fiambre*," using the Spanish slang word for corpse, the same used on menus for cold meat, "at eleven o'clock this morning."

"But you don't know about it yet," the manager said.

"No. He doesn't know," a waiter said.

"It is a very rare thing," another waiter said. "*Muy raro*."

"And sad too," the manager said. He shook his head.

"Yes. Sad and curious," the waiter said. "Very sad."

"Tell me."

"It is a very rare thing," the manager said.

"Tell me. Come on, tell me."

The manager leaned over the table in great confidence.

"In the flit gun, you know," he said. "He had eau de Cologne. Poor fellow."

"It was not a joke in such bad taste, you see?" the waiter said.

"It was really just gaiety. No one should have taken offence," the manager said. "Poor fellow."

"I see," I said. "He just wanted everyone to have a good time."

"Yes," said the manager. "It was really just an unfortunate misunderstanding."

"And what about the flit gun?"

"The police took it. They have sent it round to his family."

"I imagine they will be glad to have it," I said.

"Yes," said the manager. "Certainly. A flit gun is always useful."

"Who was he?"

"A cabinet maker."

"Married?"

"Yes, the wife was here with the police this morning."

"What did she say?"

"She dropped down by him and said, 'Pedro, what have they done to thee, Pedro? Who has done this to thee? Oh Pedro.'"

"Then the police had to take her away because she could not control herself," the waiter said.

"It seems he was feeble of the chest," the manager said. "He fought in the first days of the movement. They said he fought in the Sierra but he was too weak in the chest to continue."

"And yesterday afternoon he just went out on the town to cheer things up," I suggested.

"No," said the manager. "You see, it is very rare. Everything is *muy raro*. This I learn from the police, who are very efficient if given time. They have interrogated comrades from the shop where he worked. This they located from the card of his syndicate which was in his pocket. Yesterday he bought the flit gun and *agua de colonia* to use for a joke at a wedding. He had announced this intention. He bought them across the street. There was a label on the cologne bottle with the address. The bottle was in the washroom. It was there he filled the flit gun. After buying them he must have come in here when the rain started."

"I remember when he came in," a waiter said.

"In the gaiety, with the singing, he became gay too."

"He was gay all right," I said. "He was practically floating around."

The manager kept on with the relentless Spanish logic.

"That is the gaiety of drinking with a weakness of the chest," he said.

"I don't like this story very well," I said.

"Listen," said the manager. "How rare it is. His gaiety comes in contact with the seriousness of the war like a butterfly——"

"Oh, very like a butterfly," I said. "Too much like a butterfly."

"I am not joking," said the manager. "You see it? Like a butterfly and a tank."

This pleased him enormously. He was getting into the real Spanish metaphysics.

"Have a drink on the house," he said. "You must write a story about this."

I remembered the flit gun man with his grey wax hands and his grey wax face, his arms spread wide and his legs drawn up and he did look a little like a butterfly; not too much, you know. But he did not look very human either. He reminded me more of a dead sparrow.

"I'll take gin and Schweppes quinine tonic water," I said.

"You must write a story about it," the manager said. "Here. Here's luck."

"Luck," I said. "Look, an English girl last night told me I shouldn't write about it. That it would be very bad for the cause."

"What nonsense," the manager said. "It is very interesting and important, the misunderstood gaiety coming in contact with the deadly seriousness that is here always. To me it is the rarest and most interesting thing which I have seen for some time. You must write it."

"All right," I said. "Sure. Has he any children?"

"No," he said. "I asked the police. But you must write it and you must call it The Butterfly and the Tank."

"All right," I said. "Sure. But I don't like the title much."

"The title is very elegant," the manager said. "It is pure literature."

"All right," I said. "Sure. That's what we'll call it. The Butterfly and the Tank."

And I sat there on that bright cheerful morning, the place smelling clean and newly aired and swept, with the manager who was an old friend and who was now very pleased with the literature we were making together and I took a sip of the gin and tonic water and looked out the sandbagged window and thought of the wife kneeling there and saying, "Pedro. *Pedro*, who has done this to thee, Pedro?" and I thought that the police would never be able to tell her that, even if they had the name of the man who pulled the trigger.

EDGAR LEE MASTERS

Dreiser at Spoon River

Along with H. L. Mencken and Sinclair Lewis, Edgar Lee Masters was a major force in the New Realism which broke through the genteel literary tradition that dominated American letters at the turn of the century. In *Spoon River Anthology* (published anonymously in 1915) Masters had created his images of bitterness and frustration in a collection of epitaphs describing the secret lives of dead citizens. He made literary history in the poetic treatment of small-town America, adhering to the natural rhythms and colloquial form of spoken language.

One of the poems in *Spoon River Anthology* (Macmillan, 1915), describing Dreiser, was called 'Theodore the Poet':

As a boy, Theodore, you sat for long hours
On the shore of the turbid Spoon
With deep-set eye staring at the door of the crawfish's burrow,
Waiting for him to appear, pushing ahead,
First his waving antennae, like straw of hay,
And soon his body, colored like soap-stone,
Gemmed with eyes of jet.
And you wondered in a trance of thought
What he knew, what he desired, and why he lived at all.
But later your vision watched for men and women
Hiding in burrows of fate amid great cities,
Looking for the souls of them to come out,
So that you could see
How they lived, and for what,
And why they kept crawling so busily
Along the sandy way where water fails
As the summer wanes.

Another portrait of his friend appeared in our May 1939 issue. It arrived at *Esquire* with the following reassurance:

The enclosed piece, 'John Armstrong Entertains Dreiser at Spoon River,' is a good thing to prove to the authorities that *Esquire* is following an impeccable course. It is good history and all true.

Yours,

E. L. MASTERS

ONE TIME when Dreiser was in Chicago gathering material for a novel, our talks day by day ranged the country, and it came about that I told him of the fiddler John Armstrong, who was famous in central Illinois for his stories and his fiddling, and as the son of Hannah Armstrong, Lincoln's friend and landlady. Armstrong lived in the village of Oakford, about eight miles north of New Salem Hill, where Lincoln was postmaster in his young manhood; he had lived near Oakford all his sixty-seven years. At this time I had never seen Armstrong; I had often planned to visit him. I wanted to hear him play the fiddle and to tell stories about Menard County and New Salem, about his people and the country of Lincoln's day. Some of these racy stories had been passed on to me by people who had come in contact with Armstrong. But that was not like hearing him tell them and interlard his words with oaths. So I had been informed; and somewhat to my surprise Dreiser became greatly interested in Armstrong, and when I told him that I had to be in Springfield the next day, only twenty miles from Oakford, and thought of going on to pay the long deferred visit to Armstrong, Dreiser said that he would go too, if he could manage his engagements. The result was that I went to Springfield, and there awaited a telegram from Dreiser, while I attended to some business in the Illinois capital.

John Armstrong belonged to the Lincoln history; not only was he the son of that Hannah Armstrong who had boarded Lincoln in his New Salem days but his father was that Jack Armstrong who was the wrestler, who had wrestled with Lincoln. His brother was that Duff Armstrong who had been defended by Lincoln, using an almanac to prove that the witnesses had misstated the facts when they testified that the moon was at the meridian at the moment that Duff Armstrong struck his victim Metzger with a neck yoke and produced his death. If the moon was not at the meridian, but was setting, the witnesses could not have seen the blow struck, or with what it was struck. That was the point of the almanac, which proved that the moon was setting.

After John's father died one summer, of what John called "the lung fever", his words for pneumonia, long after Lincoln left New Salem Village for Springfield, John with his mother Hannah lived in various parts of the county of Menard, in which Oakford is situated. Sometimes he lived with his mother and Duff in what is called Sandridge Precinct, and then near the Sangamon River, just across from Mason County. Here there were camp meetings and rowdy dances where the fiddlers came and the platform dancers performed under the spell of many drinks. It was at a camp meeting that Duff Armstrong killed Metzger. John told me that at this camp meeting "they would sit around where there was preachin' for a while, and then they'd go and get some drinks".

John grew up hearing his mother tell of New Salem and the days when she darned Lincoln's socks. He became saturated with the stories and the flavour of this countryside, with all that his mother told him of the horse racing, foot racing and horseshoe pitching, and loafing in Berry's Store, where Lincoln sat around telling anecdotes —all there at New Salem twenty years before John was born. At last, a good while after Lincoln's death, Hannah died, and John married a daughter of 'Fiddler' Jones, and carried on the art of the country fiddler. For many years by the time of my visit with Dreiser to see him at Oakford he had lived there, where he ran a grain elevator, and kept open house to his friends, where his wife Aunt Caroline delighted guests with her bountiful table, and where John entertained them with fiddling and story-telling. He was supposed to have many souvenirs of the Lincoln days; but in point of fact, as it turned out, he had nothing but a picture of his mother and one of Duff, a picture of some of the jurymen who tried Duff, and a book containing Lincoln's autograph. But John as the survivor of a time that was passed was of far greater interest than such things as these. I wanted to see him in order to know just what kind of people it was that Lincoln had lived with in his youth; and above that to hear John talk and play the fiddle. Finally when I was ready to leave for Springfield, Dreiser could not accompany me. He said, however, that he would telegraph me the next day, if he could come then.

When I got to Springfield I told my father about Dreiser. As he did not real novels to any extent, but only law books and the like, he did not know Dreiser's work. He tried to get me to set off that very afternoon for Oakford, saying that John might die any time, and I would miss the chance of seeing him. Why wait for Dreiser? As a New York novelist Dreiser would not be interested in John, and would not appreciate him. What would he care for John's fiddling? However, I did not go to Oakford that afternoon. And the next morning a telegram came from Dreiser saying that he would be down from Chicago on the afternoon train. My father prepared to go with us. He telephoned John, who sent back a hearty welcome to all of us, saying that his wife would have the best dinner ready that she could prepare, and that he would meet us at the depot.

That afternoon my father got engaged in business so that he could not go. I went down to the station to meet Dreiser, from which also our train for Oakford departed. I was as surprised to see Dreiser get off the train, as I was to get his telegram. But there he was, laughing and repeating some of the jokes of Armstrong that I had told him. He was in lively spirits. We boarded the Oakford train and soon were on our way. Dreiser looked out of the window studying the country. It was not greatly different from the Indiana landscape with which he was identified as a boy and young man. But at the edge of Springfield there were a lot of Italians repairing the track. He commented on their sturdiness and vitality. When we passed through the first little village and saw the typical American idlers standing by the station to watch the train arrive he contrasted their listless behaviour with the spirited manner of the Italians we had seen. I pointed out to him places identified with my boyhood: the blacksmith shop at Cantrall where I had almost burned my fingers off; the Chautauqua Grounds near Petersburg which had been established in memory of Lincoln, and near at hand the place in the Sangamon River where I was nearly drowned. There was nothing there but the bend; for, long before, the water mill which succeeded the mill of Lincoln's day at New Salem had vanished, and even the dam was all but obliterated. At Petersburg, twenty miles from Springfield, the train stopped long enough for me to tell him about various houses and buildings; the Old Menard House where Lincoln used to stop when he came to Petersburg to court; various buildings of local note about the square; the little brick station, no longer used, standing back from the track which was used when I was a boy in Petersburg, and from which I left when we moved from Petersburg to Lewistown, fifty miles north. When we left Petersburg we came to the farm country with which I was familiar, and to the hamlet of Atterberry, where the store still stood that was there when I was a boy, and was still managed by the man who had run it all these intervening years. A few miles beyond we came to Oakford, sighting first the grain elevator which John Armstrong owned and conducted; for he was a man of means, and had led a thrifty and industrious life, along with fiddling and hunting.

John was standing on the station platform. I knew him by the pictures of him that I had seen. He was glancing about with wild-bird eyes for someone that looked like his idea of me. But I knew him at once and went to him, introducing Dreiser, who turned his eyes upon John and bored him through with scrutinising penetration. John was not conscious of Dreiser's stare, nor did he seem to betray any curiosity in Dreiser, though Dreiser's coat, with its fur collar, and his city apparel and city manner might well have caused a country-man to look the newcomer over. For himself John was freshly shaved, he had on clean linen and a good four-in-hand, his shoes were polished, he looked eminently respectable. I might have supposed that he had dressed for us, but it turned out that John was always careful of his appearance. His mother, Hannah, though a pioneer woman, had a certain breeding; and according to my grand-mother, who knew and loved her for years, she was a woman of excellent character. John had derived from his home environment under her an understanding of good habits of life, of a kind of homely etiquette, of the ways of hospitality. As a liver and a hunter, as a man who had gone about his own country for years meeting all sorts of men in that locality John would have been at ease with anyone. He took Dreiser for just another man, one perhaps of a new type, but no matter for that. So we stood momentarily on the platform of the station, where Dreiser's great height contrasted with John's low stature. John said, "They say you're a writin' feller." And when Dreiser laughed and admitted that he was, John re-marked, "Wal, by God, that was what I was told. Come on now, boys, we'll go to the house. Aunt Caroline has dinner about ready, and I've got some fine whisky for you. A feller over in the 'Burg giv' it to me."

Oakford was a village of just a few houses and about one hundred people. We passed up a street where there were two stores on one side and some houses on the other. "You remember Oakford, don't you, Lee?" John asked me. When I said I did, he went on, "Do you remember when Porky Jim Thomas run a sample room right thar?" John pointed to one of the stores which had become a drug store. With this Dreiser exploded with laughter. To which John paid no attention. "Where is Porky Jim?" I inquired. "Wal," replied John, "I don't know exactly where he is at. He died about ten years ago. We buried him here in Oakford. We'll go and look at his grave tomorrow." Though I knew why the man was called Porky Jim I asked John for Dreiser's benefit where he got such a name. "Why, Cy Skaggs giv' him that name. You see runnin' that sample room he got as big around as a barl, and as purple in the face as a gobbler. He drank a quart of whisky a day, by God, and said that no man could be healthy without it. Cy Skaggs called him that, and it stuck."

Dreiser stopped to laugh, which John seemed to take as a matter of course. He and I paused waiting for Dreiser, while John went on telling me about the last days of Porky Jim. "He had the dropsy, the doctors called it, and almost bust. They had to tap him; and a man told me they took off ten gallons of water. Once we had a hoss race here. One of the Atterberrys was raisin' quarter hosses. Porky Jim was thar takin' bets. He could hardly get around. 'Pears to me that's the last time I saw Porky before he got down at home." By this time Dreiser having laughed himself out came up to where we were standing, and on we went to John's house, which was only two blocks from the station.

John's house was a cottage of one storey, but it was freshly painted and in good repair. His yard was large and surrounded by a picket fence. There were lilac bushes and other flowering growths on the lawn. At one side was a large vegetable garden where the stalks of last summer's corn stood, blasted and shaking in the February wind. A brick walk led from the gate to the front door. From the chimney a cloud of soft coal smoke was pouring. John opened the door, held

it ajar for us to enter, and we came in and set our hand-bags down
and began to take in the room. It was small with a low ceiling. On
the wall were black crayons of relatives; in the corner was an organ;
in the centre a soft-coal base burner with windows of isinglass
through which the flames of a hot fire were flickering. On the floor
was a rag carpet of many hues, and in a good state. John went on
into the dining-room, which we could see into. There a long table
was already set, and from the kitchen beyond we could hear the
steps of John's wife, Aunt Caroline, and her daughter, and the
sizzling of food in the skillet. Dreiser looked at me and was still
laughing. We stood there, thinking that John had gone out only for
a moment. That proved to be true. He returned bearing the
promised whisky, and we drank together. John was chuckling and
talking and swearing with no stay. In a moment Aunt Caroline and
her daughter came in. I shook hands with them as Aunt Caroline
said, "I've knowed your pap since he was fifteen years old. He was
at a dance about then where my brother fiddled. I knew your grand-
pap and your grandma, but I never knowed you before. They say
you live in Chicago."

Meantime Dreiser stood unintroduced. "This here, Caroline, is a
writin' feller from New York. By God, I've forgot your name."
Dreiser told him in a quiet voice as his eyes flamed with mirth.
"Yes," said John, "Dresser. Why, Caroline, you remember them
Dressers that lived over thar by Salt Creek, just east of Dutchland.
They was Dutch. Ain't you Dutch?" Dreiser replied that he was of
German parentage. "I thought so," observed John.

Aunt Caroline and her daughter now disappeared to the kitchen
and we sat down by the fire while John talked a stream, telling about
various things that had happened in the neighbourhood, about the
horse races, the odd characters of the past. He was running over
with stories. Dreiser sat there and laughed quietly to himself. John
seemed to be oblivious of everything but the stories that he was
telling. He kept punctuating his remarks with 'by Gods', and
laughing heartily at his own humour. Finally Dreiser asked him,
"Did you know Lincoln?" "Well, I kain't say that I knowed him,"
John replied. "I seed him onct that I remember well. You see when
Duff was tried—thar's his picture on the wall—I was only nine years
old. And my mother, that's Aunt Hannah as they called her, took

me to Beardstown whar they had Duff in jail. That's when I seed Linkern." "What did he look like?" asked Dreiser, growing more interested. "Wal, by God, that's hard to answer. He looked like one of these here cranes you see along the Sangamon River—tall, you know, and thin. He didn't have no beard, that I remember. I know damn well he didn't have no beard, because my mother said so many times." "Did you see him sitting down as well as standing?" John looked at Dreiser sharply, seeing that the questions were growing acute. "You ain't no lawyer, are you, Dresser?" asked John. Dreiser answered that he wasn't a lawyer. "By God you sound like it," remarked John. "You sound like old Breese Johnson that used to be over at the 'Burg forty years ago." "I wanted to know how Lincoln looked when he was sitting down," Dreiser explained. "Wal, I expect he looked like one of these here grasshoppers with their jints stickin' up when they squat. You see Linkern had awful long legs. My mother said so. Over at Havaner thar was a man named Colonel Prickett. He told me that he seed Linkern on the platform thar onct, and that his knees stuck up halfway to his waist." This was the tenor of the talk as Aunt Caroline entered to announce that dinner was ready.

"I expect you boys want to wash," John observed. He opened doors off the living-room where we had been sitting and showed us into our separate rooms. There we found bowls and pitchers of water, and fresh towels. We also saw the very comfortable beds built up with feather ticks, and log-house quilts which Aunt Caroline had spread for us with hospitable care. We came back into the living-room, though John had been standing as we washed near our doors in order to finish one of his stories. He was swearing and talking in the husky amusing voice that was his. All the while Dreiser was smiling or chuckling, or looking about with his penetrating eyes, as if he felt that he had never seen anyone like John, or any house just like this cottage was. John now took us into the dining-room, and then as suddenly left us as he passed into the kitchen, remarking, "By God, I believe I'll wash myself." We could see him as he hid his face in his hands, and exploded the water about his face from a tin basin.

We sat down to a table of fried chicken, boiled ham and boiled beef; to potatoes, cabbage, rutabagas, carrots and onions; to hot biscuits and corn bread; to wild honey and every variety of preserves and canned berries; to pickles made of tomatoes, water-melon rinds, cucumbers; to blackberry pie and many kinds of cake; to milk and excellent cream; to coffee that was better than one usually finds in country households. John did not wait for us to begin. He started at once to feed, eating heartily, talking without remission, while Dreiser sat there silently partaking of the fare, rather delicately, not saying much, but laughing to himself at times at John's stories. His mood seemed to be one of respect for the household, of appreciation of the hospitality which was so generous, of comprehending interest in John as a veritable character. He really noted everything; even though at times seeming to be far away. Long after, he referred to this visit, and repeated some of John's picturesque vernacular, showing that it had fastened itself in his memory.

An evening then followed in which Dreiser laughed and rocked; or sat with his head against the back of the chair, folding his handkerchief into squares, or leaning forward to ask John something or to hear him better. At times he howled with delight. Aunt Caroline and her daughter washed the dishes, and came in the living-room after the fun had started. Neither said anything; while Aunt Caroline was knitting and looking down at her work in respectful silence to John. He was going on as before, growing more animated, and piling one anecdote upon another, and calling the character he was portraying, or telling about nicknames that were in themselves as funny as the comedies he sketched. By seven o'clock the hour seemed late, for it was winter and darkness by then had long come upon the prairies, and the woods which skirted the Sangamon River two miles away, and the hills just near Oakford. And such silence without, save for the wind!

"The storm without might rair and rustle" we "did na mind the storm a whistle", there comfortably grouped about the coal stove watching the flames flicker against the isinglass doors. Aunt Caroline sat attentive upon her knitting, the daughter looked down demurely, somewhat abashed by John's guests; Dreiser folded his handkerchief, and John went on telling about quarter horses, camp meetings, dances, fiddler contests in which he had figured. Sometimes as many as fifty fiddlers came together at Havana, or one of the near-by towns, there in some hall to strive for a set of harness, a whip, a five-dollar gold piece as the prize for the best fiddling. And John had often won the prize. "By God, I won 'er this time," was his comment.

Perhaps John would have talked on until sleep vanquished him, if I had not said that we wanted to hear him play the fiddle. He made no excuses, he just got up and got his fiddle. He asked his daughter to play the organ for him and to give him the key. The daughter arose without a word, with no expression on her face, just arose like a wraith and sat down at the organ and gave John the key. Then John tuned the fiddle, and sat back and began to tell stories again, rather he began to preface the playing of each piece with words concerning its origin and where it got its name, and where he heard it first. Nearly every tune was associated with something that had happened at a dance, at the county fair, at a camp meeting, a party, or a festival of some sort. For years he had attended these things, which were a continuation of the New Salem events, of dances at the Rutledge Tavern, of horse races, on the prairie west of New Salem. Thus if he had lived at New Salem when Lincoln did we should not have had a truer re-creation of those days.

John played such pieces as 'Rocky Road to Jordan', 'Way up Tar Creek', 'Foggy Mountain Top', 'Hell Among the Yearlins', 'Little Drops of Brandy', 'The Wind that Shakes the Barley', 'Good Mornin' Uncle Johnny', 'I've Fetched Your Wagon Home', as well as the more familiar pieces like 'Zip Coon', 'Turkey in the Straw'. Sometimes he sang words as he played, like this:

> "There was a woman in our town,
> In our town did dwell,
> She loved her husband dear-i-lee,
> But another man twict as well."

He played a piece which he called 'Toor-a Loor', and another called 'The Speckled Hen', and another which he called 'Chaw Roast Beef'. He sang and played 'Swingin' in the Lane'. He played and sang 'The Missouri Harmony':

> "When in death I shall calm recline
> O bear my heart to my mistress dear,
> Tell her it lived on smiles and wine
> Of brightest hue while it languished here.

Bid her not shed one tear of sorrow
        To sully a heart so brilliant and light.
    But balmy drops of the red grape borrow
        To bathe the relict from morn till night."

Concerning this, John said by way of preface before beginning, "This here is 'The Missouri Harmony'. Linkern used to sing it, but he couldn't carry no tune. That's what my mother told me. But he'd try at it."

Between playing he was piling up anecdotes about 'One-Eyed' Clemons, 'Corky Bill' Atterberry, 'Quarter Hoss' Sam Lounsbury, 'Snaggle Tooth' Engle, 'Slicky Bill' Greene. Dreiser sat there convulsed with laughter, just quietly folding his handkerchief.

John played a piece which he called 'Pete McCue's Straw Stack', and he told us before playing it, "This here is called 'Pete McCue's Straw Stack' named after old Peter McCue, who lived down by Tar Creek. They had a dance thar one time and the boys tied their horses close to a straw stack, and when they came out the hosses had et all the straw. They had been playing this piece that night, but after that they called it 'Pete McCue's Straw Stack'. I forget what they called it before this."

Resting at times from the fiddle, John held the instrument against his arm and talked, telling us what platform dancing was, and about the famous platform dancers that he had known, one of whom, growing excited with drink and music, had looked about the room and called out, "Clar the cheers out. I'm goin' to take off my shoes and come down on her." He did so and his feet went through the puncheon floor and that resulted in renaming the dance music. After that it is was called 'Skinnin' Your Shins' for the dancer had skinned his shins pretty badly. And John told about a noted strong man of Oakford who had whipped a savage bulldog with his own hands, and about Clay Bailey, who had entered the circus ring and taken an escaped leopard by the tail and dragged it back to its cage. "He couldn't have a-done that withouten he was drunk. The likker made him powerful strong and keerless." Aunt Caroline didn't bat an eye as John told these marvels. The daughter still sat at the organ waiting for John to name the next piece. Dreiser was red in the face from suppressed laughter.

John was as good a fiddler as I had ever heard; but he protested that he was a poor performer compared to his wife's brother, who had gone from Oakford years before, and had died in Iowa. "As fur as that's concerned," John confessed, "Fiddler Bill Watkins could beat me all holler, and he warn't a patchin to my wife's brother. He used to play for all the dances here and up Tar Creek—and fight! Why, by God, onct over near the Lattimore, just this side of Dutchland, they was havin' a dance, and some fellers from Mason County was thar and had cum over to break it up. 'Fiddler Bill' jest laid down his fiddle, stepped from the platform, and whooped the whole lot. Now you see my Pap was Jack Armstrong, a powerful man he was in the arms and back; and the truth is Linkern never throwed him. It was a tie. My mother told me so a hundred times before she died."

"How big was your father?" I asked John. "Why, he warn't so big," John replied. "He was short like I am, but husky, big chest, and weighed about one hundred eighty. He never was throwed, is what they tell me."

Dreiser by this time had looked at all the pictures on the wall. In an interval of fiddling he asked John about Duff Armstrong, whose picture hung near the entrance door. It was the face of a hard man, with wild eyes, rather cruel on the whole. John saw Dreiser looking at the picture and remarked, "You can believe Duff was a fightin' man. It was a fight that got him into the court at Beardstown where Linkern defended him with the almanac."

"How about that almanac?" asked Dreiser. "You were not at the trial, I have heard."

"No, I warn't," John admitted; "but I was down one time to Beardstown with my mother when Duff was thar in jail, before the trial."

"What did your mother say was done? She was present at the trial, wasn't she?"

"Yes, she was thar. She said Linkern handed a almanac to the judge which showed that the witnesses had lied about the moon."

"Yes, I know all about that," Dreiser interjected. "But do you know where he got the almanac? Did you ever hear that Lincoln had it printed for this case?"

"Yes, by God, I heard that," replied John with spirit; "but it ain't true. He got that almanac at the drug store. He went up and handed the almanac to the judge, and the judge seed that the moon was settin' and not at the meridian as the witnesses said. So how could they see Duff hit that feller with a neck yoke, because the moon was bright?"

"Yes, yes," said Dreiser, folding his handkerchief and leaning back, as if he had satisfied himself that John did not have anything of importance to reveal upon this subject.

"There's lots of stories about that almanac," said John. "Why, one time over at Springfield I seed a affidavit that said that Linkern didn't change the almanac. And right on the wall thar is a picture of one of the jurymen that tried Duff. He was a smart man, and no one could play any trick on him."

Dresier was now rocking and singing 'Turkey in the Straw' to himself. "Came to the River and couldn't get across, Paid five dollars for an old blind hoss—Turkey in the straw, Turkey in the hay . . . "etc.

I thought I'd suggest an idea, so I said, "John, here's something that hasn't been talked about much. That almanac was not legal evidence, and the judge was either fooled or else he admitted it in evidence, knowing it was illegal.

"It has turned out that an astronomical survey made at Harvard, I believe it was, showed that the moon was just where the almanac put it that night. But an Ayers or Sarsaparilla almanac would prove the state of the weather, or the position of the moon, just as much as a Montgomery Ward catalogue would prove what their prices were; that is, if you just put the catalogue in evidence without someone from the store to swear that those prices were correct."

"Is that so?" said John in great surprise. "Wal, by God, Linkern got it in evidence."

"Yes, those were the good old days. No one thought of bringing an astronomer into court to testify where the moon was on a certain night at a certain hour and minute. An almanac was believed in. But here's something else: even if the moon was setting and not at the meridian the witnesses might have seen your brother strike that man Metzger with the neck yoke. What happened was that the evidence of these witnesses was clouded by the almanac. They said the moon was at the meridian, and the almanac showed it was setting. But what of it? Your brother hit the man, didn't he?"

"You bet he did," was John's quick reply. "And I'll tell you why, by God. You see, my brother and this man was here in Oakford before that. Duff was asleep on a barl; and this man come up and cotched him while he was asleep, and pulled him off the barl. So they fit right then and thar. There was bad blood betwixt them. And that night when Duff used the neck yoke there was a general fight with several in it; and this here Metzger was hit with a slung shot by somebody, and Duff hit him with a neck yoke. But what Duff did didn't kill him. It was the slung shot. A doctor got on the witness-stand and swore that it was the slung shot that cracked his skull. Besides all that, the evidence showed that Metzger ridin' home that night fell off his hoss several times. So how could you say that ary blow at the fight killed him? He might have cracked his head fallin' off his hoss; for as fur as that's concerned he rode home after bein' hit with the slung shot and the neck yoke. And Linkern's speech, which made my mother cry, and everybody in the court room, freed Duff right thar."

"According to this, the position of the moon had as much to do with the case as the astrology of the Babylonians," I said.

"Is that so?" said John mildly. "Maybe you're right."

Dreiser began to sing:

> "The prettiest girl that ever I saw
> Was sucking cider through a straw.

"Play 'Turkey in the Straw' again, John," he requested. And John played it with more spirit than ever, if that had been possible, keeping time with a loud thud of his foot. When he was not fiddling, his daughter sat patiently at the organ waiting for John to give the signal to play. She was not saying a word. His manner of starting off would be something like this: "This here is called 'Hell Amongst the Yearlins'. I don't ricollect what it was furst called; but they had a dance over at Ben Sutton's onct, and while they was a-dancin' the cattle broke into his corn. So ever since they have called it 'Hell Amongst the Yearlins'."

It was evident by this time that John thought he had met a

strange man in the person of Dreiser. John perhaps could not see whether Dreiser was interested in his exhibition or not. He was perhaps puzzled to know in just what mood Dreiser was laughing.

"The most curious man I ever seed," he said later. "When he looks at you with his good eye he seems to know a plenty. When his cockeye turns up he looks like one of the Spilly boys. That good eye of his bores you right through. He asks questions as good as a lawyer."

The almanac case did not exhaust the subject of Duff. There was the matter of Duff's war record, and his discharge from the army by grace of Lincoln, specially exercised, at the instance of Hannah, whose journey to Washington to intercede for her son is in all the books about Lincoln. Duff had died many years before, thus leaving a world that had puzzled him, and made wastage of him. "Duff kept a-drinkin'," was John's comment. "He got so anybody could whoop him. He went around showin' his discharge from the army and pickin' up money for drinks on it." John laid the fiddle aside by this time. He brought forth some of his souvenirs: little things that belonged to his mother; a book containing Lincoln's autograph; and a very good picture of his mother when she was probably toward seventy. It was the face of a dignified pioneer woman, not without a certain charm. He then told us that she had died in Iowa, far from the scenes of her interesting life.

The evening ended at ten, and we went to bed. The partition between my room and Dreiser's was thin. Sometime after lights were out, and John had attended to the stove for the night and retired, I heard Dreiser laughing. "What is the matter, Dreiser?" I called out.

"I was thinking that we were going to see the grave of Porky Jim in the morning. My God, how funny!"

There was a breakfast of ham and eggs, and cakes, and corn bread, and all the preserves of the night before. We had about an hour, before the train left for Springfield, to see the little cemetery on a rise of ground east of the railroad tracks. We wandered around as I read the names of men and women whom I had known as a boy when I drove about the country or went to Concord Church with my grandparents. Dreiser was walking with John. I paused before a stone on which was carved the name of James Thomas; and it meant nothing to me. I remembered no James Thomas. "Who was James Thomas, John?" I asked as he came closer to me.

"Why, by God, that's Porky Jim," said John with a chuckle.

"Porky Jim," laughed Dreiser. "Oh me, oh me!"

Standing here we could see the heavy woods about four miles north along the banks of the Sangamon River. The Spoon River was at least twenty miles farther north. We had said good-bye to Aunt Caroline and her daughter when we left the house. Now at the train we parted from John, who laughed as he said, "Come again, boys."

Much later than this I was in Springfield. John's daughter came to see me to ask me to go to Oakford to console her father. She said he was not well. By this time John was quite old. It was very difficult for me to take the time to go to Oakford; but the daughter was so urgent that I did so. She said that her father would be badly hurt if I did not pay him a visit.

After a trip on the train and some motoring I arrived. John was visibly ill, and in a quietude. He didn't want to fiddle for me; but after I had begged him to do so, he got his daughter to the organ and began to play. It was slack playing at first, then he did better. Darkness was coming early. It was four o'clock, and I had to go. He followed me to the door with a sort of melancholy air. He was going to Texas the next week for the winter.

"I'll see you in the spring, John, when I come."

"No," he said, in a matter of fact way, "you won't see me no more. I won't be here in the spring." Immediately after this correct prophecy concerning himself he suddenly brightened. "What's become of that feller that was here with you?"

"Oh," I replied, "he has published a book that everyone is talking about," referring to *An American Tragedy*.

"Is that so?" said John. "Wal, he left something here, and I allus wanted to send it to him, and didn't know where he was."

"What was it?"

"Why, them things, drawers and a shirt that he slept here in."

"You mean pyjamas?"

"Is that what you call 'em? Pyjamas, eh?"

"Don't mind about sending them," I said, as I hurried down the walk to the car.

John died in January of 1926, two months after this farewell. Aunt Caroline lingered along till 1935. Thus ended the saga of the Armstrong family, which began with Aunt Hannah, who cooked and darned for Lincoln.

NELSON ALGREN

The Captain is a Card

Among the most successful ingredients in *The Man with the Golden Arm*, the book that won Nelson Algren the National Book Award in 1949, were the police line-up scenes. Actually, Algren had published several versions of this scene previously, and all the versions have certain things in common: the rapid-fire exchange of dialogue between the police captain and the assorted petty criminals is always the same in tone, always a question, the answer, a wisecrack; and the character of the captain is fairly consistent from story to story.

Algren apparently first used the situation in a story called 'Biceps', which appeared in *The Southern Review* in 1941, and then (considerably altered) under the title 'The Captain is a Card' in *Esquire*, June 1942. Later that year Algren published his novel *Never Come Morning*, in which the section appears as 'A Bottle of Milk for Mother', again considerably altered, this time to fit into the loosely structured novel. Still again the same situation, with a more or less new set of wisecracks and characters, was used in the short story called 'The Captain Has Bad Dreams, or Who Put the Sodium Amytal in the Hill & Hill', which was later included in his book of short stories *The Neon Wilderness*. He then prepared a completely new version for the police line-up sections of *The Man with the Golden Arm*.

THE UNDERSIZED MAN at the head of the first line of the evening had just been brought in off the street, and wore an oversized army overcoat dragging past his knees; its hem was frayed and caked with mud, as though he'd been sitting on a kerb with the hem in the gutter. The coat's top button dangled loosely and he twisted it tenderly; feeling perhaps that the last vestige of his respectability

F

dangled with it. If you took him seriously he looked like the original tough-luck kid, and if you didn't he looked like Amateur Night at the nearest burlesque.

What was he doing in a police line-up anyhow, the Captain wanted to know.

"Just here for protecting myself is all," the little man explained. Then he glanced uneasily towards the Captain's shadowed corner as though fearing he had, so soon in the questioning, given a wrong answer.

"Don't look over here. Tell your story to the mike."

The oversize overcoat looked into the amplifier with the face of an ageing terrier searching for ever, with brown-eyed weariness, a world of shadowed corners. Of padlocked pool-rooms, bootleg bookies, curtained brothels, darkened side-streets and unlit, littered alleys. He looked like he hadn't walked down an open street in daylight, nor had a friendly nod of recognition in his life. He looked lost.

"Do you ever go around looking for trouble?"

"No sir. I don't like trouble."

"Then what are you doing in front of a tavern at two in the morning with a Luger under your coat? Don't you know those things go off?"

"I'm a veteran."

"What's that got to do with it? I'm a veteran too. But I don't go prowling around taverns with artillery under my clothes."

The veteran eyed the Captain's corner furtively before he answered.

"He shoved me," was the explanation.

"Who's 'he'?"

"A feller I never seen him before. He brought me a drink. Because I'm a veteran."

"Then what happened?"

"He told me to go home."

"Then he slugged you?"

"No sir. He just shoved me was all."

"Then what?"

"Then nothing. That's all. I went home like he told me."

"And picked up a Luger and came back to blow his head off?"

"Yes sir. Naturally." As though that had been understood all along.

"*Naturally?* Don't you realise that if the officer hadn't happened along to take that thing off you, you'd be standing there for murder now?"

Silence. "Well?"

"Yes sir. I realise."

"You're pretty cool about it."

"Yes sir. I'm a veteran."

"What the hell *has* that got to do with it?" The Captain was exasperated at last. "I saw as much over there as you did."

The little man found the Captain with his eyes at last. And snapped like a mongrel held where it cannot move.

"It wasn't you what got shoved. It was *me.*"

"Oh." The Captain lowered his eyes as though he were, suddenly, the guilty man. Then he grinned. "*Man,*" he said quizzically, half sympathy and half surprise, "I'd hate to have you get mad at me for something worth getting mad about."

The next man was half-leaning, half-crouching against the black-and-white lines of the wall. He was a blond of perhaps twenty-two.

"Stand up there!" The Captain sounded like a public-school principal on examination day.

The blond stood as best he could. The knuckles were clenched whitely; the lips were bloodless. And the tip of the nose as white as new snow. The Captain relented.

"You must be hitting it pretty hard."

The boy's lips moved inaudibly towards the mike; it was hard to tell whether he was trying to speak or merely wetting his lips in preparation for saying something.

"What do you take?"

The answer could not be heard; the lips could not be read.

"Speak up, son. Do you sell it too?"

This time the answer came faintly, from somewhere in Cloudland.

"Once—upon—a—time."

"How's last Tuesday afternoon—is that once upon a time?"

The boy nodded solemnly, dreamily, with a slow-motion gravity all his own.

Yes.

Any Tuesday afternoon in Cloudland was once upon a time.

The next man in line was a high yellow in his early thirties.

"What you here for?"

"Havin' whisky in my home."

"You too? I thought they repealed that law. You don't carry a gun, do you?"

"No sir."

"Do you keep one on the premises?"

"I just keep it. I don't carry it. I leave it on the premises."

"But there was a .38 on the premises?"

"I wasn't nowhere near it."

"I didn't ask you how close you were. I asked whether it was there."

"Yes sir. That's what they claims. I'm in business. I got to have one."

"I thought you said it was your home. Now it's a business. Make up your mind, you can't beat both raps. It'll go lighter on you if you stick to the whisky story. What you using a private home for business for anyhow? *What* business?"

"The True-American."

"What's *that*?"

"Social 'n athletic club."

"With five women?"

"That's the social part."

"I see. Was afraid you'd tell me they were lady wrestlers."

The woman in the back giggled at the Captain's humour.

"No sir. A mixed club, *that's* what we got."

"I see. Good clean fun and lots of sunshine?"

"Yes sir. Meets in my home. We go on hikes."

"Now it's a home again. You're not selling whisky there then after all?"

"Oh no, sir. I *give* it away. They my *guests*."

"Which one of your guests filed the numbers off that .38 for you? One of the lady wrestlers?"

"Nobody. I bought it that way."

"Now we're getting somewhere for a change. Ever been in trouble before?"

"No sir," the high yellow declared.

The Captain shook his head sadly, to indicate his resignation at human mendacity. "You know, I'll begin to think you aren't telling the whole truth to these people. You're down here for strong-arm robbery on 1st June 1934. Did that happen on one of your hikes?"

"I paid a fine."

"Did you pay a fine for that no-bill for murder in 1928?"

The high yellow started almost imperceptibly. The Captain had reached him where he lived—in his courage. You could see him visibly trying to pull that courage together, like a fighter holding his guts with one hand while arranging a fixed grin for his opponent to show he isn't hurt. You can tell when they're hurt when they try to smile.

"I didn't kill her."

"You know what I mean though?"

"It's a different case."

"You know what I mean though."

The Negro's face seemed burned a rust-yellow across the forehead and nose, the way a man's face is left when he is lifted out of the chair. He stared straight into the mike, deep shadows under the eyes and the eyes themselves two yellow flares.

"Yes sir," he said at last. And waited tensely for the mike to move. The yellow flares began to die down in the eyes; when they were faded to pinpoints the Captain spoke leisurely, like a man with nowhere to go and the whole night to kill.

"Tell us more about it."

Silence.

"If you don't tell it I'll read it."

The Negro's eyes were dead embers now, and his voice a dying man's voice. He spoke without emphasis, in a dead-level monotone, and—at the first moment—with the dead woman's voice:

"Us two live t'gether 'n we sort of separated 'n got t' goin' t'gether again 'n we were drinkin' t'gether 'n I wanted t' go home n' figures I'd bluff her, teach her a lesson, scare her so's she wouldn't run off 'n always come home with me when it was time. I pulled the gun 'n levelled it 'n she grabbed for it 'n it went off 'n shot her in the stomach 'n when I went t' see her at the hospital she took my hand 'n say, 'Honey, you shouldn't a done it,' 'n that was all she ever say."

"You're a bad man. You been going wrong fifteen years."

The mike was moved to the next man.

Next was a red-headed Irish boy of eighteen, with teeth like piano keys.

"What's your trouble, Red?"

"Left a jimmy in a petrol station door."

"At night?"

"No sir. Daytime."

"Didn't have criminal intent, did you?"

"No *sir*."

"You weren't going to break into that station when it got dark, were you?"

"I just had it on my mind."

"Where were you arrested?"

"I was walkin' on the rocks off 39th. The park officer called me over."

"Where were you going when he called you?"

"Home."

"Then you got it off your mind?"

The red-head grinned amiably. He had it off his mind.

While the mike was being moved the Captain turned to his audience with the deliberation of a sideshow barker at a county fair.

"I want you to look close at this next man, ladies 'n gentlemen. This, let me tell you, is a sweetheart. Folks, meet Hardrocks O'Connor. Meet the folks, O'Connor."

A flat-faced felon in his late fifties, with no bridge to his nose and a bulge for a forehead. The voice hoarse from a hundred cells. You could tell he hit the bottle hard and you could tell he'd done his time the hard way. In the hard places. And still trying to make it the hard way. It was in his posture and in his voice; in the lean set of the jaw and across his punched-in mug like a brand.

"Tell us about yourself, Morning Glory."

O'Connor's mouth split when he said:

"Take 'em west yerself."

The Captain knew when he had a prize: he took Hardrocks west for five solid pages. Danbury, Waupun, Jeff City, Wetumpka, Leavenworth, Huntsville. For a phony bunco game. For a dice game with 'missouts'. For violation of the Narcotics Act. For forgery, for the pocket-book game, for the attention racket, for using the mails to sell a pair of missouts, for bigamy, for vag, for impersonating an officer, for breach of promise, for contributing to delinquency of a minor, for defrauding an innkeeper, for indecent exposure, for tapping a gas main. And for the phony bunco game, right back where he'd started a lifetime before.

Two years, ten days, six days, six months, thirty days, a year and a day, fifty-dollar fine, given a floater out of the state in Lubbock, only to run into two years at hard labour on the pea farm at Huntsville for taking a rancher with a phony roulette wheel at a McAllen County fair.

"Why didn't you get out of the state like they gave you a chance to do at Lubbock instead of running on down to McAllen?" The Captain was merely curious.

"Had a deal on down there."

The Captain turned to his listeners.

"Five more pages, ladies 'n gentlemen—'n not one a crime of violence. He'll sell you a little dope, take a little hisself, sell you an oilwell 'r take a merry widow for a ride on her insurance money. But he won't use a gun. He'll spot a beggar paddlin' down the street when he has t' get out of town in a hurry—but he'll stop 'n try t' take the beggar." This spectacle of a man who could steal for a lifetime without once doing so by force affected the good Captain as an obscenity. "C'mon down here," he ordered. "Let the people see you so's they'll remember you. How'd you get your nose bust, Hardrocks? Trying to take the same sucker twice?"

O'Connor paused on a step from the stage to rub the place where the bridge of his nose had once been.

"Had the bone took out when I was twenty. Wanted t' be a fighter." He hesitated as though he were about to add something.

"Keep moving', Hardrocks. No speeches. All the way down front. There, that's as near as we want you. Take off that cap. That's how he looks without a cap, folks. Now put it back on. That's how he looks with it on. Walk around, Daffodil. We want to see how you look when you walk."

O'Connor began a deliberate pacing: five steps forward and five steps back. And turned heavily at an imagined door. His life was a bull-pen, and he turned within it like a gelded bull; five dogged steps forward and five dogged steps back.

"That's enough of that, O'Connor. Now stand still and turn around with your cap in your right hand."

The old man turned, the sheen of his worn brown suit showing in the glare from above like light on an ageing animal's hide.

"That's how he looks with his back turned, folks. Put your cap on, Hardrocks. No, don't turn around yet. That's how he looks when he's walking away with your money. All right, O'Connor, back on the platform."

O'Connor returned slowly to his position before the mike.

"What did you say you were arrested for, Hardrocks? Stealing from a blind man?"

"I wasn't arrested. I walked into the station 'n give myself up. I can't make it no more. I want 'em t' come 'n get me, I want 'em all t' come 'n get me. Anyone who wants me, tell 'm 't come 'n get me. I can't make it no more."

The woman in the back stopped tittering. The Captain cocked his head to one side in mild surprise. The young men, on either side of the hardest one of them all, looked straight out over the lights as though the old man was speaking for their futures as well as for his past.

"I been a stumblin' block, I been a obstacle to the Republic. I done it all wrong, I got hard-boiled too young. I got kicked around too soon. I was a orphan 'n got kicked around. I'm an old man, I got nobody, I can't make it no more———" Hardrocks O'Connor was crying.

The next man was a young Negro in a gabardine, heavy in the shoulders and lean in the shanks.

"What you here for, Ready-Money?"

"Don't know."

"Then you'll need a lawyer to tell you. How old was the girl?"

"She looked like sixteen."

"Yeh. But she was eleven. Are you on parole?"

"Yes sir."

"Good-bye."

The last man in the line was a dwarf with the head and torso development of a man of average height. He stood two inches short

of the four-foot mark on the black-and-white diagram behind him
and looked to be in his early forties. An ugly specimen.

"What's it for, Shorty?"

"Just a pickup."

"Pickup for what?"

"Don't know. Suspicion I s'pose."

"What you sit seven years in Stateville for, Shorty?"

"Suspicion."

"Isn't seven years on suspicion a little severe?"

The dwarf's voice was as shrill as a ten-year-old's.

"Yes *sir*. It *was* severe."

"Ever get boosted through a transom, Shorty?"

"Yes *sir*."

"Who boosted you?"

"A frien'. He's still settin'."

"How many places you rob that way, Shorty?"

"I ferget."

"You shouldn't. You're still in the business. How much time you
done?"

"Year 'n a day once 'n once three years."

"You don't count Stateville?"

"You said that one."

The women tittered their enjoyment of the little man's confession.
A dwarf, standing between a seven-year-long shadow and a new
shadow just as long. Perhaps it was funny to be so little while
transoms were so high. And shadows were so long. Perhaps they
saw no shadow. Perhaps they saw no man.

Next was a middle-aged Serb, splay-footed, with the hands of a
stockyards skinner. He stood with his naked forearms folded.

"What you here for this time, Rutu?"

"Neigh—bors complain."

"Again? What about?"

"Same ol' t'ing. I fight."

"Who were you fighting with this time?"

"Same ol' t'ing. Wid wife."

"Hell, that's no crime neither. Next."

"I went and let somebody use my car."

"That puts you in, too. Next."

"What's your trouble, next man?"

"I beg your pardon?"

"Don't beg my pardon," the Captain quipped. "Beg the pardon of the woman whose purse you snatched."

"I didn't snatch it."

"How'd the officers find it in your room?"

"I stole it."

"Oh, that's different. I beg *your* pardon. *Dis*charged."

The next man was a paunchy character with the professionally friendly aspect of a floorwalker or beauty-shop operator. His iron-grey hair had been recently marcelled.

"What you here for, Flash?"

"Just riding in a cab is all."

"What did you have in your pocket?"

"Just a toy cap pistol was all."

"What was that for—Fourth of July?"

"I was on my way to give it to my little nephew in Hammond for a Christmas present."

"How many cabs you take with that toy gun, Santa?"

"Just the one I was riding in. I don't know what come over me."

"Come off it, Coneroo. How many you hold up altogether?"

"Nine."

"I said altogether."

"Oh. Altogether. Twenty-eight."

"You know what happens to habituals in Michigan?"

"Yes sir. They get life."

"Too bad you didn't wait to get to Chicago to stick up that driver. We call that a misdemeanour here. Do you think crime pays?"

The floorwalker retired gracefully from the mike and adjusted his cravat.

The last man was a Negro of perhaps nineteen, in a torn and bloodstained shirt and with one arm in a cast. He had Mongolian features, the cheek-bones set high and widely—to protect the eyes—the eyes slanted slightly and the skin like tawny parchment. The Captain explained.

"This is the sweetheart who shot Sergeant Shannon Friday night. Tell it to the people the way you told it to us, Memphis."

"Ah was out look'n fer somebody t' stick up n' had m' gun handy 'n he come along, that's all."

"Where was this?"

"South side of 59th Street. Ah was crossin' over t' the north side when ah saw Shannon, he wasn't in uniform."

"Did he call after you?"

"Yes sir. He say 'Hey Buddy, wait a minute,' 'n he had somethin' in his hand. It looked like a gun 'n ah pulled out m' pistol 'n stahted t' fire. He shot 'n hit me in the right ahm 'n ah ran 'n tried t' find some place t' hide."

"You're sure you weren't out gunning for Sergeant Shannon?"

"Oh no, sir."

"But you knew him from before?"

"From a lo-o-ong time."

"You know he may die?"

"That's what they tell me."

"Aren't worried much about it though, are you?"

"It was me 'r him."

"How'd they find you?"

"Ah leaned on a mail-box, ah was bleedin' pretty bad. Ah left stains on th' box 'n some of m' own people seen them 'n tol' a officer." The boy seemed more saddened by that single circumstance than by either the imminence of Shannon's death or of his own. Like a thing repeated many times in an effort to believe and accept:

"My *own* people."

And his voice was heavy with shame for them.

"How do you feel about getting the chair, Boy?"

"Don't care one way 'r another. Don't feel nothin', good 'r bad. Just feel a little low is all. Knew ah'd never get t' be twenty-one anyhow."

The line turned and shuffled restlessly through the door to the cells. The overhead lights went out one by one, till even the tittering women were gone. And nothing remained in the show-up room but the sounds of the city, coming up from below.

The great trains howling from track to track all night. The taut and telegraphic murmur of ten thousand city wires, drawn most cruelly against a city sky. The rush of city waters, beneath the city streets.

The passionate passing of the night's last El.

H. L. MENCKEN

An Evening on the House

Scholar, wit, journalist, editor, iconoclast, social critic and denouncer
of the species 'boobus Americanus', Mencken was an active brawling
spirit among the New Realists of the first three decades of this century
and subsequently came to personify the radical American of the twenties.

He was born in Baltimore of German descent, and lived and worked
there for the *Baltimore Sun*. With George Jean Nathan he edited *Smart
Set* from about the middle of the First World War until the magazine's
demise in the early 1920s; later Mencken and Nathan founded the
American Mercury (1924), famous for its articles debunking American
manners and culture.

Perhaps his most famous book is *The American Language,* and it made
of him, according to critic Alistair Cooke, "the classical authority on the
English of the United States". The intensity of his concern for language
and for journalistic craftsmanship was equalled only by the fury of his
criticism of the pretensions and pious hypocrisies he saw buried in the
American family, Church, and State.

In later years Mencken's biting, flamboyant style mellowed somewhat, and in his memoirs, completed in the form of a three-volume
autobiography in 1943, his lucid and ribald prose softened its attack on
the American citizen without losing any of the purity of its language.

'An Evening on the House', which appeared in the December 1943
Esquire, belongs to this later, autobiographical period, although it was
not included in the three volumes. The same is true of another autobiographical article, 'Obsequies in the Grand Manner', which appeared
in *Esquire* the subsequent month. Mencken's 'Downfall of a Revolutionary', which appeared in *Esquire* in September 1940, was reprinted
as the first selection in *Heathen Days*, one of the three autobiographical
books. 'An Evening on the House' has not been collected and is reprinted here for the first time.

IN THE DAYS OF TROLLEY PARKS, now gone for ever, there was almost as much spread between park and park, culturally speaking, as you will now find between night clubs. Some, catering to what was then called the Moral Element, showed all the hallmarks of Chautauqua, Asbury Park and Lake Mohonk, with nothing stronger on tap than ginger ale, soda pop and sarsaparilla, and no divertisement more provocative to the hormones than quoit-pitching and the flying horses. But in others there was a frank appeal to the baser nature of mankind, and at the bottom of the scale were some that, by the somewhat prissy standards of those days, were veritable sewers of wickedness. One of the latter sort was operated, in the Baltimore I adorned as a young newspaper reporter, by a cashiered police sergeant named Julius Olsen—a man who believed, as he would often say, in living and letting live. His place lay at the terminus of a Class D trolley line that meandered down the harbour side to the shore of one of the affluents of the Patapsco River. Most of his customers, however, did not patronise this trolley line, which was outfitted with senile cars that often jumped the track, and shook the bones out of their passengers when they didn't. Indeed, it was rare to encounter an actual Baltimorean in the place, which had the name of Sunset Park. Nearly all the males who frequented it were sailors from ships berthed along or anchored in the river, and nine-tenths of the females were adventuresses from either the Norfolk, Virginia, region, then famous throughout the Eastern seaboard for its levantine barbarities, or the lower tier of Pennsylvania counties, where the Vice Trust, backed by Wall Street, maintained agents in every hamlet.

If there was any among the lady visitors to Sunset who had not lost her honest name long before she ever saw it, the fault was not Julius Olsen's, for he had a ground rule rigidly excluding all others. Every evening at eight o'clock he would take his place at the garish entrance to his pleasure ground, and give his eye to each female who presented herself, whether alone or with an escort. If there was anything in her aspect that raised a suspicion of chastity he would challenge her at once, and hold her up at the gate until she convinced him that her looks were false to her inner nature. Once, as I stood there with him—for I greatly admired his insight into such things and was eager to learn its secrets—a young couple got off the trolley car and made as if to enter. To my unpractised eye they looked to be the run-of-the-mine yahoos and nothing more: I could detect no stigmata of chemical purity in the lady. But Julius saw deeper than I did, and as the couple came abreast of his sentry post his heavy paw fell upon the shoulder of the young man, and his eyebrows drew together in a fearful frown. "What in hell do you mean," he roared, "to bring a nice young girl to such a goddam dump as this? Ain't you got no goddam sense at *all*?" The young fellow, amazed and abashed, stood speechless, and Julius bellowed on. "Don't you know," he demanded, "where you are at? Ain't you ever heerd tell of Sunset Park? Goddam if I ever seen the like of it in all my born days! Do you want a gang of sailors to bash in your head and make off with your girl? What would you have to say to her mama if that happened? How would you square yourself with her pa? Goddam if I ain't got a mind to bust you one myself. Now you take her home and don't let me see you around here no more. As for *you*"—turning to the silent and trembling girl—"all I got to say is you better get yourself a better beau. Such damn fools as this one is poison to a religious young lady, and don't you go telling me that ain't what you are. *I know, I* do. Now, scat, the goddam bothen of you!"

Whereupon he half bowed and half heaved them on to the waiting trolley car, and stood by muttering until it started back to the city.

From all this the maker of snap judgments may conclude that Julius was a Puritan at heart—perhaps even that there was a Y.M.C.A. secretary hidden in him. Nothing could be more untrue. He simply did not want to clutter up his conscience, such as it was, with gratuitous and unnecessary burdens. Otherwise he was the complete antinomian, and of all the tough and abandoned trolley parks around the periphery of Baltimore, his Sunset was undoubtedly the worst. Every sort of infamy that the vice-crusaders of the time denounced, from crap shooting to hoochie-koochie dancing, and from the smoking of cigarettes by females—then still *contra bonos mores*—to riotous boozing by both sexes, went on within its gates, and there was no dilution of these carnalities by anything of an even remotely respectable nature. If a customer had called for a lemonade the waiters would have fanned him with the billies they carried up their sleeves, and if either of the two comedians in the so-called burlesque show that went on in a big shed had ventured upon a really clean joke, Julius himself would have given him the bum's rush. The strip-tease had not been invented in that remote era, but everything that the fancy of ribald men had yet concocted was offered. The stock company, like most other such organisations, played a loutish version of *Krausmeyer's Alley* every night, but it was given with variations suggested by the worst conceits of whisky drummers and medical students. The taste of the time being for large and billowy women, there was no girl in the chorus who weighed less than 170 pounds, and the rear elevation of each and every one of them was covered with bruises from head to foot, all made by the slapsticks of the comedians. In the intervals of the performance on the stage, these ladies were expected to fraternise with the customers. This fraternising consisted mainly in getting them as drunk as possible, and then turning them over to scamps who dragged them out to a dark spot behind the shed and there went through their pockets. When a customer resisted—which happened sometimes in the case of sailors—the scamps gave him a drubbing, and it was not at all unheard of for the harbour cops to find the clay of a jolly jack tar in the adjacent river, especially of a Sunday morning, for Saturday night was the big night at Sunset Park, as it was at all such places.

The land cops, who knew Julius when he was a poor flat-foot like themselves and now took a certain amount of fraternal pride in his success in life, made occasional raids upon him, but only under pressure from reformers, and never with any hope or intent of bringing him to heel. Once I was present when a party of reformers undertook a raid in person, with a squad of cops trailing along, theoretically to protect them. Julius, who was on watch as usual at his front gate, let them enter unmolested, but they had hardly snooped their first snoop before his whole company of goons, male and female, fell upon them, and in two minutes they were in full retreat, with the cops following after to clout them as they ran. The next day he swore out a warrant for their leader, charging him with lifting a diamond sunburst worth 18,000 dollars from one of the chorus girls, and under cover of the ensuing uproar their counter-charges were forgotten. Julius had a dozen witnesses willing to swear that they had seen the reformer throttle the girl with one hand and

grab the sunburst with the other, and another dozen schooled to
testify that they had recovered it only by *force majeure* and in the face
of wild slashings with a razor by the accused. The sunburst itself was
brought into court, along with five cut-rate jewellers hired to certify
to its value, and for a while things looked dark for the poor reformer, for he was a Sunday-school superintendent, and Maryland
juries, in those days, always said 'Guilty' to Sunday-school super-
intendents; but his lawyer filed a demurrer on some obscure ground
or other.

Rather curiously, there was seldom any serious disorder at Sunset
Park—that is, within Julius's definition of the term. Now and then,
to be sure, a sailor ran amuck and attempted to stage an imitation of
some massacre he had seen in Shanghai or Port Said, but he seldom
got beyond teeing off, for all of Julius's waiters, as I have said, were
armed with billies, and his head bartender, Jack Jamieson, was a
retired heavyweight, and worth a thousand men. Even the comedians
in his show lent a hand when necessary, and so did the four musicians
who constituted the orchestra—the leader, Professor Kleinschmidt,
who doubled in piano and violin and fed the comedians; the cornet
player, George Mullally; the trombonist, Billy Wilson; and the
drummer, Bing-Bing Thompson, himself a reformed sailor. Julius
himself never entered these hurly-burlies, but stood on the sidelines
to boss his lieges. Even when a customer insulted one of the lady
help, say by pasting her in the nose or biting off an ear, the head of
the establishment restrained his natural indignation, and let the *lex
situs* prevailing at Sunset Park take its course. Only once, indeed,
did I ever hear of him forgetting himself, and on that occasion I
happened to be present as his guest, for he was always very polite to
newspaper reporters, as he was to detectives, precinct leaders,
coroners and other such civic functionaries.

It was the opeing night of his 1901 season, and I made the uncomfortable trolley trip to the park in the company of Leopold
Bortsch, *Totsäufer* of the Scharnhorst Brewery, who had to attend *ex
officio*, for Julius had Scharnhorst beer on tap. Unfortunately, there
had been complaints about it of late, as there had been in Baltimore
proper, for it was then, and had been for years, the worst malt liquor
ever seen in the town. Leopold himself, who had to drink it day in
and day out on his tours of customers' saloons, and at the in-

numerable funerals, weddings, wedding anniversaries, christenings
and confirmations that went on in their families, was constrained to
admit, in candid moments, that it was certainly doing his kidneys no
good. But when a Class A customer had an opening, he had to get it
down willy-nilly, and at the same time he had to foment its consumption by all the assembled bibuli. For the first night of Sunset
Park, which in a normal week consumed two hundred half barrels,
he was expected to stage a really royal show, and to that end the
brewery allowed him 100 dollars to spend over the bar. He did not
know, as he marched up radiating his best promotional manner, that
there was trouble ahead. Specifically, he did not know that Julius,
succumbing at last to the endless complaints about Scharnhorst beer
(which had by now become so bad that even the Scotch engineers
from British ships sometimes gagged at it), had resolved to give a
look-in to seven other Baltimore breweries. Nor did he know that all
of their seven brews were already on tap at the bar, and that he
would find the *Totsäufer* of each and every one lined up before it, to
fight him to the death.

It was a shock, indeed, but Leopold was not one to be easily
flabbergasted, and his reply was characteristically prompt and bold.
The immemorial custom was for a *Totsäufer* to begin proceedings, on
such an occasion, by slapping down a five-dollar bill and inviting all
comers to have a beer. Leopold slapped down a *ten*-spot. The seven
other *Totsäufer*, thus challenged, had to respond in kind, and they
did so with panicky dispatch, each, of course, calling for his own beer.
Jack Jamieson, for the opening night, had put in two extra bar-
tenders, which, with his regular aides and himself, made five in all,
but how could five men, within the space of five minutes, draw
1,600 five-cent glasses of beer? It seemed beyond human power, but
I saw them do it, and while they were still shoving over the last
couple of hundred—by now at least 80 per cent foam—Leopold
threw down *two* ten-spots, and commanded a double ration of
Scharnhorst for all hands. What would the other *Totsäufer* do now?
What they would do was instantly apparent. Six of the seven saw
him with crisp *twenties*, and simultaneously bellowed orders for
wholesale rounds of their own beers. The seventh, Hugo Blauvogel
of the Peerless Brewery, raised by peeling off *three* tens.

The situation, as the war correspondents say, now began to

develop rapidly. Jack Jamieson relieved it somewhat by palming one of the twenties and one of the tens, and his chief assistant helped a little more by collaring another of the tens, but there remained the sum of 130 dollars for the cash-register, and a simple calculation will show that it called for 2,600 beers. Half of them had been drawn—God knows how!—before Jack thought of raising the price to ten cents, but by that time the bar was packed as tightly as a bus-load of war workers, and great gangs of reinforcements were swarming in from all parts of the park. When the news reached the hoochie-koochie show, where a hundred or more sailors from the Battleship (*censored*), then on a good-will tour of the Atlantic ports, were spoofing the performers, they arose as one man, and began a lumbering sprint for the bar. Passing the show-shed on their way, they gave the word to its patrons, and in ten seconds the girls and comedians were mauling and jawing one another to empty tables. Not a waiter was left on the floor, and in half a minute more not a girl or comedian was left on the stage, or a musician in the orchestra pit. By the time these artists arrived at the bar the crowd in front of it was twenty men deep, and all semblance of decorum had vanished. The boozers close up were so dreadfully squeezed and shoved that they could hardly get down the beers in front of them, and the later-comers on the outskirts fought in despair for better places. The sailors from the battleship, forgetting chivalry, tried to climb in over the heads of the ladies of the ensemble, and the comedians, musicians and special policemen slugged it out with the waiters. Only the eight *Totsäufer* kept their heads. They went on throwing money into the whirlpool of suds that covered the bar.

Up to this time Julius himself had been at his usual post at the park gate, searching the faces of inpouring fair ones for vestiges of innocence. But he had ears as well as eyes, and though it was a good city block from where he stood to the bar, he eventually picked up the roar that was mounting there, and made off to investigate. The crowd, by now, bulged outside the entrance like a swarm of flies around the bung of a molasses barrel, and hundreds of newcomers were arriving at a gallop and trying to horn and worm their way into it. Julius accordingly ducked to the rear, and entered behind the bar. He was just in time to hear Leopold Bortsch give the signal for the final catastrophe. It consisted of the one word 'Wine!' uttered in a kind of scream. "Wine! Wine! Wine!" echoed the massed and macerated boozers. "He's opening wine! He's setting up wine! Hooray! Hooray! Hooray!"

There were, in fact, but five bottles of wine in the whole of Sunset Park, and they had been lying in Jack's cooler for three or four years, awaiting the remote chance that John W. Gates, Stanford White or Charlie Schwab might drop around some evening. The first two were duds, but the remaining three popped with magnificent effect, and as the so-called champagne seethed out of them, the last restraints of civilised society blew off, and the whole company yielded to its *libido boozalis*. In half a minute not a single sailor from the battleship was on the floor: they were all climbing over the merchant mariners and other civilians and in dozens of cases a sailor thus climbing had another sailor climbing over *him*. Julius, with his long experience as cop and *Wirt*, saw a riot was in the making. "No more!" he roared. "Not another goddam drink! The bar is closed!"

Alas, it was a bad idea, and even if it had been a good one it would have come too late to work. As well challenge Behemoth with a spit-blower or Vesuvius with a squirt. Jack and his colleagues, in obedience to the boss's command, downed their tools instantly, but there were plenty of sailors present, both of the Navy and the Merchant Marine, who knew very well which end of a bottle had the cork, and they were over the bar in no time at all. Nor were they bound and hobbled, once they got into action, by the stiff, professional technique of Jack and company. When an outcry for gin came from the far reaches of the crowd they sent a whole bottle of it sailing through the air, and then another. Nor did they hesitate to use bottles on Julius's own head when he plunged into the thick of them, and essayed to lay them out. Of the details of this phase I can give you only hearsay, for I had been working my way out since the beginning of the action, and had by now taken a rather unfavourable post of observation some distance away, behind a large oak tree. But I went to the trouble during the weeks and months following to run down the full story, and these were its principal elements:

1. The rioters emptied not only every container of lawful goods in the park, from beer kegs to sprinklers of Angostura bitters; they also got down a barrel of cologne spirits that Julius used to sophisticate

his five-cent whisky, the contents of forty selzer siphons, and a bottle of Mickey Finns.

1. Julius's first act, on recovering his faculties, was to get a revolver from his office and go gunning for the eight *Totsäufer*. All had disappeared save Hugo Blauvogel. At him Julius fired six times, missing him every time. The next day he served notice on the Baltimore breweries that any *Totsäufer* sent to the place thereafter would be shot like a dog.

3. The sailors from the Battleship (*censored*), returning aboard at dawn, took with them five of the ladies of the Sunset Park ensemble and both comedians. The officer of the deck refused admission to the ladies, but apparently swore in the comedians as mess attendants, yeomen, chaplain's mates or something of the sort, for a couple of weeks later the men of the whole North Atlantic Fleet staged a show at the Guantanamo base that is still remembered in the Navy as the damndest ever seen. Its stars were two comics of unprecedented virtuosity. From the first glimpse of their red noses to the last reverberation of their slapsticks, they had the assemblage rolling in the aisles.

SINCLAIR LEWIS

Gentlemen, this is Revolution

Esquire has had a small army of regular book reviewers: James T. Farrell, Burton Roscoe, William Lyon Phelps, Bennett Cerf, Sinclair Lewis, A. J. Liebling, and currently, Dorothy Parker. Sinclair Lewis began his reviews in the issue of June 1945 with this review of Richard Wright's *Black Boy*, and three other books on the Negro in America: Walter White's *A Rising Wind*; Gunnar Myrdal's *An American Dilemma*; and a symposium, *What the Negro Wants*, by several Negro educators and journalists. The enthusiasm with which he welcomes this 'revolution' against what the subtitle called "the old dominion of white smugness" is obvious.

In his memoir of Sinclair Lewis (*Esquire*, October 1958) George Jean Nathan wrote of Lewis' dedication to the Negro cause:

"There was only one time when Lewis's humor seemed to have completely deserted him. This was when he had completed one of his later novels, *Kingsblood Royal*, and had become such a negrophile that not only did he collect autographs of Buck and Bubbles and Bill Robinson, and other celebrities of the day, but chose his Negro chauffeur, Joseph, as his constant companion and bosom friend. He introduced him into what, he had heard and regarded, was fashionable society. He furthermore became so touchy on the subject of his new comrades that he quarreled with any of his former friends who carelessly ventured to refer to them in slangy terms. One such was his old friend Mencken, who had sent him a box of burnt cork with the suggestion that Red use it when next he turned actor."

Lewis' last review for *Esquire* was in December 1945, when he stopped to "go back to work on a novel". *Kingsblood Royal* was published in 1947.

*"*BLACK BOY,*"* the story of his own youth in the South by Richard Wright, the enormously talented young Negro who also wrote *Native*

Son, has been greeted by several placidly busy white reviewers and by a couple of agitated Negro reviewers as betraying too much "emotion", too much "bitterness".

Now this is the story of a coloured boy who, just yesterday, found in his native community not merely that he was penalised for having the same qualities that in a white boy would have warmed his neighbours to universal praise—the qualities of courage, energy, curiosity, refusal to be subservient, the impulse to record life in words —but that he was in danger of disapproval, then of beatings, then of being killed, for these qualities, for being 'uppity'. Not bitterness but fear charges the book, and how this young crusader can be expected to look back only a few years to the quiet torture with anything except hatred is beyond me.

When we have a successful comedy by an ex-prisoner about the kindness and humour of the warders in a German concentration camp, then I shall expect Mr. Wright to mellow and to speak amiably of the teachers who flattened him, his coloured neighbours and relatives who denounced him, the merchants who cheated him, the white fellow-mechanics who threatened him for wanting to learn their skills, and the librarian who suspected him—quite rightly—of reading that militant and bewhiskered Bolshevik, that polluter of temples and Chambers of Commerce, Comrade H. L. Mencken.

There has recently appeared, at the same time as *Black Boy*, the skilled and important report by the secretary of the National Association for the Advancement of Colored People, my friend Walter White, upon what has been happening to American Negro soldiers in our camps at home and in England, and at the battle-front in Italy and Africa. There are in this report numerous exact incidents of Jim Crowism lugged into our Army of Democracy. The main impressions that come out of reading it are the continued segregation of Negro soldiers from their white comrades in Red Cross clubs and even in adjacent villages, and the fact that, except for a few sectors in which Negroes have brilliantly fought and flown, they have been restricted to labour units instead of being trusted as fighters.

Soldier workers, lugging supplies ashore during landings, or driving trucks or repairing roads under fire, get killed just as frequently

—it may even be just as painfully—as the white fighters, but there is no credit in it. They are expected to live like dogs and not even to die as heroes.

The assertions of Mr. White are amply backed up by a woman, a white woman, a woman from a Navy family, in another just-issued book, *Jim Crow Grows Up*, by Ruth Danenhower Wilson.

If there had appeared only these three books, these three disturbing Border Incidents, they would still be enough to make the wise observer fear that a revolution in Negro affairs is threatened. But one may go beyond them to a score of other related books published in the past three years, and if America can possibly take the time from its study of comic strips to discover even the titles of these books, it may realise that this is a revolution, and that it is not coming—it is here.

The unwritten manifesto of this revolution states that the Negro, backed by a number of whites in every section of the land, is finished with being classed as not quite human; that he is no longer humble and patient—and unlettered; and that an astonishingly large group of Negro scholars and journalists and artists are expressing their resolution with courage and skill. They are no longer 'coloured people'. They are *people*.

Lillian Smith's novel, *Strange Fruit*, still a best seller and as such revealing new audiences, is not merely a small tragedy about two lovers separated by a colour line which bothered everybody except the lovers themselves. It is a condensation of the entire history of one-tenth of our population.

That amusing and amazingly informative book, *New World A-Coming*, by Roi Ottley, published in 1943, is not just a report of the new Negro life in Harlem. It is a portent of an entire new life for all American Negroes, and it was written by what is naïvely known as a 'coloured man'—that is, a man who has by nature the fine rich skin that the rest of us try to acquire by expensive winter trips to Florida.

And the 1943 biography of Dr. George Washington Carver by Rackham Holt—who, like Lillian Smith, is very much the White Lady—portrays, on the positive side of the question, what one Negro could do, given any chance at all, even so small a chance that to a white man it would have seemed a balk. Dr. Carver, whose discovery of the food and the plastics to be found in the once disenfranchised peanut was salvation for large sections of the South, was the greatest agricultural chemist of our time. It is doubtful whether any flamboyant soldier or statesman or author has done more solid good for America than this Negro, the child of slaves.

But in one thing the intellectual or just the plain reasoning Negro today has broken away from the doctrines of Dr. Carver. This newcomer has progressed or seriously retrogressed, whichever you prefer. He is no longer, like Dr. Carver, ecstatic with gratitude to the white men who permit him the singular privilege of enabling them to make millions of dollars.

To such innocent readers as have not known that the Negro doesn't really like things as they are, such as have been shocked by the 'bitterness' of Mr. Wright's *Black Boy*, there is to be recommended a book much more shocking. But here the shocks are communicated by graphs and columns of figures and grave chapters of sociology, which add up to exactly the same doctrines as Mr. Wright's.

This is *An American Dilemma*, a 1,483-page treatise by Professor Gunnar Myrdal of Sweden and a staff of American assistants. Mr. Myrdal was invited by the Carnegie Corporation to come to America precisely because he was a foreigner, and less subject to our own prejudices.

Anyone who reads through this vast work will really know something about the identity and the social position of the Negro, and anyone who desires to 'argue the question' is invited to read it, whether he was born in Maine or Mississippi. Probably no other book has more exact information, more richness of Negro lore. Here is his complex origin, whereby the yardman whom you think so clownish may have in him the blood of Arabian princes as well as of Bantu warriors; here are his economic status today, his religion and culture, his past and present share in politics, his social conflicts, his actual and possible jobs, his dollars-and-cents budget today. It is all as impersonal as penicillin, and as powerful.

To this sober pair of volumes should be added the enlightenment and stimulation and considerable entertainment in a book published a few months ago by that excellent Southern institution, the University of North Carolina Press, at Chapel Hill; a book called

What the Negro Wants. In this, fourteen distinguished Negro writers such as Langston Hughes, A. Philip Randolph, Dr. W. E. B. Du Bois, Mary Bethune, Roy Wilkins tell precisely what they think of it all.

They are all serious, honest, and informed, but among them I prefer George Schuyler of the Pittsburgh *Courier,* who, despite his wit and easy urbanity, is perhaps the most serious of the lot. How any person so cultured that he can add two and two and get as much as three out of it can read the deft pages of Mr. Schuyler and still accept any of the Comical Coon, the Dancing Dinge, the Grateful Bellhop, the 'Mah brethrens, Ah absquatulates tuh consider' theory of Negro culture, I cannot understand.

His thesis, bland as dynamite soup, is that there is no Negro Problem at all, but there decidedly is a Caucasian Problem: that of the universal American-English-Belgian-Dutch-French-German-Portuguese exploiter who smugly talks about the 'white man's burden' while he squats on the shoulders of all the 'coloured men' in the world. Mr. Schuyler suggests that in Kenya and Burma and Jamaica and Java and Peking just as much as in America these coloured races are now effectively sick of it. He is, however, too polite to point up the facts that there are a lot more of them than there are of us, and that a machine-gun does not inquire into the complexion of the man who uses it.

Here, all of these books begin to fit into a pattern. This suggestion of a universal revolt against the domination of white smugness is also the conclusion of *A Rising Wind,* even though the author is so gay and gentle a leader as Walter White. Quoting from Pearl Buck, another white woman who is not content to be nothing more than that, Mr. White indicates with what frightening care the entire 'coloured' world'—including Japan—is watching and reporting upon our treatment of our own Negroes in Army and Navy, in hotel and bus, in factory and pulpit and congressional committee room.

Gentlemen, my pukka English-Irish-Yank-Swede-Dutch brethren, it behooves us to find out what this larger part of the world is thinking and most articulately saying about us. A slight injection of knowledge may hurt our feelings, but it may save our lives.

I am delighted that in my first column for that stately household compendium, *Esquire,* I have been able to uphold the standards of refined and uncontaminated rhetoric and, here in my ivory tower in Duluth, to keep from taking sides and to conceal my personal views upon Messrs. White, Wright, Schuyler and Myrdal. Let us by all means avoid distasteful subjects and think only of the brightest and best.

J. D. SALINGER

This Sandwich Has No Mayonnaise

J. D. Salinger's 'This Sandwich Has No Mayonnaise', which appeared in *Esquire* in October 1945, marked the author's second appearance in the magazine. His first was 'The Heart of a Broken Story', published in September 1941. In the 'Backstage with *Esquire*' notes on the contributors, Salinger said: "I am a dash man and not a miller, and it is probable that I will never write a novel." He of course then went on to write his well-remembered *The Catcher in the Rye*, about Holden Caulfield, a figure who in this story is already dead, or at least missing-in-action. This is especially interesting because Salinger does the same thing again in his saga of the Glass family. 'A Perfect Day for Bananafish' is one of the earliest of these stories, and there Seymour—really the key figure in the Glass family—is a suicide. Salinger's characters seem to have a life outside of the stories in which they appear, as if Salinger was just giving us bits and pieces out of the continuity of their lives, with things happening to them that no reader knows about. 'This Sandwich Has No Mayonnaise' takes place *after* the end of *The Catcher in the Rye*, and in it Holden Caulfield's brother remembers things that happened *before The Catcher in the Rye*. It is an early example of Salinger's methods of developing his sagas, and it is here reprinted for the first time.

I AM INSIDE THE TRUCK, too, sitting on the protection strap, trying to keep out of the crazy Georgia rain, waiting for the lieutenant from Special Services, waiting to get tough. I'm scheduled to get tough any minute now. There are thirty-four men in this here veehickle, and only thirty are supposed to go to the dance. Four must go. I plan to knife the first four men on my right, simultaneously singing 'Off We Go into the Wild Blue Yonder' at the top of my voice, to drown out their silly cries. Then I'll assign a detail of two men (preferably college graduates) to push them off this here veehickle into the good wet Georgia red clay. It might be worth forgetting that I'm one of the Ten Toughest Men who ever sat on this protection strap. I could lick my weight in Bobbsey Twins. Four must go. From the truck of the same name. . . . Choose yo' pahtnuhs for the Virginia Reel! . . .

And the rain on the canvas top comes down harder than ever. This rain is no friend of mine. It's no friend of mine and these other gents (four of whom must go). Maybe it's a friend of Katharine Hepburn's, or Sarah Palfrey Fabyan's, or Tom Heeney's, or of all the good solid Greer Garson fans waiting in line at Radio City Music Hall. But it's no buddy of mine, this rain. It's no buddy of the other thirty-three men (four of whom must go).

The character in the front of the truck yells at me again.

"What?" I say. I can't hear him. The rain on the top is killing me. I don't even want to hear him.

He says, for the third time, "Let's get this show on the road! Bring on the women!"

"Gotta wait for the lieutenant," I tell him. I feel my elbow getting wet and bring it in out of the downpour. Who swiped my raincoat? With all my letters in the left-hand pocket. My letters from Red, from Phoebe, from Holden. From Holden. Aw, listen, I don't care about the raincoat being swiped, but how about leaving my letters alone? He's only nineteen years old, my brother is, and the dope can't reduce a thing to a humour, kill it off with a sarcasm, can't do anything but listen hectically to the maladjusted little apparatus he wears for a heart. My missing-in-action brother. Why don't they leave people's raincoats alone?

I've got to stop thinking about it. Think of something pleasant, Vincent old troll. Think about this truck. Make believe this is not the darkest, wettest, most miserable Army truck you have ever ridden in. This truck, you've got to tell yourself, is full of roses and blondes and vitamins. This here is a real pretty truck. This is a swell truck. You were lucky to get this job tonight. When you get back from the dance—Choose yo' pahtnuhs, folks!—you can write an immortal poem about this truck. This truck is a potential poem. You can call it, 'Trucks I Have Rode In', or 'War and Peace', or 'This Sandwich Has No Mayonnaise'. Keep it simple.

Aw, listen. Listen, rain. This is the ninth day you've been raining. How can you do this to me and these thirty-three men (four of whom must go)? Let us alone. Stop making us sticky and lonely.

—Somebody is talking to me. The man is within knifing distance. (Four must go.) "What?" I say to him.

"Where ya from, Sarge?" the boy asks me. "—Your arm's gettin' wet."

I take it in again. "New York," I tell him.

"So'm I! Whereabouts?"

"Manhattan. Just a couple of blocks from the Museum of Art."

"I live on Valentine Avenue," the boy says. "Know where that is?"

"In The Bronx, isn't it?"

"Naa! *Near* The Bronx. *Near* The Bronx, but it ain't *in* it. It's still Manhattan."

Near The Bronx, but isn't in it. Let's remember that. Let's not go around telling people they live in The Bronx when in the first place they don't live there, they live in Manhattan. Let's use our heads, buddy. Let's get on the ball, buddy.

"How long have you been in the Army?" I ask the boy. He is a private. He is the soakingest wettest private in the Army.

"Four months. I come in through Dix and then they ship me down to Mee-ami. Ever been in Mee-ami?"

"No," I lie. "Pretty good?"

"Pretty *good*?" He nudges the guy on his right. "Tell 'im, Fergie."

"What?" says Fergie, looking wet, frozen and fouled.

"Tell the Sarge about Mee-ami. He wantsa know if it's any good or not. Tell 'im."

Fergie looks at me. "Ain'tya never been there, Sarge?"—You poor miserable sap of a sergeant.

"No. Pretty good down there?" I manage to ask.

"What a town," says Fergie softly. "You could get anything you want down there. You could really amuse yourself. I mean you could really amuse yourself. Not like this here hole. You couldn't amuse yourself in this here hole if you tried."

"We lived in a hotel," the boy from Valentine Avenue says. "Before the War you probly paid five, six dollars a day for a room in the hotel we was at. *One room.*"

"Showers," says Fergie, in a bitter-sweet tone which Abelard, during his last years, might have used to mention Héloïse's handle. "You were all the time as clean as a kid. Down there you had four guys to a room and you had these showers in between. The soap was free in the hotel. Any kinda soap you wanted. Not G.I."

"*You're alive, ain'tcha?*" the character in the front of the truck yells at Fergie. I can't see his face.

Fergie is above it all. "Showers," he repeats. "Two, three times a day I took 'em."

"I used to sell down there," a guy in the middle of the truck announces. I can barely see his face in the darkness. "Memphis and Dallas are the best towns in Dixie, for my dough. In the winter-time Miami gets too crowded. It used to drive you crazy. In the places it was worth goin', you could hardly get a seat or anything."

"It wasn't crowded when we were there—was it, Fergie?" asks the kid from Valentine Avenue.

Fergie won't answer. He's not altogether with us on this discussion. He's not giving us his all.

The man who likes Memphis and Dallas sees that, too. He says to Fergie, "Down here at this Field I'm lucky if I get a shower once a day. I'm in the new area on the west side of the Field. All the showers aren't built yet."

Fergie is not interested. The comparison is not apt. The comparison, I might and will say, stinks, Mac.

From the front of the truck comes a dynamic and irrefutable observation, "No flying again tonight! Them cadets won't be flyin' again tonight, all right. The eighth day no night flyin'."

Fergie looks up, with a minimum of energy. "I ain't hardly seen a plane since I'm down here. My wife thinks I'm flyin' myself nuts. She writes and tells me I should get outta the Air Corps. She's got me on a B–17 or something. She reads about Clark Gable and she's got me a gunner or something on a bomber. I ain't got the heart to tell her all I do is empty out stuff."

"What stuff?" says Memphis and Dallas, interested.

"Any stuff. Any stuff that gets filled up." Fergie forgets Mee-mi for a minute and shoots Memphis and Dallas a withering look.

"Oh," says Memphis and Dallas, but before he could continue Fergie turns to me. "You shoulda seen them showers in Mee-ami, Sarge. No kiddin'. You'd never wanna take a bath in your own tub again." And Fergie turns away, losing interest in my face—which is altogether understandable.

Memphis and Dallas leans forward, anxiously, addressing Fergie. "I could get you a ride," he tells Fergie. "I work at Dispatchers. These here lieutenants, they take cross-countries about oncet a month and sometimes they don't already have a passenger in the back. I been lotsa times. Maxwell Field. Everywhere." He points a finger at Fergie, as though accusing him of something. "Listen. If you wanna go sometime, gimme a ring. Call Dispatchers and ask for me. Porter's the name."

Fergie looks phlegmatically interested. "Yeah? Ask for Porter, huh? Corporal or something?"

"Private," says Porter—just short of stiffly.

"Boy," says the kid from Valentine Avenue, looking past my head into the teeming blackness. "Look at it come down!"

—Where's my brother? Where's my brother Holden? What is this missing-in-action stuff? I don't believe it, I don't understand it, I don't believe it. The United States Government is a liar. The Government is lying to me and my family.

I never heard such crazy, liar's news.

Why, he came through the war in Europe without a scratch, we all saw him before he shipped out to the Pacific last summer—and he looked fine. Missing.

Missing, missing, missing. Lies! I'm being lied to. He's never been missing before. He's one of the least missing boys in the world. He's here in this truck; he's home in New York; he's at Pentey Preparatory School ("You send us the Boy, We'll mould the Man— all modern fireproof buildings . . ."); yes, he's at Pentey, he never left school; and he's at Cape Cod, sitting on the porch, biting his fingernails; and he's playing doubles with me, yelling at me to stay back at the baseline when he's at the net. Missing! Is that missing? Why lie about something as important as that? How can the Government do a thing like that? What can they get out of it, telling lies like that?

"Hey, Sarge!" yells the character in the front of the truck. "Let's get this show on the road! Bring on the dames!"

"How are the dames, Sarge? They good-lookin'?"

"I don't really know what this thing is tonight," I say. "Usually they're pretty nice girls." That is to say, in other words, by the same token, usually they're usually. Everybody tries very, very hard. Everybody is in there pitching. The girls ask you where you come from, and you tell them, and they repeat the name of the city, putting an exclamation point at the end of it. Then they tell you about Douglas Smith, Corporal, AUS. Doug lives in New York, and do you know him? You don't believe so, and you tell her about New York being a very big place. And because you didn't want Helen to marry a soldier and wait around for a year or six, you go on dancing with this strange girl who knows Doug Smith, this strange nice girl who's read every line Lloyd C. Douglas has written. While you dance and the band plays on, you think about everything in the world except music and dancing. You wonder if your little sister Phoebe is remembering to take your dog out regularly, if she's remembering not to jerk Joey's collar—the kid'll kill the dog some-day.

"I never saw rain like this," the boy from Valentine Avenue says. "You ever see it like this, Fergie?"

"See what?"

"Rain like this."

"Naa."

"*Let's get this show on the road! Bring on the dames!*" The noisy guy leans forward and I can see his face. He looks like everybody else in the truck. We all look alike.

"What's the looey like, Sarge?" It was the boy from near the Bronx.

"I don't really know," I say. "He just hit the Field a couple of days ago. I heard that he lived right around here somewhere when he was a civilian."

"What a break. To live right near where you're at," says the boy from Valentine Avenue. "If I was only at Mitchel Field, like. Boy. Half hour and I'm home."

Mitchel Field. Long Island. What about that Saturday in the summer at Port Washington? Red said to me, *It won't hurt you to see the Fair either. It's very pretty.* So I grabbed Phoebe, and she had some kid with her named Minerva (which killed me), and I put them both in the car and then I looked around for Holden. I couldn't find him; so Phoebe and Minerva and I left without him. . . . At the Fair we went to the Bell Telephone Exhibit, and I told Phoebe that *This Phone* was connected with the author of the *Elsie Fairfield* books. So Phoebe, shaking like Phoebe, picked up the phone and trembles into it, *Hello, this is Phoebe Caulfield, a child at the World's Fair. I read your books and think they are very excellent in spots. My mother and father are playing in* Death Takes a Holiday *in Great Neck. We go swimming a lot, but the ocean is better in Cape Cod. Good-bye!* . . . And then we came out of the building and there was Holden, with Hart and Kirky Morris. He had my terry-cloth shirt on. No coat. He came over and asked Phoebe for her autograph and she socked him in the stomach, happy to see him, happy he was her brother. Then he said to me, *Let's get out of this educational junk. Let's go on one of the rides or something. I can't stand this stuff.* . . . And now they're trying to tell me he's missing. Missing. Who's missing? Not him. He's at the World's Fair. I know just where to find him. I know exactly where he is. Phoebe knows, too. She would know in a minute. What is this missing, missing, missing stuff?

"How long's it take you to get from your house to Forty-Second Street?" Fergie wants to know from the Valentine Avenue kid.

Valentine Avenue thinks it over, a little excitedly. "From my house," he informs intensely, "to the Paramount Theaytre takes exactly forty-four minutes by subway. I nearly won two bucks betting with my girl on that. Only I wouldn't take her dough."

The man who likes Memphis and Dallas better than Miami speaks up, "I hope all these girls tonight ain't chicken. I mean kids. They look at me like I was an old guy when they're chicken."

"I watch out that I don't perspire too much," sayd Fergie. "These here G.I. dances are really hot. The women don't like it if you perspire too much. My wife don't even like it when I perspire too much. It's all right when *she* perspires—that's different! . . . Women. They drive ya nuts."

A colossal burst of thunder. All of us jump—me nearly falling off the truck. I get off the protection strap, and the boy from Valentine

Avenue squeezes against Fergie to make room for me. . . . A very drawly voice speaks up from the front of the truck:

"Y'all ever been to Atlanta?"

Everybody is waiting for more thunder. I answer. "No," I say.

"Atlanta's a good town."

—Suddenly the lieutenant from Special Services appears from nowhere, soaking wet, sticking his head inside the truck—*four of these men must go.* He wears one of those oilskin covers on his visored cap; it looks like a unicorn's bladder. His face is even wet. It is a small-featured, young face, not yet altogether sure of the new command in it issued to him by the Government. He sees my stripes where the sleeves of my swiped raincoat (with all my letters) should be.

"You in chahge heah, Sahgeant?"

Wow. Choose yo' pahtnuhs . . .

"Yes, sir."

"How many men in heah?"

"I'd better take a re-count, sir." I turn around, and say, "All right, all you men with matches handy, light 'em up—I wanna count heads." And four or five of the men manage to burn matches simultaneously. I pretend to count heads. "Thirty-four including me, sir," I tell him finally.

The young lieutenant in the rain shakes his head. "Too many," he informs me—and I try to look very stupid. "I called up every orderly room myself," he reveals for my benefit, "and distinctly gave orduhs that only fahve men from each squadron were supposed to go." (I pretend to see the gravity of the situation for the first time. I might suggest that we shoot four of the men. We might ask for a detail of men experienced in shooting people who want to go to dances.) . . . The lieutenant asks me, "Do you know Miz Jackson, Sahgeant?"

"I know who she is," I say as the men listen—without taking drags on their cigarettes.

"Well, Miz Jackson called me this mawnin' and asked for just thi'ty men even. I'm afraid, Sahgeant, we'll have to ask four of the men to go back to their areas." He looks away from me, looks deeper into the truck, establishing a neutrality for himself in the soaking dark. "I don't care how it's done," he says to the truck, "but it'll have to be done."

I looked cross-eyed at the men. "How many of you did not sign up for this dance?"

"Don't look at me," says Valentine Avenue. "I signed up."

"Who didn't sign up?" I say. "Who just came along because somebody told him about it?" That's cute, sergeant. Keep it up.

"Make it snappy, Sahgeant," says the lieutenant, letting his head drip inside the truck.

"C'mon now. Who didn't sign up?" C'mon now, who didn't sign up. I never heard such a gross question in my life.

"Heck, we all signed up, Sarge," says Valentine Avenue. "The thing is, around seven guys signed up in my squadron."

All right. I'll be brilliant. I'll offer a handsome alternative. "Who's willing to take in a movie on the Field instead?"

No response.

Response.

Silently, Porter (the Memphis-Dallas man) gets up and moves towards the way out. The men adjust their legs to let him go by. I move aside, too. . . . None of us tells Porter, as he passes, what relatively big, important stuff he is.

More response. . . . "One side," says Fergie, getting up. "So the married guys'll write letters t'night." He jumps out of the truck quickly.

I wait. We all wait. No one else comes forward. "Two more," I croak. I'll hound them. I'll hound these men because I hate their guts. They're all being insufferably stupid. What's the matter with them? Do they think they'll have a terrific time at this sticky little dance? Do they think they're going to hear a fine trumpet take a chorus of 'Marie'? What's the matter with these idiots? What's the matter with *me*? Why do I want them all to go? Why do I sort of want to go myself? Sort of! What a joke. You're aching to go, Caulfield . . .

"All right," I say coldly. "The last two men on the left. C'mon out. I don't know who you are."—I don't know who you are.— Phew!

The noisy guy, who has been yelling at me to get the show on the road, starts coming out. I had forgotten that he was sitting just there. But he disappears awkwardly into the India ink storm. He is followed, as though tentatively, by a smaller man—a boy, it proves in the light.

His overseas cap on crooked and limp with wet, his eyes on the lieutenant, the boy waits in the rain—as though obeying an order. He is very young, probably eighteen, as he doesn't look like the tiresome sort of kid who argues and argues after the whistle's blown. I stare at him, and the lieutenant turns around and stares at him, too.

"I was on the list. I signed up when the fella tacked it up. Right when he tacked it up."

"Sorry, soldier," says the lieutenant. "—Ready, Sahgeant?"

"You can ask Ostrander," the boy tells the lieutenant, and sticks his head inside the truck. "Hey, Ostrander! Wasn't I the first fella on the list?"

The rain comes down harder than ever, it seems. The boy who wants to go to the dance is getting soaked. I reach out a hand and flip up his raincoat collar.

"Wasn't I first on the list?" the boy yells at Ostrander.

"What list?" says Ostrander.

"The list for fellas that wanna go to the dance!" yells the boy.

"Oh," says Ostrander. "What about it? I was on it."

Oh, Ostrander, you insidious bore!

"Wasn't I the first fella on it?" says the boy, his voice breaking.

"I don't know," says Ostrander. "How should I know?"

The boy turns wildly to the lieutenant.

"I was the first one on it, sir. Honest. This fella in our squadron —this foreign guy, like, that works in the orderly room—he tacked it up and I signed it right off. The first fella."

The lieutenant says, dripping, "Get in. Get in the truck, boy."

The boy climbs back into the truck and the men quickly make room for him.

The lieutenant turns to me and asks, "Sahgeant, wheah can I use a telephone around heah?"

"Well. Post Engineers, sir. I'll show you."

We wade through the rivers of red bog over to Post Engineers.

"Mama?" the lieutenant says into the mouthpiece. "Buddy . . . I'm fine. . . . Yes, mama. Yes, mama. I'm fixin' to be. Maybe

Sunday if I get off like they said. Mama, is Sarah Jane home? . . .
Well, how 'bout lettin' me talk to her? . . . Yes, mama. I will if I
can, mama; maybe Sunday."

The lieutenant talks again.

"Sarah Jane? . . . Fine. Fine . . . I'm fixin' to. I told mama
maybe Sunday if I get off. Listen, Sarah Jane. You got a date
t'night? . . . It sure is pretty bad. It sure is. Listen, Sarah Jane.
How's the car? You get that thing fixed? That's fine, that's fine;
that's mighty cheap, with the plugs and all." The lieutenant's voice
changes. It becomes casual. "Sarah Jane, listen. I want you to
drive oveh to Miz Jackson's t'night. . . . Well, it's like this: I got
these boys heah for one of those pahties Miz Jackson gives. You
know? . . . Only this is what I want to tell you: they's one boy too
many. . . . Yes. . . . Yes. . . . Yes. . . . I know that, Sarah
Jane; I know that; I know it's rainin'. . . . Yes. . . . Yes. . . ."
The lieutenant's voice gets very sure and hard suddenly. He says
into the mouthpiece, "I ain't *askin'* you, girl. I'm *tellin'* you. Now I
want you to drive ovuh to Miz Jackson's right quick—*heah*? . . . I
don't care. . . . All right. All right. . . . I'll see y'll later." He
hangs up.

Drenched to the bone, the bone of loneliness, the bone of silence,
we plod back to the truck.

Where are you, Holden? Never mind this Missing stuff. Stop
playing around. Show up. Show up somewhere. Hear me? Will
you do that for me? It's simply because I remember everything. I
can't forget anything that's good, that's why. So listen. Just go up
to somebody, some officer or some G.I., and tell them you're Here—
not Missing, not dead, not anything but Here.

Stop kidding around. Stop letting people think you're Missing.
Stop wearing my robe to the beach. Stop taking the shots on my side
of the court. Stop whistling. Sit up to the table . . .

NORMAN MAILER

The Language of Men

Norman Mailer is commonly recognised as one of the most talented young writers in America today. A product of Brooklyn and Harvard, he saw Army service during World War II, mostly in the Pacific, and wrote of it in *The Naked and the Dead*, one of the outstanding war novels published in the United States. His second novel, *Barbary Shore* (1951), had the distinction, according to the author, "of receiving possibly the worst reviews of any serious novel in recent years." His third novel, *The Deer Park* (1955), one of the most outspoken books on the sexual manners, mores, and myths of Hollywood, returned Norman Mailer's name to the best-seller lists and succeeded in splitting American critics into two almost equally divided groups pro and con, a not inconsiderable feat.

Dwight McDonald especially singles Mailer out as one of the best of the young writers, and speaks of his constant experimenting, his search for new forms and ideas. In 1956 and 1957 Mailer wrote several articles about hipsterism in the magazine *Dissent* and in the weekly *Village Voice*: "I take hip very seriously; the hipsters may be the beginning of a new world revolution, like the early Christians."

'The Language of Men' appeared in *Esquire* in April 1953 and seems more closely related to Mailer's earliest book in its delineation of the character and habits of men in the Army. It is one of the relatively few short stories he has published.

IN THE BEGINNING, Sanford Carter was ashamed of becoming an Army cook. This was not from snobbery, at least not from snobbery of the most direct sort. During the two and a half years Carter had been in the Army he had come to hate cooks more and more. They

existed for him as a symbol of all that was corrupt, overbearing,
stupid, and privileged in Army life. The image which came to mind
was a fat cook with an enormous sandwich in one hand, and a bottle
of beer in the other, sweat pouring down a porcine face, foot on a
flour barrel, shouting at the K.P.s, "Hurry up, you men, I ain't got
all day." More than once in those two and a half years, driven to
exasperation, Carter had been on the verge of throwing his food into
a cook's face as he passed on the serving line. His anger often derived
from nothing: the set of a pair of fat lips, the casual heavy thump of
the serving spoon into his plate, or the resentful conviction that the
cook was not serving him enough. Since life in the Army was in most
aspects a marriage, this rage over apparently harmless details was
not a sign of unbalance. Every soldier found some particular habit
of the Army spouse impossible to support.

Yet Sanford Carter became a cook and, to elaborate the irony, did
better as a cook than he had done as anything else. In a few months
he rose from a Private to a first cook with the rank of Sergeant,
Technician. After the fact, it was easy to understand. He had
suffered through all his Army career from an excess of eagerness.
He had cared too much, he had wanted to do well, and so he had
often been tense at moments when he would better have been
relaxed. He was very young, twenty-one, had lived the com-
paratively gentle life of a middle-class boy, and needed some success
in the Army to prove to himself that he was not completely worthless.

In succession, he had failed as a surveyor in Field Artillery, a clerk
in an Infantry headquarters, a telephone wireman, and finally a
rifleman. When the war ended, and his regiment went to Japan,
Carter was still a rifleman; he had been a rifleman for eight months.
What was more to the point, he had been in the platoon as long as
any of its members; the skilled hard-bitten nucleus of veterans who
had run his squad had gone home one by one, and it seemed to him
that through seniority he was entitled to at least a corporal's rating.
Through seniority he was so entitled, but on no other ground.
Whenever responsibility had been handed to him, he had discharged it miserably, tensely, overconscientiously. He had always
asked too many questions, he had worried the task too severely, he
had conveyed his nervousness to the men he was supposed to lead.
Since he was also sensitive enough and proud enough never to curry

favour with the noncoms in the platoons, he was in no position to sit in on their occasional discussions about who was to succeed them. In a vacuum of ignorance, he had allowed himself to dream that he would be given a squad to lead, and his hurt was sharp when the squad was given to a replacement who had joined the platoon months after him.

The war was over, Carter had a bride in the States (he had lived with her for only two months), he was lonely, he was obsessed with going home. As one week dragged into the next, and the regiment, the company, and his own platoon continued the same sort of training which they had been doing ever since he had entered the Army, he thought he would snap. There were months to wait until he would be discharged and meanwhile it was intolerable to him to be taught for the fifth time the nomenclature of the machine-gun, to stand a retreat parade three evenings a week. He wanted some niche where he could lick his wounds, some Army job with so many hours of work and so many hours of complete freedom, where he could be alone by himself. He hated the Army, the huge Army which had proved to him that he was good at no work, and incapable of succeeding at anything. He wrote long, aching letters to his wife, he talked less and less to the men around him and he was close to violent attacks of anger during the most casual phases of training—during close-order drill or cleaning his rifle for inspection. He knew that if he did not find his niche it was possible that he would crack.

So he took an opening in the kitchen. It promised him nothing except a day of work, and a day of leisure which would be completely at his disposal. He found that he liked it. He was given at first the job of baking the bread for the company, and every other night he worked till early in the morning, kneading and shaping his fifty-pound mix of dough. At two or three he would be done, and for his work there would be the tangible reward of fifty loaves of bread, all fresh from the oven, all clean and smelling of fertile accomplished creativity. He had the rare and therefore intensely satisfying emotion of seeing at the end of an Army chore the product of his labour.

A month after he became a cook the regiment was disbanded, and those men who did not have enough points to go home were sent to

other outfits. Carter ended at an ordnance company in another
Japanese city. He had by now given up all thought of getting a non-
com's rating before he was discharged, and was merely content to
work each alternate day. He took his work for granted and so he
succeeded at it. He had begun as a baker in the new company
kitchen; before long he was the first cook. It all happened quickly.
One cook went home on points, another caught a skin disease, a
third was transferred from the kitchen after contracting a venereal
infection. On the shift which Carter worked there were left only
himself and a man who was illiterate. Carter was put nominally in
charge, and was soon actively in charge. He looked up each menu
in an Army recipe book, collected the items, combined them in the
order indicated, and after the proper time had elapsed, took them
from the stove. His product tasted neither better nor worse than
the product of all other Army cooks. But the mess sergeant was impressed. Carter had filled a gap. The next time ratings were given
out Carter jumped at a bound from Private to Sergeant T/4.

On the surface he was happy; beneath the surface he was overjoyed. It took him several weeks to realise how grateful and
delighted he felt. The promotion coincided with his assignment to a
detachment working in a small seaport up the coast. Carter arrived
there to discover that he was in charge of cooking for thirty men, and
would act as mess sergeant. There was another cook, and there were
four permanent Japanese K.P.s, all of them good workers. He still
cooked every other day, but there was always time between meals to
take a break of at least an hour and often two; he shared a room with
the other cook and lived in comparative privacy for the first time in
several years; the seaport was beautiful; there was only one officer,
and he left the men alone; supplies were plentiful due to a clerical
error which assigned rations for forty men rather than thirty; and in
general everything was fine. The niche had become a sinecure.

This was the happiest period of Carter's life in the Army. He came
to like his Japanese K.P.s. He studied their language, he visited
their homes, he gave them gifts of food from time to time. They
worshipped him because he was kind to them and generous, because
he never shouted, because his good humour bubbled over into
games, and made the work of the kitchen seem pleasant. All the
while he grew in confidence. He was not a big man, but his body

filled out from the heavy work; he was likely to sing a great deal, he cracked jokes with the men on the chow line. The kitchen became his property, it became his domain, and since it was a warm room, filled with sunlight, he came to take pleasure in the very sight of it. Before long his good humour expanded into a series of efforts to improve the food. He began to take little pains and make little extra efforts which would have been impossible if he had been obliged to cook for more than thirty men. In the morning he would serve the men fresh eggs scrambled or fried to their desire in fresh butter. Instead of cooking sixty eggs in one large pot he cooked two eggs at a time in a frying-pan, turning them to the taste of each soldier. He baked like a housewife satisfying her young husband; at lunch and dinner there was pie or cake, and often both. He went to great lengths. He taught the K.P.s how to make the toast come out right. He traded excess food for spices in Japanese stores. He rubbed paprika and garlic on the chickens. He even made pastries to cover such staples as corn beef hash and meat and vegetable stew.

It all seemed to be wasted. In the beginning the men might have noticed these improvements, but after a period they took them for granted. It did not matter how he worked to satisfy them; they trudged through the chow line with their heads down, nodding coolly at him, and they ate without comment. He would hang around the tables after the meal, noticing how much they consumed, and what they discarded; he would wait for compliments, but the soldiers seemed indifferent. They seemed to eat without tasting the food. In their faces he saw mirrored the distaste with which he had once stared at cooks.

The honeymoon was ended. The pleasure he took in the kitchen and himself curdled. He became aware again of his painful desire to please people, to discharge responsibility, to be a man. When he had been a child, tears had come into his eyes at a cross word, and he had lived in an atmosphere where his smallest accomplishment was warmly praised. He was the sort of young man, he often thought bitterly, who was accustomed to the attention and the protection of women. He would have thrown away all he possessed—the love of his wife, the love of his mother, the benefits of his education, the assured financial security of entering his father's business—if he had been able just once to dig a ditch as well as the most ignorant farmer.

Instead, he was back in the painful unprotected days of his first entrance into the Army. Once again the most casual actions became the most painful, the events which were most to be taken for granted grew into the most significant, and the feeding of the men at each meal turned progressively more unbearable.

So Sanford Carter came full circle. If he had once hated the cooks, he now hated the troops. At meal-times his face soured into the belligerent scowl with which he had once believed cooks to be born. And to himself he muttered the age-old laments of the house-wife: how little they appreciated what he did.

Finally there was an explosion. He was approached one day by Corporal Taylor, and he had come to hate Taylor, because Taylor was the natural leader of the detachment and kept the other men endlessly amused with his jokes. Taylor had the ability to present himself as inefficient, shiftless, and incapable, in such a manner as to convey that really the opposite was true. He had the lightest touch, he had the greatest facility, he could charm a geisha in two minutes and obtain anything he wanted from a supply sergeant in five. Carter envied him, envied his grace, his charmed indifference; then grew to hate him.

Taylor teased Carter about the cooking, and he had the knack of knowing where to put the knife. "Hey, Carter," he would shout across the mess hall while breakfast was being served, "you turned my eggs twice, and I asked for them raw." The men would shout with laughter. Somehow Taylor had succeeded in conveying all of the situation, or so it seemed to Carter, insinuating everything, how Carter worked and how it meant nothing, how Carter laboured to gain their affection and earned their contempt. Carter would scowl, Carter would answer in a rough voice, "Next time I'll crack them over your head." "You crack 'em, I'll eat 'em." Taylor would pipe back, "but just don't put your fingers in 'em." And there would be another laugh. He hated the sight of Taylor.

It was Taylor who came to him to get the salad oil. About twenty of the soldiers were going to have a fish fry at the geisha house; they had bought the fish at the local market, but they could not buy oil, so Taylor was sent as the deputy to Carter. He was charming to

Carter, he complimented him on the meal, he clapped him on the back, he dissolved Carter to warmth, to private delight in the attention, and the thought that he had misjudged Taylor. Then Taylor asked for the oil.

Carter was sick with anger. Twenty men out of the thirty in the detachment were going on the fish fry. It meant only that Carter was considered one of the ten undesirables. It was something he had known, but the proof of knowledge is always more painful than the acquisition of it. If he had been alone his eyes would have clouded. And he was outraged at Taylor's deception. He could imagine Taylor saying ten minutes later, "You should have seen the grease job I gave to Carter. I'm dumb, but, man, he's dumber."

Carter was close enough to giving him the oil. He had a sense of what it would mean to refuse Taylor, he was on the very edge of mild acquiescence. But he also had a sense of how he would despise himself afterwards.

"No," he said abruptly, his teeth gritted, "you can't have it."

"What do you mean we can't have it?"

"I won't give it to you." Carter could almost feel the rage which Taylor generated at being refused.

"You won't give away a lousy five gallons of oil to a bunch of G. I.s having a party?"

"I'm sick and tired," Carter began.

"So am I." Taylor walked away.

Carter knew he would pay for it. He left the K.P.s and went to change his sweat-soaked work shirt, and as he passed the large dormitory in which most of the detachment slept he could hear Taylor's high-pitched voice. Carter did not bother to take off his shirt. He returned instead to the kitchen, and listened to the sound of men going back and forth through the hall and of a man shouting with rage. That was Hobbs, a Southerner, a big man with a big bellowing voice.

There was a formal knock on the kitchen door. Taylor came in. His face was pale and his eyes showed a cold satisfaction. "Carter," he said, "the men want to see you in the big room."

Carter heard his voice answer huskily. "If they want to see me, they can come into the kitchen."

He knew he would conduct himself with more courage in his own kitchen than anywhere else. "I'll be here for a while."

Taylor closed the door, and Carter picked up a writing board to which was clamped the menu for the following day. Then he made a pretence of examining the food supplies in the pantry closet. It was his habit to check the stocks before deciding what to serve the next day, but on this night his eyes ranged thoughtlessly over the canned goods. In a corner were seven five-gallon tins of salad oil, easily enough cooking oil to last a month. Carter came out of the pantry and shut the door behind him.

He kept his head down and pretended to be writing the menu when the soldiers came in. Somehow there were even more of them than he had expected. Out of the twenty men who were going to the party, all but two or three had crowded through the door.

Carter took his time, looked up slowly. "You men want to see me?" he asked flatly.

They were angry. For the first time in his life he faced the hostile expressions of many men. It was the most painful and anxious moment he had ever known.

"Taylor says you won't give us the oil," someone burst out.

"That's right, I won't," said Carter. He tapped his pencil against the scratchboard, tapping it slowly and, he hoped, with an appearance of calm.

"What a stink deal," said Porfirio, a little Cuban whom Carter had always considered his friend.

Hobbs, the big Southerner, stared down at Carter. "Would you mind telling the men why you've decided not to give us the oil?" he asked quietly.

"'Cause I'm blowed if I'm going to cater to you men. I've catered enough," Carter said. His voice was close to cracking with the outrage he had suppressed for so long, and he knew that if he continued he might cry. "I'm the acting mess sergeant," he said as coldly as he could, "and I decide what goes out of this kitchen." He stared at each one in turn, trying to stare them down, feeling mired in the rut of his own failure. They would never have dared this approach to another mess sergeant.

"What crud," someone muttered.

"You won't give a lousy five-gallon can of oil for a G.I. party," Hobbs said more loudly.

"I won't. That's definite. You men can get out of here."

"Why, you lousy little snot," Hobbs burst out, "how many five-gallon cans of oil have you sold on the black market?"

"I've never sold any." Carter might have been slapped with the flat of a sword. He told himself bitterly, numbly, that this was the reward he received for being perhaps the single honest cook in the whole United States Army. And he even had time to wonder at the obscure prejudice which had kept him from selling food for his own profit.

"Man, I've seen you take it out," Hobbs exclaimed. "I've seen you take it to the market."

"I took food to trade for spices," Carter said hotly.

There was an ugly snicker from the men.

"I don't mind if a cook sells," Hobbs said, "every man has his own deal in this Army. But a cook ought to give a little food to a G.I. if he wants it."

"Tell him," someone said.

"It's bull," Taylor screeched. "I've seen Carter take butter, eggs, every damn thing to the market."

Their faces were red, they circled him.

"I never sold a thing," Carter said doggedly.

"And I'm telling you," Hobbs said, "that you're a two-bit crook. You been raiding that kitchen, and that's why you don't give to us now."

Carter knew there was only one way he could possibly answer if he hoped to live among these men again. "That's a goddam lie," Carter said to Hobbs. He laid down the scratchboard, he flipped his pencil slowly and deliberately to one corner of the room, and with his heart aching he lunged towards Hobbs. He had no hope of beating him. He merely intended to fight until he was pounded unconscious, advancing the pain and bruises he would collect as collateral for his self-respect.

To his indescribable relief Porfirio darted between them, held them apart with the pleased ferocity of a small man breaking up a fight. "Now, stop this! Now, stop this!" he cried out.

Carter allowed himself to be pushed back, and he knew that he had gained a point. He even glimpsed a solution with some honour.

He shrugged violently to free himself from Porfirio. He was in a rage, and yet it was a rage he could have ended at any instant. "All right, you men," he swore, "I'll give you the oil, but now that we're at it, I'm going to tell you a thing or two." His face red, his body perspiring, he was in the pantry and out again with a five-gallon tin. "Here," he said, "you better have a good fish fry, 'cause it's the last good meal you're going to have for quite a while. I'm sick of trying to please you. You think I have to work——" he was about to say, my fingers to the bone—"well, I don't. From now on, you'll see what chow in the Army is supposed to be like." He was almost hysterical. "Take that oil. Have your fish fry." The fact that they wanted to cook for themselves was the greatest insult of all. "Tomorrow I'll give you real Army cooking."

His voice was so intense that they backed away from him. "Get out of this kitchen," he said. "None of you has any business here."

They filed out quietly, and they looked a little sheepish.

Carter felt weary, he felt ashamed of himself, he knew he had not meant what he said. But half an hour later, when he left the kitchen and passed the large dormitory, he heard shouts of raucous laughter, and he heard his name mentioned and then more laughter.

He slept badly that night, he was awake at four, he was in the kitchen by five, and stood there white-faced and nervous, waiting for the K.P.s to arrive. Breakfast that morning landed on the men like a lead bomb. Carter rummaged in the back of the pantry and found a tin of dehydrated eggs covered with dust, memento of a time when fresh eggs were never on the ration list. The K.P.s looked at him in amazement as he stirred the lumpy powder into a pan of water. While it was still half-dissolved he put it on the fire. While it was still wet, he took it off. The coffee was cold, the toast was burned, the oatmeal stuck to the pot. The men dipped forks into their food, took cautious sips of their coffee, and spoke in whispers. Sullenness drifted like vapours through the kitchen.

At noon-time Carter opened cans of meat-and-vegetable stew. He dumped them into a pan and heated them slightly. He served the stew with burned string beans and dehydrated potatoes which tasted like straw. For dessert the men had a single lukewarm canned peach and cold coffee.

So the meals continued. For three days Carter cooked slop, and suffered even more than the men. When meal-time came he left the chow line to the K.P.s and sat in his room, perspiring with shame, determined not to yield and sick with the determination.

Carter won. On the fourth day a delegation of men came to see him. They told him that indeed they had appreciated his cooking in the past, they told him that they were sorry they had hurt his feelings, they listened to his remonstrances, they listened to his grievances, and with delight Carter forgave them. That night, for supper, the detachment celebrated. There was roast chicken with stuffing, lemon meringue pie and chocolate cake. The coffee burned their lips. More than half the men made it a point to compliment Carter on the meal.

In the weeks which followed the compliments diminished, but they never stopped completely. Carter became ashamed at last. He realised the men were trying to humour him, and he wished to tell them it was no longer necessary.

Harmony settled over the kitchen. Carter even became friends with Hobbs, the big Southerner. Hobbs approached him one day, and in the manner of a farmer talked obliquely for an hour. He spoke about his father, he spoke about his girl friends, he alluded indirectly to the night they had almost fought, and finally with the courtesy of a Southerner he said to Carter, "You know, I'm sorry about shooting off my mouth. You were right to want to fight me, and if you're still mad I'll fight you to give you satisfaction, although I just as soon would not."

"No, I don't want to fight with you now," Carter said warmly. They smiled at each other. They were friends.

Carter knew he had gained Hobbs' respect. Hobbs respected him because he had been willing to fight. That made sense to a man like Hobbs. Carter liked him so much at this moment that he wished the friendship to be more intimate.

"You know," he said to Hobbs, "it's a funny thing. You know I really never did sell anything on the black market. Not that I'm proud of it, but I just didn't."

Hobbs frowned. He seemed to be saying that Carter did not have to lie. "I don't hold it against a man," Hobbs said, "if he makes a little money in something that's his own proper work. Hell, I sell gas from the motor pool. It's just I also give gas if one of the G.Is. wants to take the jeep out for a joy ride, kind of."

"No, but I never did sell anything," Carter had to explain. "If I ever had sold on the black market, I would have given the salad oil without question."

Hobbs frowned again, and Carter realised he still did not believe him. Carter did not want to lose the friendship which was forming. He thought he could save it only by some further admission. "You know," he said again, "remember when Porfirio broke up our fight? I was awful glad when I didn't have to fight you." Carter laughed, expecting Hobbs to laugh with him, but a shadow passed across Hobbs' face.

"Funny way of putting it," Hobbs said.

He was always friendly thereafter, but Carter knew that Hobbs would never consider him a friend. Carter thought about it often, and began to wonder about the things which made him different. He was no longer so worried about becoming a man; he felt that to an extent he had become one. But in his heart he wondered if he would ever learn the language of men.

EVELYN WAUGH

St. Francis Xavier's Bones

Evelyn Waugh's interest in travel and in religious shrines and figures
dates from the early thirties. In 1930, at the age of 26, he was received
into the Roman Catholic Church; he had begun his travels a year or
two before. "From 1928 until 1937," he says, "I had no fixed home and
no possessions which would not conveniently go on a porter's barrow."

In December 1952 Waugh made a trip to Goa, and in December of
the following year 'St. Francis Xavier's Bones' appeared in *Esquire* (it
has not been anthologised, and is reprinted here for the first time).
Earlier, in 1950, he had published a religious novel, *Helena*, a fictional-
ised life of the now canonised mother of Constantine (who found the
wood of the true Cross). Still following his religious predilections,
Waugh journeyed to Jerusalem in 1951, where he recorded his impressions for *Life* magazine. With additional comments they were published
in the book *The Holy Places* in 1953.

Waugh, of course, is much better known for his early comic novels,
Decline and Fall, *Vile Bodies*, *Scoop*, *Handful of Dust*, etc.—wildly satiric
pictures of life among the bright young Londoners of the twenties and
thirties. But it is often pointed out that his serious, religious non-fiction
and the hilarious, bitingly satiric fiction spring from the same source:
his aversion to many aspects of the modern world, and his devout
Catholicism.

DIU, Daman, Goa, Mahé, Karikal, Pondichéry, Yanam—how odd
these places, strung out along the coast of India, used to look in the
school atlas; as though small, alien teeth had been nibbling at the
edges of the huge vermilion expanse of British India.

"Couldn't we turn them out, sir?"

"Of course. Any time we wanted to."

"Then why don't we, sir?"

And we were told that these quaint survivals were a part of history, of the remote days when France and Portugal competed with us for empire; furthermore that their neglected condition provided a salutary example to any Indian who was crass enough to doubt the benevolence of the British Raj.

"Are there really Indians like that, sir?"

"A few Bengali babus."

That was how the geography lesson ran nearly forty years ago.

> *The tumult and the shouting dies,*
> *The captains and the kings depart . . .*

Today, after all the pageantry of British surrender, these places remain the solitary outposts of European authority.

I had long wanted to visit them; Goa especially, for I had been endeared to many Goans in many parts of the world; I had read travellers' tales of the Golden City that had once been the capital and emporium of all the widespread Portuguese empire of the East, and now stood quite deserted; I had seen prints and photographs of the great baroque buildings engulfed in jungle, and lately I had read Father James Broderick's biography of St. Francis Xavier, whose body is Goa's greatest treasure. December, 1952, was the saint's particular month, the four hundredth anniversary of his death, when his relics were to be exposed to veneration for the last time in their long and strange history. It was then or never to make the pilgrimage.

Goa can be reached by sea from Bombay or overland from Belgaum, a straggling cantonment on the air route to the south. The bus at Belgaum was full of pilgrims. A polite youth distributed printed warnings of the brutality of the 'Fascist' régime ahead of us. He was one of the dissident Goans, a small organised group of whom exists in Bombay. This was my introduction to the threat which hangs over the European territories. Covetous eyes are on them in Delhi, where the Congress politicians are more ambitious than their predecessors in power, the British imperialists. Even in happy Goa, at the time of the British withdrawal, many Hindus and some

Christians were excited by the jubilation beyond their frontiers. A dozen agitators were deported and now live in Portugal in complete freedom, subject to a ban on their returning home to resume their activities. A small section only of the population is interested in public affairs. The wisest of these have patiently compared the new Republic of India with their own, giving particular attention to the state of order, the purity of the financial administration, the welfare of the poorest classes, the penal system and the respect shown to minority communities such as the Eurasians. In none of these respects have they found reason for envy. There are very few European officials in the territory. Goans have strong local patriotism but they are, in fact, Portuguese. They are not a subject or 'protected' people. They enjoy full and equal citizenship with the descendants of the Conquistadors and can rise to any position in the Republic. There is no exclusive club. In one thing only are they deficient in comparison with the Indians. Politics are the cocaine of the people and this unhealthy stimulant is little used in Goa. Wherever he goes in India, the Western visitor is beset by begging students. At first, remembering, perhaps, Ignatius Loyola at the University of Paris, he is warmed with sympathy at the traditional spectacle of poverty in pursuit of knowledge. Then he asks: what subject are they studying? What profession do they aspire to practise? And often the chilling answers are: politics, politicians. The ambitions of Indian youth are no longer confined to a clerkship and a pension. There are larger prizes, very remote but very brilliant, at Delhi and in the Indian Embassies.

For a few Goan youths it may seem sad to grow up deprived of the mass oratory and demonstrations, overturned buses, tear-gas and *lathi*-charges which enrich the frugal life of the Indian student. These, if they go to Bombay for their education, become recruits for the Congress Party. The more experienced value their Portuguese citizenship for the privileges it confers. There is little extravagant devotion to Lisbon. Portuguese rule was violent in its early days, neglectful later; only in the present generation has it begun to redeem its past. Goans of Brahman descent never fail to announce the fact, while those of mixed blood are silent on the subject. Patriotism at home and among the Diaspora—the thousands of Goans in Africa, Bombay, and along the trade routes of British shipping—is Goan. But, paradoxically, the only guarantee of local integrity is Portuguese nationality.

These are the impressions of several subsequent weeks of inquiry and discussion. On that first morning there was barely time to glance at the Congress leaflet before the bus started and all attention was devoted to the hard work of travel. This was called a 'luxury coach', and later acquaintance with the normal service confirmed its claim to certain superior amenities. The number of passengers was limited to the number of seats and that morning the passengers were all Goans visiting their homes for the festival, all in Western dress, all very polite and in the best of spirits except when, rather often, they were being sick. Clinging to the hard, narrow seats we bounced and banged our way to the frontier in a brown dust storm of our own making.

In two hours we reached the Indian road block.

Smuggling is said to be well organised and profitable. Most things are cheaper in Goa but the main illicit export is whisky, for the State of Bombay has used its new-found freedom to decree Prohibition—an ineffective piece of bigotry and an odd one, for there is nothing in Hindu religion or tradition to discourage fermented liquors. The smugglers do not follow the highway or use public transport; the traffic goes one way only, but even in our exodus the Indian officials were tediously vigilant. The Festival of St. Francis Xavier was not officially popular in India. Indeed, the Indians were then staging what looked rather like a specially contrived counter-attraction—a festival at Ernakulam to celebrate the nineteen hundredth anniversary of the arrival there of St. Thomas the Apostle. St. Thomas is the patron of sceptics. He will not, I think, condemn the doubt of his ever having reached India; still less of his having done so in December, 52 A.D. But Indians rejoice in festivals and both occasions were enthusiastically thronged.

We changed into a more comfortable vehicle and half an hour later reached the Goan frontier post, where easy-going cordiality prevailed. A booth sold beer and wine and most of the male passengers celebrated their return to civilised ways. Then we began our headlong descent through scenery quite unlike what we had passed hitherto. It is a countryside of enchanting natural beauty; our dust cloud turned to powdered chocolate from the deep red-brown earth and rock in which the road is cut. High on one side, deep on the other, rose and fell dense green plantations of indigenous palm and plantain and the sturdy little cashew trees which the Portuguese brought from Brazil. The watery depths of the valley were brilliant with young rice. The whole landscape tilted forward before us to where the two fine rivers break into a jumble of islands and streams and broad creeks, with beyond them the open sea.

Goa, particularly in the 'Old Conquests', is better populated than appears from the road. Neat homesteads are hidden everywhere in the trees. There are half a million inhabitants, most of whom eschew the towns. In our descent we were passing through the 'New Conquests'. There is a considerable difference between the two areas. The Old Conquests were Albuquerque's territory. He took them from Mohammedan invaders. To the Portuguese of that period all Mohammedans were the hated Moors. Albuquerque exterminated the males and gave the women as wives to his men. Hindus he treated with greater clemency but in effect they were given the choice of emigration or baptism. Within a generation almost all his subjects bore Portuguese names, professed the Christian faith and were the ancestors of the most devout and moral people in India. He destroyed all the temples, many of which are reputed to have been splendid works of art. In extenuation of this æsthetic outrage it may be said that Hindu art probably struck him and his contemporaries as being not only expressive of an erroneous theology, but also preposterously obscene. The Old Conquests preserve their ancient egalitarian system of land tenure; each man, however far he travels, is bound to his ancestral village by his share in the common lands; each village committee preserves the list of its community and relieves its poor.

The New Conquests were added in 1795, an age of 'enlightenment'. There are many temples, not very ancient but gracious and commodious, still served by the dancing girls whose role has been abolished in most parts of India. We passed one near Ponda, a glimpse at the end of a fine avenue quickly obliterated by our cloud of dust. There is a child Raja living without ostentation beside the temple of Sunda and farther south a feudal nobleman, a gunner officer in the Indian army. The villages and farms of the New Conquests are shabbier than those of the Old, for the wealthier

Hindus congregate in the towns, where most of the shops are in their hands. There are plenty of Hindus among the Christians and some Christians among the Hindus, living independently but amicably side by side. In general, however, the old frontier holds and divides two distinct cultures.

We crossed it at the bridge over the Combarjua and almost at once were skirting Old Goa: another glimpse through the dust—white cupolas, an arch, laterite walls hairy as coconuts with dry weed— then a metalled road beside the river Mandovi, a great stretch of tidal water full of small sails, with wooded hills beyond; and so to New Goa or Pangim, the modern capital.

There is nothing outstandingly modern in Pangim except the hotel, which is so new that it was still being loudly built during the festival month which it had been designed to serve. That alone breaks the charm of the water front, whose remarkable features are the fine, placid old Government House and a wildly vivacious new statue of the Abbé Farias, a Goan mesmerist of the Napoleonic era, mentioned by Dumas and caught here in hot bronze at the climax of an experiment, rampant over an entranced female.

Pangim makes no pretensions to gaiety. The transient Portuguese officials are economical, the Goan residents home-loving. Week-end tourists from Bombay have grown in numbers since Prohibition. These alone, in normal times, disturb the tranquillity of the town. In honour of the Festival loudspeakers had been set up in the main squares. In one of these was a neat little Industrial Exhibition and a temporary café. There was also an exhibition of modern art which deserved more attention than it got. All other activity was on the quay and at the bus station, for Pangim, that month, was purely a place for passage for Old Goa, eight miles upstream.

There are many vivid accounts of Old Goa both in its prosperity and its ruin. Its prosperity lasted barely one hundred and fifty years. Its ruin was swift, caused by Dutch rivalry and the sheer lack of Portuguese manpower, and accelerated by plague and fever. Most travellers reached it after a voyage of great privation and danger. Perhaps they tended to exaggerate the splendours they found. There was treasure certainly and warehouses full of expensive Eastern merchandise; but there was little that could be called 'civilisation', either Asiatic or European. The masons built solidly but they

followed without imagination a limited range of models. Most of
the portraits of Viceroys and Patriarchs are of historical interest
only. In population Old Goa equalled Elizabethan London, but
most of its inhabitants were servile, and the social life, even of the
prosperous and important, sounds devoid of charm. Those swelter-
ing, swaggering *fidalgos* and their sickly womenfolk with their
palanquins and sweets and scents and retinues of handmaids were
not real ladies and gentlemen but the riffraff of Portugal, over-
dressed and over-privileged. The Church alone sustained what there
was of culture; and the Church alone displays some of its former
grandeur today.

The city was abandoned in 1759. Its palaces and colleges were
used as quarries. The jungle closed in, thrusting roots between the
laterite blocks. Vaults and façades crumbled into the steep streets.
A hundred years later Richard Burton, then a subaltern on sick
leave from Bombay, found only the huge Convent of St. Monica
inhabited. He did not know it—he was too busy listening to
scandalous stories to inquire—but there were barely a dozen nuns
living there at the time of his impertinent visit. The last of them
survived alone into the late '70s, when the illustrious foundation
came to an end. The vast, buttressed walls stood firm but the
paintings flaked away in the cloisters and the odorous enclosed
garden ran all to weed. It had enjoyed a remarkable history, guard-
ing its strict and secret piety among the gaming houses and brothels,
receiving splendid benefactions, passing through the little revolving
hatch that was its access to the world of commerce special sweet-
meats for sale and delicate pieces of needlework; sheltering once a
stigmatic German sister and a crucifix which is said to have rebuked
a mitigation of rule with fresh-flowing blood.

It was the last religious house to survive the legislation of the anti-
clerical faction in Portugal. When Santa Monica stood empty the
soul of Old Goa seemed finally to have departed. Memories of fever
and plague haunted it. No one cared to stay there after sunset. The
Canons of the Cathedral came punctually to their stalls and sang
their daily office but returned to Pangim to sleep. Like Gibbon
ruminating on the steps of Ara Coeli, many romantic trippers in the
last hundred years have stood under the Arch of the Viceroys,
considered the vanity of earthly empire and indulged in forebodings

of the future of British India. The last of these was Robert Byron, who, quite without foundation, reported that the Cathedral housed a mechanical organ.

In the last two years there has been a stir in the city's sleep. Officials have exterminated the mosquitoes. Vegetation and rubble have been cleared so that the four great remaining churches stand in an open space. Several of the chapels that lie around them are being repaired. There is a plan to use Santa Monica as the archdiocesan seminary. But during the festival month the area was transformed into a fairground and bivouac. The pilgrims were in possession, an ever-changing population of some fifty thousand men, women and children.

The Papal Delegation and high officers had been there for the opening ceremonies and were gone before I arrived. Day after day I watched the changing parade of Christian India with inexhaustible fascination. Sometimes a wealthy family or an official from the Government of India would arrive in a private car, enter privately ahead of the queue, pay their homage and turn home. One day half a village community of black little aboriginals were led in by the priest who had just converted them. They had never before left their ancestral forest and had no idea that the world contained so many other Christians.

There were prosperous Goan parishes marching in procession, men and women apart, carrying wands and banners, singing litanies and wearing the insignia of pious sodalities. For these a whole bazaar had been constructed selling souvenirs and rosaries and beer. But the traders were not doing quite as well as they had hoped. At last, after two hundred years, the Jesuits were again in charge, and everything was more efficiently ordered than on previous occasions. And the overwhelming majority of pilgrims were very poor people who had pinched and saved and borrowed to raise their fares. They carried bundles of provisions and when they were not praying they were cooking and eating. They prayed long and often with rapt devotion, resolutely visiting all the altars and all the statues, kissing the stones; and they ate long and often, squatting in groups over the wood smoke and spicy steam, chattering in half a dozen languages.

When a bishop passed—and prelates were plentiful there all that month—they would rise and dart to kiss his ring. They came from all over India and Ceylon but mostly from the southern coast between Bombay and Madras which had heard the preaching of St. Francis Xavier. They were the descendants of his converts. Always, from before dawn until late evening, patient queues formed and moved slowly forward to the side door of the Cathedral. Hitherto the relics had been exposed in the Jesuit church of Bom Jesus. Now for the first and last time they stood in the transept of the Cathedral. They were the goal of the pilgrimage. Three quarters of a million Indians were coming to thank a Spaniard, who had died far away, just four hundred years ago, for their gift of Faith.

Francis Xavier is no figure of tradition and legend. Generations of patient scholars, culminating in Father George Schurhammer, S.J., have collected and collated the evidence. Last year the fruit of their work was set before English readers in the lively narrative of Father James Brodrick, S.J. 'Lively' is the right word, not merely for the vivacious humour of the writing, but for the whole image he has created, a study 'from the life', complete in the round, seeming palpable. Francis Xavier lived in an age of great adventurers. In England we incline to regard our Elizabethan sea dogs as unique national heroes. The Portuguese went first and went farther, and among those fierce and fearless men, Francis Xavier was pre-eminent in daring and endurance. In him renaissance exuberance co-existed with medieval faith—faith like a meteorite, compact, impermeable, incorruptible. But there was another component which belongs to no period in time—an insatiable love for his fellow men. Love raised him to the altars of the Church and love keeps him alive in the hearts of his devotees today. He believed that those who died in the darkness of heathenism were in danger of eternal damnation. The most perfect gift Love could bring was Christian Truth. That was the single, irresistible force that drove him across seas wide open to piracy, through forts seething with disease and sin, along inland tracks devoid of food and shelter, to wherever he could find a foothold and a hearing.

Ten years were the total span of his stupendous mission. He came to the East under obedience, a Jesuit priest, one of the earliest companions of St. Ignatius Loyola. The King of Portugal required Jesuits in his Eastern empire. There were few to choose from then.

Even so Francis Xavier was a second choice. Had a colleague not fallen ill he might have completed his life in a European university.

Goa was his base. There he began his work and there, three times, he returned to re-equip himself for his great journeys and to attend to local ecclesiastical affairs. His mission lay wherever there were souls to be saved. The colonists, their slaves and prisoners, the newly converted Indians, the heathen—all were in his charge, and his methods were as diverse as the peoples. He walked the streets of Goa with a hand bell, calling all and sundry to prayer. He dined with the luxurious and laughed them out of their excesses. He lay night-long beside the dying in the crowded and stifling hospitals, hearing confessions and whispering comfort. He stood among the fishing boats and taught through an interpreter the simple prayers that are used there today. Basque was his mother tongue, to which he reverted as he lay dying. His Portuguese, as appears in his letters, was imperfect. Of the numberless languages of Asia he had a bare smattering, but nowhere except among the Japanese did he meet with misunderstanding. He had the gift of tongues which springs from love and burns its way into the mind without the intermediary of words. He was possessed by the Word. He covered, in his ten years, all that was known of Asia, he penetrated unknown Japan and fell at last with his dying eyes on China, quite worn out at the age of forty-six and still yearning for further conquests.

During his lifetime he was recognised as a saint. When the news of his death reached Malacca his bones were sent for, from where he had been buried in lime on the island of Sancian. Thus was first observed the phenomenon whose strangeness caught the imagination of East and West alike. After ten weeks he was found as fresh and supple and flushed as on the day he died. The body was taken to Malacca and reburied there, bent double and pressed down under the floor of the church. There it remained until news of his death reached Goa. The capital of the Indies required it, and five months later it was again dug up and again found incorrupt and unchanged except for some wounds caused by its clumsy burial.

The body, now acclaimed as miraculous, was borne to Goa and rapturously welcomed. It was also carefully examined by doctors and pronounced to be untouched by any embalmer. On several subsequent occasions it was re-examined by critical foreigners and found in a state of preternatural preservation. An elaborate silver casket was made for it and later mounted on a monument of Tuscan marble. There it stands today in the old Jesuit church of Bom Jesus.

For a hundred and fifty years it defied corruption though much mishandled by the curious and the pious. One over-pious lady bit off a toe and smuggled it away to Lisbon. The Pope sent for an arm. On both occasions there was a flow of fresh blood.

But some signs of a desiccation had begun to appear. Early in the eighteenth century the Jesuits submitted that the spectacle had ceased to be edifying, and should be decently abandoned. The King of Portugal ordered that the casket should be opened only at the command of the Viceroy. Then in 1757 Pombal, the anti-clerical minister of the King of Portugal, had the Jesuits expelled from the King's dominions. Pombal fell in 1777, and in 1782 the casket was once more laid open to the lips of the people. The body was by then quite dry and stiff. Since then there has been an exposition every ten years.

The body is now officially spoken of merely as 'the relics' of the saint. At their final exposition the face, an arm and a foot were all that appeared from the sumptuous vestments. The side panels of the casket were removed; the open coffin was pulled out a few inches to allow the pilgrims to kiss the withered foot. This was what they had come for; not to see a miracle but to say thank you and to seek protection. Hour after hour they filed past, paying their inherited debt of love. On 6th January the casket was carried back to Bom Jesus, its doors locked, and the saint's restless bones at last found peace, not to be touched or seen again until the Day of Judgment.

His beloved Goans stand guard over him and he over them. He is their single renowned possession. India is littered with prodigious monuments—Buddhist, Jain, Hindu, Mohammedan and the Anglo-Saxon engineer have responded to the vast wealth of the place, expanded and sought to perpetuate themselves.

Goa has St. Francis Xavier and his spirit can be recognised in every face; not his exuberance, perhaps, though Goans are great travellers, but his faith and love. Goans have a peculiar, pervading, unobtrusive benignity which is not found anywhere except in deeply Christian places. They had a special place in his story. They made a home for him. They were his beginning, not the remote un-attainable end of his striving. To them he returned to take stock and recuperate. To them finally he was borne in triumph. And they are making a congenial home for him still.

ALBERT CAMUS

The Spirit of Algiers

Just after Albert Camus was awarded the Nobel Prize for literature, *Esquire* published the following note on Camus as a preface to a short story of his in the February 1958 issue:

"It is a testimony to the immediacy of Albert Camus's writing, as well as to the quality, that he should have been honoured with the 1957 Nobel Prize in Literature so early in his career (he is only forty-four), and on the basis of so few books. He has published only one full-length novel (*The Plague*), two novelettes (*The Stranger* and *The Fall*), and two essays (*The Myth of Sisyphus* and *The Rebel*). A collection of his short stories (*Exile and the Kingdom*), in which 'The Growing Stone' will be included, will appear in this country next month.

"The Nobel Committee cited Camus's markedly personal approach to the great fundamental problems of life; and one sees how in his work the paradox of life is dramatized by man's situation: man finds himself pressed, suddenly, into corners, his life flared in one illuminating moment, and it is his action—or lack of action—in that moment which defines him for Camus. The irony appears (in his fiction) when each crisis seems a *new* test, with no particular continuity between past and present, present and future. For, in the end, Camus would say, Man's situation is absurd. He is lent dignity and stature only as he becomes conscious of his absurdity, when he perceives the tragic nature of life and of his individual and necessary role within it."

Five years earlier, in the December 1953 issue, his essay 'The Spirit of Algiers' had appeared without any accompanying note. If one had been included it would have referred to the article's original date of composition, 1936 (when Camus was twenty-three years of age), and then remarked that 'The Spirit of Algiers' was published originally in a collection of essays, *Noces*. In 1942 it was reprinted in France as part of *The Myth of Sisyphus*, which was translated into English in 1955. In the last book, the essay is entitled 'Summer in Algiers', and though in a different translation, it is essentially the same work.

Camus himself was born and educated in Algeria, and the sense of physicality, of the sun and of the flesh, that emerges here is an image of Algeria that has persisted in his later work. It is the dominant external impression of his years in Algeria, or so one gathers from his novels and essays.

Some of the ideas and associations which appear later in Camus' writing are also present in this essay, although in a somewhat different form. But the people of Algiers described here embody certain of his imperatives, and the piece is almost a hymn to their passionate living. One must live, Camus believes, and the important thing is not to live better but to live more. To live without illusions and without myths, without consolations and without self-deceptions; rather one must start with the present and live fully within it. This is the 'spirit of Algiers', as well as a portrait of Camus at twenty-three, living in a world curved with sun and opulence, and viewed (by him) with admiration, sensually.

———————

THEY ARE OFTEN SECRET, the loves you share with a place. Cities like Paris, Prague, and even Florence are turned in upon themselves, and so limit the society which is natural to them. But Algiers, and with it certain privileged places, cities on the sea, open out into the sky like a mouth or a wound. The things one loves in Algiers are the things everyone lives by: the sea at every turning, a certain burden in the sunshine, the beauty of the people. And, as always, in this shamelessness, in this offering, there is an even more secret perfume. In Paris, one can have a longing for space and the beating of wings. Here man is overwhelmed, and, assured of his desires, he can take stock of his riches.

Undoubtedly you must live in Algiers for a long time to under-stand how withering an excess of natural goods can be. There is nothing here for the man who wants to learn, to educate himself, or to better himself. This is a country without lessons. It neither makes promises nor drops hints. It is satisfied with giving, but in pro-fusion. It is completely given over to the eyes, and you know it as soon as you enjoy it. Its pleasures are past remedy, and its joys without hope. It calls for spirits that are clear-sighted, that is, bereft of consolation. It requires one to make an act of lucidity as one makes an act of faith. A strange land that bestows upon the man it sustains both his grandeur and his misery! It is not surprising that the sensuous riches with which a sensitive man is provided in this country coincide with the most extreme poverty. There is no truth which does not bring with it its own bitterness. Why then be surprised if I no longer love the face of this land except among its poorest people?

Throughout their youth here men find a life in proportion to their beauty; and afterwards there is a decline and a forgetting. They put their stakes on the flesh, but they knew they were going to lose. In Algiers, to the man who is young and alive, everything offers an escape and an excuse for triumphs: the bay, the sun, the red and white play of terraces towards the sea, the flowers and the sports grounds, the girls with cool legs. But for him who has lost his youth, there is nothing to cling to and nowhere for melancholy to escape from itself. Elsewhere, on Italian terraces, in the cloisters of Europe, or along the outline of Provençal hills, there are many places where man can flee from his humanity and gently get free of himself. But everything here calls for solitude and the blood of young men. Goethe, on his deathbed, cried out for light, and that has become a historic saying. In Belcourt and in Bab-el-Oued, old men sitting at the backs of cafés listen to the boastings of young men with plastered hair.

These beginnings and these ends, it is summer that brings them to us in Algiers. During these months the wealthy desert the city. But the poor remain, and the sky. Along with them we go down together towards the port and man's treasures: the warmth of the water and the brown bodies of women. And at night, gorged with these riches, they go back to the oilcloth and the oil lamp that furnish all the scenery of their lives.

In Algiers, you bathe in the harbour and then go and rest on a raft. When you go near a raft where there is a pretty girl, you shout to your friends, "I tell you, she's a peach." Those are healthy pleasures. One must believe that they constitute the ideal of these young people since most of them continue this life during the winter, and every day at noon they gather naked in the sun for a frugal meal. Not that they have read the dull tracts of the nudists, those Protestants of the flesh (there is a systemisation of the body which is as irritating as that of the mind). But they are happy in the sun.

Not nearly enough importance will ever be placed upon this habit

H

of our age. For the first time in two thousand years the body may be seen naked on the beaches. For twenty centuries men have striven to make Greek insolence and naïveté decent, to diminish the importance of the flesh and to complicate dress. Today, after all this history, the stretches of young people on Mediterranean beaches go back to the magnificent gestures of the athletes of Delos. And living in this way, beside the flesh and by the flesh, they see that the flesh has its shades, its life and—to venture a bit of nonsense—a psychology of its own.

May I lay myself open to ridicule by saying that I do not like the way in which Gide exalts the flesh? He calls upon it to delay desire in order to sharpen desire. Thus he is like those who, in the slang of the brothel, are called complicated or cerebral. Christianity also wants to defer desire. But it is more natural and sees in this deference a mortification. My friend Vincent, who is a cooper and a junior swimming champion, has an even clearer view of things. He drinks when he is thirsty, if he desires a woman he tries to sleep with her, and would marry her if he were in love with her (that hasn't happened yet). Afterwards, he always says, "That's better"—which sums up forcefully the apology one might make for satiety.

The evolution of the flesh, like that of the mind, has its history, its setbacks, its advances and its losses. With this difference only: colour. When you go to the harbour baths during the summer, you become aware of the simultaneous passing of every skin from white to gold, then to brown, and finally to tobacco colour, the ultimate effort of transformation of which the body is capable. The harbour is dominated by the play of the white cubes of the Casbah. When you are at water level, against the crude white background of the Arab city, the bodies unfold a copper frieze. And as August advances and the sun grows greater, the white of the houses becomes more blinding, and the skins take on a more sombre warmth. How then escape identifying yourself with this dialogue of stone and flesh, as the sun and the seasons pass? The whole morning is spent diving, in blossoming laughter amid sprays of water, in long paddle strokes around red and black cargo vessels (those that come from Norway are all scented with wood; those from Germany are filled with the smell of oil; those that hug the coast smell of wine and old casks). When sunshine is spilling from every corner of the sky, an orange canoe laden with brown bodies draws us into a crazy race. Then the cadenced beating of the double paddle, the blades the colour of fruit, is suspended sharply and we glide along in the still water of the harbour: how can I have any doubts that I am piloting over the smooth waters a wild cargo of gods in whom I recognise my brothers?

But at the other end of the town, summer is already offering us her other riches: I mean her moments of silence and her boredom. These moments of silence differ in quality, according to whether they spring from shadow or shade of the bordering trees. Arabs sell for five francs glasses of iced lemonade flavoured with orange flowers. Their cry, "Ice cold, ice cold!" carries across the empty square. After their cries, silence falls again under the sunshine: in the vendor's jug, the ice turns round and I hear its tiny noise. There is the silence of siesta. In the streets along the sea front, outside the hairdressers' dirty shops, it can be measured by the musical buzzing of flies behind the curtains made of hollow reeds. Elsewhere, in the Moorish cafés of the Casbah, it is the flesh that is silent, that cannot tear itself away from these places, leave the glass of tea and discover time again in the sounds of its own blood. But, above all, there is the silence of summer evenings.

These brief moments, when day slips into night, are they thronged with secret signs and calls—is that why Algiers is so bound to them in my imagination? Sometimes when I am far away from this country, I conjure up its twilights like promises of happiness. Over the hills which dominate the city there are roads among the mastic and olive trees. And it is towards them that my heart turns. I see sprays of black birds climb towards the green horizons. In the sky, empty suddenly of sunshine, something gradually relaxes. A tiny host of red clouds string out until they are absorbed back into the air. Almost immediately afterwards appears the first star, and then, in one stride, comes the devouring night.

Fleeting evenings in Algiers, what unequalled quality do they possess to stir so many things in me? The sweetness that they leave on my lips I have not time to weary of before it disappears in the night. Is that the secret of its persistence?

On Padovani beach the dance hall is open every day. And in the huge rectangular night club, open to the sea its whole length long, the poor young people of the district dance until evening. Often I

used to wait there for an unusual moment. During the day the hall
is protected by sloping wooden screens. When the sun has disappeared, they are raised. Then the hall is filled with a strange
green light, born of the double shell of sea and sky. Sitting away
from the windows, you see only the sky and the faces of the passing
dancers, as in a shadow theatre. Night comes quickly then and with
it the lights.

I cannot put into words how moving and how secret this subtle
moment is to me. I remember, though, a tall splendid girl who had
danced all afternoon. She wore a jasmine necklace over her clinging
blue dress that was wet with sweat from her hips down her legs. She
laughed as she danced and tossed back her head. When she came
close to the table, she left floating after her the mingled smell of
flowers and flesh. When evening arrived, I could no longer see her
body pressed against her partner's, but against the sky moved the
alternate spots of white jasmine and black hair, and when she threw
back her full bosom I could hear her laugh and see her partner's
profile bend down suddenly. My idea of innocence I owe to nights
like these. In any event, I learn no longer to separate these beings
laden with violent feelings from the sky where their desires whirl.

In suburban cinemas in Algiers they sometimes sell peppermints
which bear, marked in red, everything essential to the birth of love:
1) questions, "Do you love me?" "When will you marry me?"; 2)
answers, "Madly"; "In the spring." After preparing the ground,
you pass them to your neighbour, who replies in a similar fashion or
simply plays the fool. In Belcourt they have seen marriages
arranged in this way and whole lives committed by the exchange of
peppermint sweets. And this gives a good picture of the childlike
people of this country.

The sign of youth is, perhaps, a splendid inclination towards easily
won happiness. But, above all, it is an eagerness to live which comes
near squandering. In Belcourt, as in Bab-el-Oued, they marry
young. They go to work very early, and they use up in ten years the
experience of a man's life. A thirty-year-old workman has already
played all his cards. He awaits the end with his wife and his
children. His happiness has been short and merciless. So has his life.
And you understand that he is born of this country where everything

is given only to be taken away. In this abundance and profusion, life takes the curve of the great passions, sudden, exacting, generous. It is not to be built, but to be burned. So there is no question of contemplating and of becoming better.

The idea of hell, for example, is only a mild joke here. An imagination of this kind is allowed only to the very virtuous. And I believe that virtue is a word without meaning all over Algeria. Not that these men lack principles. They have their morality, and a very special one. They do not neglect their mothers. They see that their wives are respected in the streets. They are considerate to pregnant women. They do not attack an adversary in pairs, because 'that isn't done'. The one who does not observe these elementary rules 'is not a man' and that settles the affair. This seems just and strict to me. We are still very far from obeying unconsciously this code of the street, the only disinterested one I know. I have seen people's faces around me soften with pity whenever a man went by surrounded by policemen and, before they knew whether the man had stolen, was a parricide or simply a nonconformist, "Poor chap!" they said, or again, with a shade of admiration, "That one's a pirate."

There are races born to pride and life. They are the ones that foster the most remarkable inclination towards boredom. They are the ones, too, in whom the attitude towards death is most repellent. Putting the joys of the senses aside, the amusements of these people are among the silliest. A bowling club, association banquets, the shilling cinema and community fêtes have for years provided adequate recreation for those over thirty. Sundays in Algiers are among the most sinister days in the world. How then could these unthinking people clothe with myths the deep horror of their life? Everything connected with death here is a subject of fun or of hate. These people without religion or idols die alone after living in a crowd.

I well know that such a people cannot be accepted by everyone. Here intelligence has no place, as it has in Italy. This race is indifferent to the mind. It has a cult and an admiration of the flesh. From flesh it draws its strength, its naïve cynicism and a childish vanity which deserves to be judged severely. Here it is a people without a past, without a tradition, and yet not without poetry—but a poetry whose quality is hard and sensual, far from tenderness, the same as their sky, the only poetry that truly moves me and makes me at one with myself. The opposite of a civilised people is a creative people. These barbarians sprawling on the beaches—I have the foolish hope that, perhaps without their knowing, they are in the act of fashioning the face of a culture in which man's grandeur will at last find its true countenance. These people entirely given over to their present live without myths, without consolation. They have put all their goods on this earth, and accordingly they are defence-less against death.

Everything made here shows a distaste for stability and a heedless-ness of the future. There is a rush to live, and if an art was to be born here, it would obey that hatred of duration that drove the Dorians to carve their first column in wood. Between this sky and these faces turned towards it there is nothing on which to hang a mythology, a literature, a philosophy, or a religion, but stones, flesh, stars and those truths that the hand can touch.

Oneness is expressed here in terms of sunshine and of sea. It is felt in the heart in a certain human desire which contains its own bitter-ness and its own grandeur. Gradually I come to the knowledge that there is no superhuman happiness, no eternity outside the curve of days. These absurd, essential goods, these relative truths, are the only ones that move me. The others, ideals, I have not enough heart to understand. I do not wish to play the fool, but I cannot find any sense in the happiness of angels. I know only that this will endure longer than I. And what shall I call eternity, if not what goes on after my death?

I am not expressing the satisfaction of an individual with his lot. It is something very different. It is not always easy to be a man, still less to be a pure man. But to be pure is to rediscover the country of the soul where the relationship of the world becomes perceptible, where the beating of the blood meets the violent pulsations of the two-o'clock sun. It is a well-known fact that you always recognise your native land when you are about to lose it. For those who are too tortured by themselves, their native land is the one that rejects them. I should not like to be brutal nor seem to exaggerate. But, in short, those things in this life that reject me are first of all those things which make me die. Everything that exalts life at the same time increases its absurdity. In the Algerian summer I learn that one thing is more tragic than suffering, and that is the life of a happy man. But this may also be the road to a larger life, since it leads one not to cheat.

Many, in fact, pretend to a love of living in order to elude love itself. They try to enjoy themselves and to 'make experiments'. But this is a point of view of the mind. One needs an exceptional gift to be a sensualist. A man's life comes to an end without the help of his mind, with its retreats and advances, its simultaneous solitude and presence. To see these men of Belcourt working, supporting their wives and their children, I believe it possible to feel a secret shame. I have no illusions; there is not much love in the lives I am speaking of. I ought to say there is no longer very much. But at least they have evaded nothing. There are words that I have never understood very well, like sin. Yet I believe I know that these men have not sinned against life. For if there is one sin against life, it is not so much in despairing as in hoping for another life and slipping away from the implacable grandeur of this one. These men have not cheated. They were summer gods at twenty because of their eagerness to live, and thus they remain deprived of all hope. I have seen two of them die. They were filled with horror, but silent. It is better thus. From Pandora's box in which swarmed the evils of humanity, the Greeks let out hope after all the others, as the most terrible of all. I know of no more moving symbol. For hope, contrary to what people believe, is the equivalent of resignation. And to live is not to be resigned.

Here is the bitter lesson of Algerian summers. But already the season is trembling and summer is slipping away. The first September rains, after so much violence and tenseness, are like the first tears of the liberated earth, as if for a few days this country were stirring with tenderness. At the same time the acacias spread an odour of love over the whole of Algeria. In the evening or after the rain, the entire earth, her belly wet with a seed perfumed with bitter almond, rests from having given herself all summer long to the sun. And once again this odour consecrates the marriage of man and earth and awakes in us the only truly virile love in this world, perishable and bounteous.

ALBERTO MORAVIA

The Chinese Dog

'Alberto Moravia' (a pen name for Alberto Pincherle) first received attention outside Italy when the English translation of his *Woman of Rome* appeared in 1949, although he had achieved recognition in Italy as early as 1929 with the publication of his first novel when he was twenty-two. Since then he has been widely read abroad with such novels as *The Fancy Dress Party*, *Conjugal Love*, and the recent *Two Women*.

He has published many short stories, not all of which have yet appeared in America. Farrar, Straus and Cudahy published his *Bitter Honeymoon and Other Stories* in 1954 and another selection, *Roman Tales*, in 1957. When *Roman Tales* was published in Italy it was issued in three volumes and contanied many stories which were omitted from the single-volume Farrar, Straus edition. 'The Chinese Dog', which appeared in the Italian edition, was one of those omitted from the American; thus it appears here reprinted for the first time since its appearance in *Esquire* in January 1956.

THAT WINTER, in order to make a living, I finally had to resort to dog catching. Not on the payroll of the city, which then has the dogs exterminated, but on my own, in view of the tips I was given for each of the dogs stolen by me. I would go to one of the prosperous sections of town at the time of day when the maids take the dogs walking, and in my pocket I would have a cord with a slide knot tied into it. As soon as one of those maids came out, I would start following her, at a distance. Maidservants, as is known, have few chances to take their minds off things, and take advantage of these respites to meet with some woman friend or else with their male friends. The maid would let the dog run loose, and immediately he would trot on ahead, sniffing and stopping to lift his leg at each corner or tree. When I saw that the maid was deep in conversation, I would approach the dog, slip the cord over his head, and duck round the street corner. Then the next problem was getting to Tormarancio, where I lived. Partly by foot, and partly with the help of some taxi-drivers who lived out that way, I would get as far as the Garbatella stop, and from there on one of those open trucks that did bus service I would finally get home. Home? Don't make me laugh. Let's put it this way: I would finally get to that corner of a room that, along with a narrow cot, I rented from Bonifazi, a worker friend of mine. That same room served as sleeping quarters for him, his wife and his three children; with the result that at night the floor was one whole spread of mattresses and if you wanted to get out, some one of them had to get up and make a roll of his mattress, to let you through. I would leave the dog with Bonifazi, who knew of this traffic, and the following day I would go back to that building from which I had seen the maid emerge. I would tell the superintendent how I had found such and such a dog. Immediately they would send for me, let me into an entrance hall that was all marble and mirrors, and almost throw their arms around me out of gratitude. The morning after, I would bring back the dog, pocket the tip, and start in all over again.

One day, with this system of the cord, I rounded up a strange dog, of a kind I had never seen before. He looked like a lion—large head, round and covered with fur, a smoothly shaved body, a stubby snout, and a tongue that was purplish black. He was a good animal, but not very lively; more on the sad side, and almost thoughtful. He followed me with his head hanging low, as though he knew what was in store for him.

That day it was raining. All I had on my back was a thin ragged jacket and an undershirt; my shoes were full of holes—in a word I got so drenched that on the truck my teeth started chattering, and when I moved my toes I could feel the water ooze through my socks and out through the shoe leather. Then in Tormarancio, which is in one of those low spots, the rain, as usual, had flooded the houses, and, instead of warmth, what I found was more water; and Bonifazi's wife shouting in despair, the children in tears, and Bonifazi himself trying to construct some sort of gangway across the flooded floor. I went straight to bed, without eating. That same night I broke out in a fever, and the following day I stayed in bed. The fever did not leave me for an entire week. I was in that corner, on that bed; with two clothes-lines strung up over me and my belongings hanging on them. From the depths of my fever I stared out at the room, with all its mattresses stacked into the corners, with other lines and other clothes on them, crisscrossing in all directions. It was almost always dark, since the rain did not let up, and two out of the three windows had cardboard panes. Bonifazi's wife did the cooking in the next room, which meant that I was always alone, but I didn't mind, for when I feel bad I prefer not to talk. As for the dog, he was really good and, in order to keep the humidity from getting at him and making him ill, I had made a bed for him out of old rags and shavings which I kept under my cot. I kept giving money to Bonifazi's wife to buy food for him; not because I had the tip on my mind, but because I like animals and hate to make them suffer. On the seventh day I started raving, and I got the fixation that they wanted to take the dog away from me. I asked Bonifazi to have him put on my bed. Bonifazi did that, and I put my arms around the dog's body, pressed my face into that warm fur of his, and fell asleep hugging him. The dog didn't budge. During the night, perhaps owing to that fur of his, I sweated so much that I was soaked; then I felt as though I were released from a grip, and in the morning the fever had gone. All night long the dog had not moved.

For the next few days I took it easy, and meanwhile the sun had come out again, and I went walking in the neighbourhood, pulling the dog behind me, on the cord. Just outside Tormarancio there are a number of shacks that make the Tormarancio ones look good by comparison. Do I have to describe them?—wooden crates and gas containers, topped off by sheets of corrugated roofing, surrounded by cane fences, and with doorways so low that you have to stoop to get in. In one of these shacks there was a Chinese, of the kind that sells ties in Rome. He had come there a few years before, and then had stayed, and he lived with a woman who was called Fesseria. She plied the usual trade; was thin, white, underfed; with a long face and a pair of heavy black eyebrows, and black eyes. Her hair was thick, black and as soft as silk, and when she put on some lipstick she even managed to be good-looking. The Chinese was pure Chinese; seen from the rear he might have been taken for one of those peasants from up north, squat and sturdy; but then he turned and you saw that he was Chinese. Well, with the dog I went walking in front of the Chinaman's shack, and without delay both of them came out—she with a pail full of water that almost landed, when she emptied it, on my legs; and he holding a pot, since he was always cooking. The Chinese came up to me and, speaking good Italian since he talks the way I do, said, "This breed of dog comes from my country . . he is Chinese." And he explained that in China these dogs are as common as poodles here. He also said that, if I wanted, he was willing to take him, since the dog reminded him of his country, and that he would cherish him. But all he had to give in exchange was a couple of those raw-silk ties. I refused; what good were the ties when what I wanted was the cash reward? Fesseria, holding the pail, called out to me, "Luigi . . . so you won't give us the dog?" She was tantalising, gay, jumping around from one puddle to the next on those long thin legs of hers. Even though I still felt pretty low, I couldn't help feeling attracted by her, so thin and white, with that pair of black eyebrows. However, I said nothing at all, and went back to Bonifazi's.

The next day I went into Rome, to the building where I had first seen the maid. But then things start going wrong. . . . "He belonged to an American family," the woman of the building told me, "and the family had to leave; yesterday. After all the fuss they made about the dog. . . . But anyway they had to leave, and they did."

So there I was; a fine specimen of a dog on my hands, and no idea what to do with him. At first I tried selling him, but that was no go. People took one look at my tattered clothes and said that the dog was stolen goods, as was true. On the other hand, I did not want to take him to the dog pound, since there they would have put him to death, poor thing, whereas I still remembered the night when he had cured me with the warmth of his fur, and had never moved. Meanwhile, however, he was costing me money, since he ate a great deal and was not small-sized.

One of those afternoons, I decided against going to the city. I left Tormarancio, which the sun had transformed from a swamp into a desert of dust, and climbed up to one of the nearby hills. By then it was springtime; without a cloud in the sky, with all that soft air and sunshine. Seen from up there even Tormarancio, with its long low houses and red roofs, seemed less of a prison camp than usual. The hill was covered with fresh tender green grass that was pleasing to see, and in places it looked as though there had been a snowfall, because of an outcropping of small daisies so thick that the grass was hidden by them. I roamed around from hill to hill, my hands in my pockets, whistling. The illness had done me good and I could feel my heart filling with a kind of vague hope, looking out towards the horizon full of sun, and watching large white butterflies as they headed right into it. The dog had become quite lively for a change, and raced ahead. At a certain point I went downhill and started following a brook that flowed between two high hills. Then I heard the dog bark, raised my eyes, and saw Fesseria, who was out walking too, alone, her hair loose on her shoulders, a blade of grass set between her teeth, her hands in the pockets of a striped smock of the kind worn by factory girls. She stopped and started playing with the dog, and then said, laughing, "Well, are you going to give us the dog?" Without pausing to think, I said, "I'll give him to you, on one condition."

To make a long story short, we made love; on the ground, between those two high hills, beside the brook. The dog, meanwhile, had started lapping up the water in the brook with his purple tongue; then settled back and sat there on the grass, eyeing us; to the point that it almost unnerved me. And I did what I did not only because that woman appealed to me, but also because I liked the idea of giving the dog away in return for some love-making; since by then I had grown fond of him and it seemed to me that that was the right price for him. In the end, we got up and Fesseria took the cord for the dog, saying, "He will be glad because it reminds him of his country." I stayed there, watching her go off with the dog, and I still had that feeling for her. Then I stretched out on the ground and slept for a couple of hours.

The next morning I went into the city and stayed there overnight, with a dachshund that I had picked up near Piazza Santíago del Cile. I slept in a city dormitory, and then went back to Tormarancio. That afternoon I went out walking again, with the dachshund, and happened to find myself in front of the shack of the Chinaman.

Fesseria was away, probably having gone to Rome. But he was

there, and he came out with a garbage can, which he emptied behind
the shack. Why, I don't know, but I would have liked him to thank
me for the dog, so I asked him where he was. He smiled and made a
gesture which I didn't understand, and went back into the shack.
The dachshund was poking around in the garbage. I went over and
then I saw, in among the refuse, the paw of the dog, smeared with
blood but with all its hair.

Later I was told that in their country the people eat dogs, everybody does, and there is no harm in it. But, at the time, the blood
mounted to my head. I entered the shack; he had his back to me
and was bent over the stove. He turned round, smiling, with a plate
that contained a piece of dark-coloured meat, in a sauce; and I
realised that it was the meat of the dog and that he was inviting me
to eat it. With my fist I sent the plate into his face, shouting,
"Murderer! What have you done to the dog?" Immediately I
realised that he did not understand why I was so mad. He ducked,
ran out of the shack and headed towards Tormarancio. I scooped
up a stone and hurled it at him; then I caught up with him and
seized him by the neck. People rushed out and he kept hollering,
"Grab him, he's crazy!" and I kept shaking him by the neck and
shouting, "What did you do to the dog? Murderer! What did you
do to the dog?" Finally they separated us, and got me on to the
truck for Rome.

That same day I took the dachshund back to its owners and they
gave me a tip. But I did not go back to Tormarancio. I had no
belongings anyway, and had left nothing at Bonifazi's. I owed him
one month's rent and thought that, after all, not all ills are one
hundred per cent harmful. At the same time, that affair of the
Chinese dog had given me a feeling of disgust for my livelihood, and
I decided to change. I set myself up as a pedlar, pushing around a
cart filled with amost everything—green olives, melon seeds, peeled
chestnuts, peanuts, dried figs and walnuts. I twirled the wrapping
paper into cones all day long, at the new bridge, at the entrance to
the Aurelia tunnel, and more or less succeeded in keeping body and
soul together. In that period I was always sad and life had little
meaning for me, perhaps because of the dog. Only once I saw Fesseria,
from a distance, but I did not speak to her. If she had told me that
she too had eaten the dog, I think I would have killed her.

ALDOUS HUXLEY

Brave New World Revisited

This is one in a series of monthly essays which appeared in *Esquire* under the heading, 'From the Study of Aldous Huxley', between July 1955 and April 1957.

Whether he writes about Freudian theory or canned fish, Huxley's approach is always original, now heavily influenced by the Eastern Mysticism which goes into his Perennial Philosophy. Most controversial of all the essays in this series was 'Brave New World Revisited', his re-evaluation of the satirically projected nightmare which he wrote twenty-four years earlier, *Brave New World*.

We selected this essay from among some forty-five pieces Huxley has contributed to our pages (as early as 1935, one of his short stories, 'Visiting Stranger', appeared in *Esquire*) because it seems to us one of the most curious reversals in literature, and until now it has been seen only by those who read the July 1956 issue of *Esquire*.

This essay bears no relation to Huxley's more recently published discussion of modern liberty, also entitled *Brave New World Revisited*.

THE MOST DISTRESSING THING that can happen to a prophet is to be proved wrong; the next most distressing thing is to be proved right. In the twenty-five years that have elapsed since *Brave New World* was written, I have undergone both these experiences. Events have proved me distressingly wrong; and events have proved me distressingly right.

Here are some of the points on which I was wrong. By the early Thirties Einstein had equated mass and energy, and there was already talk of chain reactions; but the Brave New Worlders knew nothing of nuclear fission. In the early Thirties, too, we knew all about conservation and irreplaceable resources; but their supply of metals and mineral fuel was just as copious in the seventh century After Ford as ours is today. In actual fact the raw material situation will already be subcritical by AF 600 and the atom will be the principal source of industrial power. Again, the Brave New Worlders had solved the population problem and knew how to maintain a permanently favourable relationship between human numbers and natural resources. In actual fact, will our descendants achieve this happy consummation within the next six centuries? And if they *do* achieve it, will it be by dint of rational planning, or through the immemorial agencies of pestilence, famine and internecine warfare? It is, of course, impossible to say. The only thing we can predict with a fair measure of certainty is that humanity (if its rulers decide to refrain from collective suicide) will be travelling at vertiginous speed along one of the most dangerous and congested stretches of its history.

The Brave New Worlders produced their children in biochemical factories. But though bottled babies are not completely out of the question, it is virtually certain that our descendants will in fact remain viviparous. Mother's Day is in no danger of being replaced by Bottle Day. My prediction was made for strictly literary purposes, and not as a reasoned forecast of future history. In this matter I knew in advance that I should be proved wrong.

From biology we now pass to politics. The dictatorship described in *Brave New World* was global and, in its own peculiar way, benevolent. In the light of current events and developing tendencies, I sadly suspect that in this forecast, too, I may have been wrong. True, the seventh century After Ford is still a long way off, and it is possible that, by then, hard economic necessity, or the social chaos resulting from nuclear warfare, or military conquest by one Great Power, or some grisly combination of all three, will have bludgeoned our descendants into doing what we ought to be doing now, from motives of enlightened self-interest and common humanity—namely, to collaborate for the common good. In time of peace, and when things are going tolerably well, people cannot be expected to vote for measures which, though ultimately beneficial, may be expected to have certain disagreeable consequences in the short run. Divisive forces are more powerful than those which make for union. Vested interests in languages, philosophies of life, table manners, sexual habits, political, ecclesiastical and economic organisations are sufficiently powerful to block all attempts, by rational and peaceful methods, to unite mankind for its own good. And then there is nationalism. With its Fifty-Seven Varieties of tribal gods, nationalism is the religion of the twentieth century. We may be Christians, Jews, Moslems, Hindus, Buddhists, Confucians or Atheists; but the fact remains that there is only one faith for which large masses of us are prepared to die and kill, and that faith is nationalism. That nationalism will remain the dominant religion of the human race for the next two or three centuries at the very least seems all too probable. If total, nuclear war should be avoided, we may expect to see, not the rise of a single world state, but the continuance, in worsening conditions, of the present system, under which national states compete for markets and raw materials and prepare for partial wars. Most of these states will probably be dictatorships. Inevitably so; for the increasing pressure of population upon resources will make domestic conditions more difficult and international competition more intense. To prevent economic breakdown and to repress popular discontent, the governments of hungry countries will be tempted to enforce ever-stricter controls. Furthermore, chronic undernourishment reduces physical energy and disturbs the mind. Hunger and self-government are incompatible. Even where the average diet provides three thousand calories a day, it is hard enough to make democracy work. In a society most of whose members are living on seventeen hundred to two thousand calories a day it is simply impossible. The undernourished majority will always be ruled, from above, by the well-fed few. As population increases (twenty-seven hundred millions of us are now adding to our numbers at the rate of forty millions a year, and this increase is increasing according to the rules of compound interest); as geometrically increasing demands press more and more heavily on static or, at best, arithmetically increasing supplies; as standards of living are forced down and popular discontent is forced up; as the general scramble for diminishing resources becomes ever fiercer, these national dictatorships will tend to become more oppressive at home, more ruthlessly competitive abroad. "Government," says one of the Brave New Worlders, "is an affair of sitting, not hitting.

You rule with the brains and the buttocks, not the fists." But where there are many competing national dictatorships, each in trouble at home and each preparing for total or partial war against its neighbours, hitting tends to be preferred to sitting, fists, as an instrument of policy, to brains and the "masterly inactivity" (to cite Lord Salisbury's immortal phrase) of the hindquarters. In politics, the near future is likely to be closer to George Orwell's *1984* than to *Brave New World*.

Let me now consider a few of the points on which, I fear, I may have been right. The Brave New Worlders were the heirs and exploiters of a new kind of revolution, and this revolution was, in effect, the theme of my fable. Past revolutions have all been in fields external to the individual as a psychophysical organism—in the field, for example, of ecclesiastical organisation and religious dogma, in the field of economics, in the field of political organisation, in the field of technology. The coming revolution—the revolution whose consequences are described in *Brave New World*—will affect men and women, not peripherally, but at the very core of their organic being. The older revolutionaries sought to change the social environment in the hope (if they were idealists and not mere power seekers) of changing human nature. The coming revolutionaries will make their assault directly on human nature as they find it, in the minds and bodies of their victims or, if you prefer, their beneficiaries.

Among the Brave New Worlders, the control of human nature was achieved by eugenic and dysgenic breeding, by systematic conditioning during infancy and, later on, by 'hypnopædia', or instruction during sleep. Infant conditioning is as old as Pavlov, and hypnopædia, though rudimentary, is already a well-established technique. Phonographs with built-in clocks, which turn them on and off at regular intervals during the night, are already on the market and are being used by students of foreign languages, by actors in a hurry to memorise their parts, by parents desirous of curing their children of bed-wetting and other troublesome habits, by self-helpers seeking moral and physical improvement through autosuggestion and 'affirmations of positive thought'. That the principles of selective breeding, infant conditioning and hypnopædia have not yet been applied by governments is due, in the democratic countries, to the lingering, liberal conviction that persons do not exist for the state, but that the state exists for the good of persons; and in the totalitarian countries to what may be called revolutionary conservatism—attachment to yesterday's revolution instead of the revolution of tomorrow. There is, however, no reason for complacently believing that this revolutionary conservatism will persist indefinitely. In totalitarian hands, applied psychology is already achieving notable results. One third of all the American prisoners captured in Korea succumbed, at least partially, to Chinese brainwashing, which broke down the convictions installed by their education and childhood conditioning, and replaced these comforting axioms by doubt, anxiety and a chronic sense of guilt. This was achieved by thoroughly old-fashioned procedures, which combined straightforward instruction with what may be called conventional psychotherapy in reverse, and made no use of hypnosis, hypnopædia or mind-modifying drugs. If all or even some of these more powerful methods had been employed, brain-washing would probably have been successful with all the prisoners, and not with a mere thirty per cent of them. In their vague, rhetorical way, speech-making politicians and sermon-preaching clergymen like to say that the current struggle is not material, but spiritual—an affair not of machines, but of ideas. They forget to add that the effectiveness of ideas depends very largely on the way in which they are inculcated. A true and beneficent idea may be so ineptly taught as to be without effect on the lives of individuals and societies. Conversely, grotesque and harmful notions may be so skilfully drummed into people's heads that, filled with faith, they will rush out and move mountains—to the greater glory of the devil and their own destruction. At the present time the dynamism of totalitarian ideas is greater than the dynamism of liberal, democratic ideas. This is not due, of course, to the intrinsic superiority of totalitarian ideas. It is due partly to the fact that, in a world where population is fast outrunning resources, ever larger measures of governmental control become necessary—and it is easier to exercise centralised control by totalitarian than by democratic methods. Partly, too, it is due to the fact that the means employed for the dissemination of totalitarian ideas are more effective, and are used more systematically, than the means employed for disseminating democratic and liberal ideas. These more effective methods of totalitarian propaganda, education and brain-washing are, as we have seen, pretty old-fashioned. Sooner or later, however, the dictators will abandon their revolutionary conservatism and, along with it, the old-world procedures inherited from the pre-psychological and palaeo-pharmacological past. After which, heaven help us all!

Among the legacies of the proto-pharmacological past must be numbered our habit, when we feel in need of a lift, a release from tension, a mental vacation from unpleasant reality, of drinking alcohol or, if we happen to belong to a non-Western culture, of smoking hashish or opium, of chewing coca leaves or betel or any one of scores of intoxicants. The Brave New Worldlers did none of these things; they merely swallowed a tablet or two of a substance called Soma. This, needless to say, was not the same as the Soma mentioned in the ancient Hindu scriptures—a rather dangerous drug derived from some as yet unidentified plant native to South Central Asia—but a synthetic, possessing "all the virtues of alcohol and Christianity, none of their defects". In small doses the Soma of the Brave New Worlders was a relaxant, an inducer of euphoria, a fosterer of friendliness and social solidarity. In medium doses it transfigured the external world and acted as a mild hallucinant; and in large doses it was a narcotic. Virtually all the Brave New Worlders thought themselves happy. This was due in part to the fact that they had been bred and conditioned to take the place assigned to them in the social hierarchy, in part to the sleep-teaching which had made them content with their lot and in part to Soma and their ability, by its means, to take holidays from unpleasant circumstances and their unpleasant selves.

All the natural narcotics, stimulants, relaxants and hallucinants known to the modern botanist and pharmacologist were discovered by primitive man and have been in use from time immemorial. One of the first things that Homo sapiens did with his newly-developed rationality and self-consciousness was to set them to work finding out ways to by-pass analytical thinking and to transcend or, in extreme cases, temporarily obliterate the isolating awareness of the self. Trying all things that grew in field or forest, they held fast to that which, in this context, seemed good—everything, that is to say, that would change the quality of consciousness, would make it different, no matter how, from everyday feeling, perceiving and thinking.

Among the Hindus, rhythmic breathing and mental concentration have, to some extent, taken the place of the mind-transforming drugs used elsewhere. But even in the land of yoga, even among the religious and even for specifically religious purposes, cannabis indica has been freely used to supplement the effects of spiritual exercises. The habit of taking vacations from the more or less purgatorial world which we have created for ourselves is universal. Moralists may denounce it; but, in the teeth of disapproving talk and repressive legislation, the habit persists, and mind-transforming drugs are everywhere available. The Marxian formula, "Religion is the opium of the people", is reversible, and one can say with even more truth that "Opium is the religion of the people". In other words, mind-transformation, however induced (whether by devotional or ascetic or psycho-gymnastic or chemical means), has always been felt to be one of the highest, perhaps the very highest, of all attainable goods. Up to the present, governments have thought about the problem of mind-transforming chemicals only in terms of prohibition or, a little more realistically, of control and taxation. None, so far, has considered it in its relation to individual well-being and social stability; and very few (thank heaven!) have considered it in terms of Machiavellian statecraft. Because of vested interests and mental inertia, we persist in using alcohol as our main mind-transformer—just as our neolithic ancestors did. We know that alcohol is responsible for a high proportion of our traffic accidents, our crimes of violence, our domestic miseries; and yet we make no effort to replace this old-fashioned and extremely unsatisfactory drug by some new, less harmful and more enlightening mind-transformer. Among the Brave New Worlders, Noah's prehistoric invention of fermented liquor has been made obsolete by a modern synthetic, specifically designed to contribute to social order and the happiness of the individual, and to do so at the minimum physiological cost.

In the society described in my fable, Soma was used as an instrument of statecraft. The tyrants were benevolent, but they were still tyrants. Their subjects were not bludgeoned into obedience; they were chemically coerced to love their servitude, to co-operate willingly and even enthusiastically in the preservation of the social hierarchy. By the malignant or the ignorant, anything and everything can be used badly. Alcohol, for example, has been used, in small doses, to facilitate the exchange of thought in a symposium (literally, a drinking party) of philosophers. It has also been used, as the slave traders used it, to facilitate kidnapping. Scopolamine may be used to induce 'twilight sleep'; it may also be used to increase suggestibility and soften up political prisoners. Heroin may be used to control pain; it may also be used (as it is said to have been used by the Japanese during their occupation of China) to produce an incapacitating addiction in a dangerous adversary. Directed by the wrong people, the coming revolution could be as disastrous, in its own way, as a nuclear and bacteriological war. By systematically using the psychological, chemical and electronic instruments already in existence (not to mention those new and better devices which the future holds in store), a tyrannical oligarchy could keep the majority in permanent and willing subjection. This is the prophecy I made in *Brave New World*. I hope I may be proved wrong, but am sorely afraid that I may be proved right.

Meanwhile it should be pointed out that Soma is not intrinsically evil. On the contrary, a harmless but effective mind-transforming drug might prove a major blessing. And anyhow (as history makes abundantly clear) there will never be any question of getting rid of chemical mind-transformers altogether. The choice confronting us is not a choice between Soma and nothing; it is a choice between Soma and alcohol, Soma and opium, Soma and hashish, ololiuqui, peyote, datura, agaric and all the rest of the natural mind-transformers; between Soma and such products of scientific chemistry and pharmacology as ether, chloral, veronal, Benzedrine and the barbiturates. In a word, we have to choose between a more or less harmless all-round drug and a wide variety of more or less harmful and only partially effective drugs. And this choice will not be delayed until the seventh century After Ford. Pharmacology is on the march. The Soma of *Brave New World* is no longer a distant dream. Indeed, something possessing many of the characteristics of Soma is already with us. I refer to the most recent of the tranquillising agents —the Happiness Pill, as its users affectionately call it, known in America under the trade names of Miltown and Equinel. These Happiness Pills exert a double action: they relax the tension in striped muscle and so relax the associated tensions in the mind. At the same time they act on the enzyme system of the brain in such a way as to prevent disturbances arising in the hypothalamus from interfering with the workings of the cortex. On the mental level, the effect is a blessed release from anxiety and self-regarding emotivity.

In my fable the savage expresses his belief that the advantages of Soma must be paid for by losses on the highest human levels. Perhaps he was right. The universe is not in the habit of giving us something for nothing. And yet there is a great deal to be said for a pill which enables us to assume an attitude towards circumstances of detachment, ataraxia, 'holy indifference'. The moral worth of an action cannot be measured exclusively in terms of intention. Hell is paved with good intentions, and we have to take some account of results. Rational and kindly behaviour tends to produce good results, and these results remain good even when the behaviour which produced them was itself produced by a pill. On the other hand, can we with impunity replace systematic self-discipline by a chemical? It remains to be seen.

Of all the consciousness-transforming drugs the most interesting, if not the most immediately useful, are those which, like lysergic acid and mescalin, open the door to what may be called the Other World of the mind. Many workers are already exploring the effects of these drugs, and we may be sure that other mind-transformers, with even more remarkable properties, will be produced in the near future. What man will ultimately do with these extraordinary elixirs, it is impossible to say. My own guess is that they are destined to play a part in human life at least as great as the part played up till now by alcohol, and incomparably more beneficent.

JOHN STEINBECK

The Case of Arthur Miller

John Steinbeck was one of the earliest contributors to *Esquire* and several of his most famous stories, later collected in *The Long Valley*, first appeared in *Esquire*: 'The Lonesome Vigilante' (October 1936); 'The Ears of Johnny Bear' (September 1937); and 'A Snake of One's Own' (February 1938).

When Arthur Miller's case for contempt of Congress was coming up for a final hearing in the spring of 1957, *Esquire's* editors, seeking someone to comment on the case for them, turned to Steinbeck. After asking his friend Miller whether such a piece would help him or embarrass him, Steinbeck agreed to the assignment and wrote this personal essay, almost as an editorial, which the magazine published in the issue of June 1957.

THE TRIAL of Arthur Miller for contempt of Congress brings close to all of us one of the strangest and most frightening dilemmas that a people and a government has ever faced. It is not the first trial of its kind, nor will it in all probability be the last. But Arthur Miller is a writer—one of our very best. What has happened to him could happen to any writer; could happen to me. We are face to face with a problem by no means easy of solution. 'Is a puzzlement!'

No man knows what he might do in a given situation, and surely many men must wonder how they would act if they were in Arthur Miller's shoes. I wonder what I would do.

Let me suppose that I were going to trial for contempt of Congress as he is. I might be thinking somewhat as follows:

There is no doubt that Congress has the right, under the law, to ask me any question it wishes and to punish my refusal to answer with a contempt charge. The Congress has the right to do nearly anything conceivable. It has only to define a situation or an action as a 'clear and present danger' to public safety, public morals, or public health. The selling or eating of mince pie could be made a crime if Congress determined that mince pie was a danger to public health—which it probably is. Since many parents raise their children badly, mother love could be defined as a danger to the general welfare.

Surely, Congress has this right to ask me anything on any subject. The question is: Should the Congress take advantage of that right?

Let us say that the Congressional Committee feels that the Communist Party and many groups which have been linked with it— sometimes arbitrarily—constitute a clear and present danger to the nation. Now actually it is neither virtue nor good judgment on my part that has kept me from joining things. I am simply not a joiner by nature. Outside of the Boy Scouts and the Episcopal choir, I have never had an impulse to belong to things. But suppose I had. And suppose I have admitted my association with one or more of these groups posted as dangerous. As a writer, I must have been interested in everything, have felt it part of my profession to know and understand all kinds of people and groups. Having admitted these associations, I am now asked by the Committee to name individuals I have seen at meetings of such groups. I hope my reasoning then would go as follows:

The people I knew were not and are not, in my estimation, traitors to the nation. If they were, I would turn them in instantly. If I give names, it is reasonably certain that the persons named will be called up and questioned. In some cases they will lose their jobs, and in any case their reputations and standing in the community will suffer. And remember that these are persons who I honestly believe are innocent of any wrongdoing. Perhaps I do not feel that I have that right; that to name them would not only be disloyal but actually immoral. The Committee then is asking me to commit an immorality in the name of public virtue.

If I agree, I have outraged one of our basic codes of conduct, and if I refuse I am guilty of contempt of Congress, sentenced to prison and fined. One way outrages my sense of decency and the other brands me as a felon. And this brand does not fade out.

Now suppose I have children, a little property, a stake in the community. The threat of the contempt charge jeopardises everything I love. Suppose, from worry or cowardice, I agree to what is asked. My deep and wounding shame will be with me always.

I cannot be reassured by the past performance of the Committee. I have read daily for a number of years the testimony of admitted liars and perjurers whose charges have been used to destroy the peace and happiness of people I do not know, and many of whom were destroyed without being tried.

Which path am I to choose? Either way I am caught. It may occur to me that a man who is disloyal to his friends could not be expected to be loyal to his country. You can't slice up morals. Our virtues begin at home. They do not change in a court-room unless the pressure of fear is put upon us.

But if I am caught between two horrors, so is the Congress caught. Law, to survive, must be moral. To force personal immorality on a man, to wound his private virtue, undermines his public virtue. If the Committee frightens me enough, it is even possible that I may make up things to satisfy the questioners. This has been known to happen. A law which is immoral does not survive and a government which condones or fosters immorality is truly in clear and present danger.

The Congress had a perfect right to pass the Alien and Sedition Act. This law was repealed because of public revulsion. The Escaped Slave laws had to be removed because the people of free states found them immoral. The Prohibition laws were so generally flouted that all law suffered as a consequence.

We have seen and been revolted by the Soviet Union's encouragement of spying and telling, children reporting their parents, wives informing on their husbands. In Hitler's Germany it was considered patriotic to report your friends and relations to the authorities. and we in America have felt safe from and superior to these things. But are we so safe or superior?

The men in Congress must be conscious of their terrible choice. Their legal right is clearly established, but should they not think of their moral responsibility also? In their attempts to save the nation from attack, they could well undermine the deep personal morality which is the nation's final defence. The Congress is truly on trial along with Arthur Miller.

Again let me change places with Arthur Miller. I have refused to name people. I am indicted, convicted, sent to prison. If the charge were murder or theft or extortion I would be subject to punishment, because I and all men know that these things are wrong. But if I am imprisoned for something I have been taught from birth is a good thing, then I go to jail with a deep sense of injustice and the rings of that injustice are bound to spread out like an infection. If I am brave enough to suffer for my principle, rather than to save myself by hurting other people I believe to be innocent, it seems to me that the law suffers more than I, and that contempt of the law and of the Congress is a real contempt rather than a legalistic one.

Under the law, Arthur Miller is guilty. But he seems also to be brave. Congress feels that it must press the charge against him, to keep its prerogative alive. But can we not hope that our representatives will inspect their dilemma? Respect for law can be kept high only if the law is respectable. There is a clear and present danger here, not to Arthur Miller, but to our changing and evolving way of life.

If I were in Arthur Miller's shoes, I do not know what I would do, but I could wish, for myself and for my children, that I would be brave enough to fortify and defend my private morality as he has. I feel profoundly that our country is better served by individual courage and morals than by the safe and public patriotism which Dr. Johnson called "the last refuge of scoundrels".

My father was a great man, as any lucky man's father must be. He taught me rules I do not think are abrogated by our nervous and hysterical times. These laws have not been annulled; these rules of attitudes. He taught me—glory to God, honour to my family, loyalty to my friends, respect for the law, love of country and instant and open revolt against tyranny, whether it come from the bully in the schoolyard, the foreign dictator, or the local demagogue.

And if this be treason, gentlemen, make the most of it.

RICHARD H. ROVERE

The Question of Ezra Pound

In the spring of 1957 one of *Esquire's* editors cast about for someone to do a piece on 'the question' of Ezra Pound and the rights and wrongs of his incarceration in St. Elizabeth's Hospital, near Washington. He decided on Richard Rovere, author of a regular 'Letter from Washington' for *The New Yorker*, of various articles for *Harper's* and the *Atlantic*, and of the book *The Eisenhower Years* (1956).

Rovere's article appeared in *Esquire* for September 1957 and evoked such a response that a special AFTERMATH section of the Sound and Fury letters to the editor department was established to group the letters separately. In December 1957, January 1958, and February 1958, letters were published from John Dos Passos, Van Wyck Brooks, Marianne Moore, Osbert Sitwell, Joseph Frank, Howard Nemerov, Richard Wilbur, Wallace Fowlie, Mark Schorer, Warren Bower, Norman Mailer, Kenneth Rexroth, Robert Graves, Patrick Murphy Malin, Babette Deutsch, J. V. Cunningham, Andrew Lytle, William Carlos Williams, Robert L. Allen, Richard Chase, T. D. Horton, and Selden Rodman.

In the spring of 1958 Pound was released from St. Elizabeth's. Richard Rovere's article was of great use in the preparation of the case for his release.

IT WOULD BE HARD to name a living man who embodies more polarities of mind, temperament, and function than Ezra Pound, the poet, scholar, and sometime reformer who has spent the last twelve of his seventy-two years confined, as certifiably insane, in St. Elizabeth's Hospital, the huge asylum maintained by the federal government on a rise of land in the south-east corner of Washington.

This inmate is one of the great champions and liberators of the modern spirit; he is also a crackpot poisoner of the well of opinion— a political crank who has proceeded from funny-money theories to a full-blown chauvinsim. This xenophobe Pound is one of the truly cosmopolitan figures of the century—as the pre-eminent translator of his time, he has been a heroic builder of bridges to other civilisations; there is, however, a chamber of his poet's soul in which a yahoo dwells—a buckwheat oaf sounding off like a Kleagle of the Klavern or a New York street-brawler back in the days of the Christian Front. This cosmopolitan Pound is a true patriot—he has a love for the United States that is genuine and affecting and that has had a great deal to do with the making of American culture over the last fifty years; yet he has been, since 26th November 1945, under indictment for nineteen separate counts of treason—the charge growing out of the uncontested fact that he made propaganda broadcasts for the fascist enemy from the enemy's camp in wartime.

In Ezra Pound's extraordinary person, the antipodal qualities clang and clatter, the denial crowds the affirmation, antithesis is always on the heels of thesis. Throughout his life he has esteemed the Confucian ideal of order, and much of his work reflects it; yet his life and his work, taken as a whole, are sheer chaos—though sometimes a glorious chaos, as in what William Butler Yeats called the "stammering confusion" of the *Cantos*, the most imposing of all his work. This great man has stood at once for love and for hate, for friendship and for misanthropy, for reason and for befuddlement, for unexampled purity and for pure muck, for luminous spirits like Yeats and Robert Frost and for deranged ones like Benito Mussolini and for fanatics like John Kasper, the muddled youth who recently was denied appeal of a one-year sentence for contempt of court committed in the aftermath of his efforts, undertaken a year or so ago—largely, he says, at Ezra Pound's encouragement—to stir the lily-white animals to riot and bloodshed in defence of segregation in the South.

In the world as Pound, in his better moments, wants it, first things would be first, and the first thing about him is that he is a great poet. It is by no means certain, though, that he or we can have it that way. The object of public interest today, of syndicated newspaper articles and comment in the mass-circulation magazines, is Pound the crazy writer who appears in relationship to the White Citizens Councils and the general revival of Kluxery to be somewhat as Lenin was to the Bolsheviks before 1917. The comparison is, of course, absurd, and probably the connection between Pound and Kasper is not everything that young Mr. Kasper, hungering for a god and perhaps for a father, claims it to be. The White Citizens Councils should not be hung around Pound's neck simply on John Kasper's say-so. The records of St. Elizabeth's Hospital reveal no more than a half-dozen visits by Kasper to Pound, and though there may have been more, no number of visits would constitute acceptable evidence of Pound's direct responsibility. The shrine is not to be blamed for everything the pilgrim does and is. There is bigotry in Ezra Pound, and that is bad enough, but in justice it has to be acknowledged that he has never been known to address himself to the question of public-school integration. Still, the world does have a way, sometimes, of putting last, or secondary, things first, and to the world at the moment Pound *is* the inmate, the mental patient, the crazy writer who once committed treason or something and who now appears to be tied up with Kasper, the race agitator.

The world's way is to be noted, but not in all cases, and certainly not in such cases as this, followed. The main thing about Ezra Pound is that he is a poet of towering gifts and attainments. Poetry is not a horse-race or any other sort of competition, and it is silly to argue over which poet runs the fastest, jumps the highest, or dives the deepest. Still, a respectable case could be made out to the effect that the century has produced no talent larger or more fecund than Pound's. Certainly the fit comparisons would be with no more than half a dozen other men who write in English. These, as the literary Establishment sees the matter today, would be T. S. Eliot, Yeats, Frost (some dissent here, probably), W. H. Auden, and Dylan Thomas; later on, some of these names may be removed and replaced by some from the second rank, such as Wallace Stevens, Robert Graves, Walter de la Mare, Marianne Moore, William Carlos Williams, E. E. Cummings, and Robert Lowell.

Pound's position is secure, not only because of the power of his own work but because of his service as a midwife to genius and as an influence on other poets. Not long ago, the government which detains Pound in St. Elizabeth's circulated abroad, as part of its effort to persuade the world that we Americans really care about the finer things, a flossy periodical in which it was asserted that Ezra Pound "has done more to serve the cause of English poetry than anyone else alive". (The article, by Hayden Carruth, a gifted critic, also said, "It is hard to think of a good reason why Pound should not have his freedom immediately.") The statement on his service is broad but difficult to gainsay. Of the poets of comparable stature, at least half have at one time or another been Pound's disciples; others were greatly aided by him. The best known and most influential poem of our time, Eliot's *The Waste Land*, took the shape in which the world knows it under his expert hand. Eliot submitted it to Pound at many stages, and in its penultimate stage it was, according to Eliot, "a sprawling, chaotic poem . . . which left Pound's hands, reduced to about half its size, in the form in which it appears in print". The dedication of *The Waste Land* reads, "For Ezra Pound—*il miglior fabbro*". Pound deeply influenced Yeats in the later phases of Yeats' career. But for Pound, the recognition of Robert Frost would have come more belatedly than it did. It was Pound who first got Frost published in the United States and Pound also who found a London publisher for James Joyce. Amy Lowell, E. E. Cummings, and William Carlos Williams sat, often in extreme discomfort, at his feet. W. H. Auden is of a later generation, but he has asserted that "there are few living poets . . . who could say, 'My work would be exactly the same if Mr. Pound had never lived.' "

And all of this influencing and literary politicking in addition to his own work: it is now just short of fifty years since the publication of his first book, *A Lume Spento*, and the flame is still bright and hot. He began with a rage to "purify the language of the tribe" and to make that purified language part of the stuff of life itself. Poetry was to *be* existence, not *about* existence. "Poetry is . . . as much 'criticism of life' as red-hot iron is a criticism of fire." The age, he said, in one of his most famous poems:

> . . . *demanded an image*
> *Of its accelerated grimace,*
> *Something for the modern stage,*
> *Not, at any rate, an Attic grace;*

> *Not, not certainly, the obscure reveries*
> *Of the inward gaze;*
> *Better mendacities*
> *Than the classics in paraphrase!*
>   . . .
> *A prose kinema, not, not assuredly, alabaster*
> *Or the 'sculpture' of rhyme.*

He provided for the age what he thought it demanded—volume upon volume of poetry, some of incomparable loveliness, some of un-excelled ugliness, and much besides. And he still does. In these last few melancholy years many magical and magnificent things have gone out to the world from his bedlam in Washington. He has pressed forward with his *Cantos*, with his criticism, and with his indefatigable labours of translation, the latest fruit of which is a stunning version of Sophocles' *Trachiniæ*. If the New York *Herald Tribune* now sees his wretched quarters in Anacostia as the place where young men like John Kasper are corrupted, others may some day compare them with the cells in which Cervantes wrote *Don Quixote* or Bunyan *Pilgrim's Progress*.

But Pound is alive and controversial in our world and much too thorny a subject to be dealt with only in terms of his major work. His madness, if it exists, will not be exorcised by his verses—any more than his verses can be hidden under his madness. Poetry, one can begin by saying, is, among other things, an act of the controlled intelligence. This is particularly true in the case of Pound, who has never failed to demand of himself and of his work cool, hard, purposeful thought, and who has, additionally, an analytical mind of immense power. However, a controlled and discriminating intelligence is not a sure defence against insanity. Both madness and genius can be spasmodic or simultaneous in a compartmented being like Pound.

The question of whether Pound is insane by any acceptable legal or psychiatric definition is a vexed one. Reputable authorities dis-agree. Four psychiatrists, one of them appointed by Pound's counsel, filed a unanimous report which led to his commitment to St. Elizabeth's, sparing the defendant and the country the pain of a trial for a capital offence. But some doctors have maintained that

Pound is quite a long way from being insane by the standards that court examiners are compelled to use and that justice was jobbed when Pound went to the hospital rather than to the gallows. From the layman's point of view, the matter is a good deal simpler. Whether Pound meets the legal and institutional tests for a criminally inculpable and confinable psychotic—and it seems highly doubtful that he does—he is a pathological personality who has, by the reasonable standards of most reasonable men, lost contact with reality at many crucial points. In the vernacular, he is off his rocker —or if he isn't, the rest of us are off ours. The paranoid's delusions, his morbid suspicions, his view of life as a conspiracy, are all apparent, even in the fine poetry which more and more over the last twenty-five years has dealt with Pound's political and economic obsessions. In Pound, those suspicions and delusions are evidence of mania. For a village eccentric to assert that Franklin Roosevelt was a tool of international Jewry, that we got into the Second World War because of a crooked financial deal pulled off by Roosevelt and Henry Morgenthau, that all world history would be changed if Martin Van Buren's autobiography had been published a few years sooner than it was—all this would not be conclusive proof of insanity. Such beliefs may merely show misguidance. But it is quite another thing for a man of Pound's cultivation to believe them and to make them the stuff of his poetry.

Since the onset of the great Depression, Pound has been making silk purses from sow's ears. His major theme—as distinct from the secondary and supporting themes involving Roosevelt and Morgenthau and Van Buren—has been that mankind's troubles, all of them, are traceable to the hiring out of money at interest ("the beast with a hundred legs, USURA") by commercial lenders ("every bank of discount is downright corruption/every bank of discount is downright iniquity") and that life on earth would be sweet and noble and æsthetically rich if we had the wisdom to adopt the fiscal reforms advocated by Silvio Gesell, Major C. H. Douglas, and other hopeful currency tinkerers. These are his political convictions as well as the meat of his poetry, and since when, asks Dr. Frederic Wertham, one of the dissenting psychiatrists, has a political conviction, however aberrant, been regarded as proof of paranoia? The answer the layman can give, without attempting to satisfy either psychiatry or law, is that a political conviction is lunatic when it leads a man to tell a friend, as Pound once told William Carlos Williams, that at a given moment he preferred the sanctuary of St. Elizabeth's to the world beyond its Nichols Avenue gates, where he believed he would be shot by agents of the "international crew".

The obsessions make him see the surface of life in a world that endures usury as "infinite pus flakes, scabs of a lasting pox", and the flux of life in this motion:

> as the earth moves, the centre
> passes over all parts in succession
> a continual bum-belch
> distributing its production.

Still, the purses are silk beyond all cavil or dispute:

> The ant's a centaur in his dragon world.
> Pull down thy vanity, it is not man
> Made courage or made order, or made grace.
> Pull down thy vanity, I say pull down.
> Learn of the green world what can be thy place
> In scaled invention or true artistry.
> Pull down thy vanity,
> Paquin pull down!
> The green casque has outdone your elegance.

It is characteristic of the great egotists to have little traffic with their own years of innocence and learning. When they deal with the period at all, they are likely to follow the example of Rousseau and foreshorten and revise experience in such a way as to make worldliness follow directly upon infancy. Pound is of the classic breed—though not, as it happens, in any other way a brother to Rousseau. One cannot accuse him of selfishness or of excessive self-portraiture; his ego has asserted itself massively, in cocksureness, in literary and political arrogance, in conceits of dress such as red velvet robes and conceits of leadership such as walking one pace ahead of his followers in every procession, and, in these later years, in his paranoid delusions about the malign sources of the world's resistance to his

I

remedies. This kind of self-concern has led him to consider himself
and his life at great length, to record his own comings and goings, to
preserve the least of his *obiter dicta*, and to reflect in hundreds of
thousands of words on the meaning of his own strange journey.

Yet the shaping years are nowhere dealt with. In every autobiographical statement the infant born in Hailey, Idaho, in 1885,
the son of Homer and Isabel Weston Pound, becomes in a sentence
or two a central figure in American letters. Idaho could have influenced him not at all, for in 1887 the family moved to Wyncotte,
Pennsylvania, and Pound's father took up his duties as assayer of the
United States Mint at Philadelphia. It is clear from a handful of
letters to his parents, published a few years ago in his collected
correspondence, that they were bookish, serious-minded people. His
mother, who was somehow related to Henry Wadsworth Longfellow,
was a musician of sorts, and his father had a lively and informed
interest in contemporary literature. Does the fact that Pound's
father had a professional concern with the value of currency explain
Pound's obsession to any degree? This has been rumoured, but
Pound himself has cast no light upon it. All that is really known of
him in the early years is that he survived.

He was a gifted child and entered the University of Pennsylvania
at fifteen. From this point on, he is not reticent in dealing with
experience, but neither, one suspects, is he particularly reliable. He
paints himself as an enormously learned young man, which he no
doubt was, and as an enormously sophisticated one, which he
evidently was not. He did not enroll as a regular undergraduate at
Pennsylvania. He wanted no truck with most of what they had to
teach, so he was a 'special student', working mostly in languages.
He claims to have had contempt for most of his teachers and for most
of his fellow students. Yet there are contemporaries who remember
him as a boy, gangling and shy and humiliated by his life under a
carpet of bright red hair, who was terribly eager for acceptance and
who, indeed, was so eager to be pledged to a fraternity that, when he
was finally rebuffed, he transferred to Hamilton College. The story
may be untrue; it all happened in another world anyway, and
memories are not all they might be. But the quality of memories
counts. William Carlos Williams, a medical student at Pennsylvania
at the time, has the recollection that when Pound thought the

moment had at last arrived to try his luck at picking up a girl, he implored Williams to come along for protection.

At all odds, Pound did transfer to Hamilton, where he took prescribed courses and in 1905 was awarded a degree. After Hamilton, he went back to Pennsylvania and got a master's degree. (It is curious that in a one-page autobiography prepared for his *Selected Poems* in 1949, Pound, while skipping over some of the principal episodes in his life, should have listed three academic degrees, two earned, from Hamilton and Pennsylvania, and an honorary Litt. D. from Hamilton in 1939. Before 1939 he had been writing of American universities as nothing but fancy beaneries. In April, 1929, he advised the Alumni Secretary of the University of Pennsylvania that "All the U. of P. or your god damn college or any other god damn American college does or will do for a man of letters is to ask him to go away without breaking the silence." It was a different story when Hamilton asked the man of letters to accept its recognition. Among his many dualities are a contempt for authority and an almost sickening respect for it. When he lived in Italy, he had embossed on his stationery a gamy platitude from Mussolini—'Liberty is not a right but a duty'.) In those student years he wrote some of the poems that were to appear in his first book in 1908. It would be interesting, at least from the viewpoint of the gossip that lurks in each of us, to know how close he was to the trembling adolescent recalled by Williams and how far from this, which is from the period:

> For I was a gaunt, grave councillor,
> Being in all things wise, and very old,
> But I have put aside this folly and the cold
> That old age weareth for a cloak.
> . . .
> I was quite strong—at least they said so—
> The young men at the sword-play. . . .

Pound had tried out for the fencing team at Pennsylvania.

Poems are born of hopes and imaginings, and so long as Pound had these within him, as he did in wild abundance, it should matter little to anyone—save those in a position to offer therapy—what else he was in that far-away time. After Philadelphia, he travelled abroad for a year, in Italy, Spain, and Provence, and then accepted an instructorship at Wabash College, in Indiana. Within a few months of his appointment, he was asked to resign, which he did. His story is that he had invited to his lodgings a penniless girl, stranded from a burlesque show, whom he had found on the streets of town while going out in a raging blizzard to mail a letter. He claimed that he had been stirred by nothing more than an impulse to hospitality, and in the centennial history of the college the authorities, eager to reclaim a genius, explained that the girl slept chastely in Pound's bed and Pound on the floor. It sounds plausible, but it scarcely matters. Pound's landlady discovered her. The college providentially booted him, and he returned to Europe, there to remain, except when he returned for his honorary Litt. D., until he was flown to Washington as a prisoner under armed guard on 18th November 1945.

"London, deah old Lundon, is the place for poesy"—thus Pound, to a stay-at-home friend on 3rd February 1909. London was the place for Pound—or at any rate, *a* place. It is difficult to believe that his awesome energies were greatly dependent on environment. At all odds, he pursued poesy; he gave it chase like a Nimrod being shot at from the rear. It is doubtful if any other American writer ever knew a period as fertile as the decade that followed Pound's move to London. He produced his finest half-dozen volumes of poetry, quite enough to sustain his reputation. ("Thirty pages are enough for any of us to leave," he once wrote. "There is scarce more of Catullus or Villon." There are perhaps a thousand pages of Pound's own poetry, with more coming all the time.) He translated: from medieval French, from Latin, from Greek, and from Chinese and Japanese, which he could not read but which he nevertheless rendered from the literal translations of Ernest Franciso Fenollosa, an American Orientalist who had taught philosophy at the Imperial Normal School in Tokyo and who made Pound his executor. He was the European editor of *Poetry*, the Chicago magazine which Harriet Monroe, a noble dilettante lady, offered this philistine republic as "a place of refuge, a green isle in the sea, where Beauty may plant her gardens." He dug up Frost and Eliot for the magazine; he pestered established British writers for manuscripts. He got Wyndham Lewis, John Masefield, Ford Madox Ford, Rabindranath Tagore. He and

Amy Lowell put their heads together, a consummation blessed by T. E. Hulme, a British philosopher with poetic leanings, and produced Imagism, a school. The doctrine was that poetic images should not be adornments but the guts of the work itself. The language, in Hulme's words, was to be "cheerful, dry and sophisticated," or, in Pound's single word, "perfect". "It stands," he said, amplifying, "for hard, clear edges." And the best of it did have hard, clear edges; sometimes, though, the quest for perfection was destructive; the individual poem was lightened and hardened to the point where it was fleshless and boneless. Once Pound had the thought of describing some faces he had looked upon in the Paris Metro. He wrote a poem of thirty lines. It seemed rather fatty to him, so he put it aside, while he awaited further light on the problem. After a time, he went over it and cut it to fifteen lines. Still imperfect. He put it away again for a year or so, and then did some drastic surgery, so that the poem, called *In a Station of the Metro*, now reads, in its entirety:

> *The apparition of these faces in the crowd:*
> *Petals on a wet, black bough.*

There were such miscarriages. But more often there was success. Pound soon abandoned the school in favour of one he called Vorticism, which he proclaimed as vastly superior. He was alone in grasping the distinction; if there was one, it did not show in his work, in which he continued to make breathtaking approaches to perfection.

"Dear Miss Lowell," Pound wrote in November 1913, "I agree with you . . . that 'Harriet' is a bloody fool. Also I've resigned from *Poetry* in Hueffer's [Ford Madox Ford's] favor, but I believe he has resigned in mine. . . ." It was this sort of thing down through the years, Imagism to Vorticism and on along to Social Credit and Gesellism, thence to fascism. And from *Poetry* to *BLAST*, the official Vorticist organ, which had no bang at all and petered out in two issues, and back to *Poetry* and on to *The Egoist* and *The Little Review*. In between and amongst these, there were side enthusiasms—the music of George Antheil and Arnold Dolmetsch, the sculpture of Henri Gaudier-Brzeska. Pound learned to play the bassoon and for a time fancied himself a composer. He was everlastingly transient. It was not for long that London was good for poesy. By 1913, England was "this stupid little island . . . dead as mutton". After the war he moved to Paris—accompanied by the wife he had acquired in London, Dorothy Shakespear, who lives today in the wastes of south-east Washington and never misses a visiting period at St. Elizabeth's. And a few years after that to Rapallo, on the Italian Riviera.

"One has to keep going East," he told Mary Colum, "to keep one's mind alive." Any direction would have done, for it was really a matter of the restlessness of the literary plotter and organiser of movements. As Robert Graves saw it, "Slowly the frustrated Pound went mad-dog and bit the other dogs of his day; he even fastened his teeth in Yeats' hand, the hand that had fed him." This is too dour a picture of it. Pound was not, at bottom, disloyal. Indeed, even in his present madness he remains fast to many of his oldest friends and his oldest principles. The cream of the ugly jest is that he remains intensely loyal to some of the principles he has been accused of betraying and, in fact, in his fashion did betray. When he insists, as he always does nowadays, that everything he did and was in politics had as its object the "saving of the United States Constitution", he is representing himself as honestly as he can. Even in the zaniest of the *Cantos*, in the crazy, ranting passages about Adams and Jefferson and poor old Van Buren, one has a sense of him as a genuine American reformer, a zealous improver, the perpetual liberal optimist of American letters carrying on in the spirit of 1912. "Any agonising," he wrote in that year, "that tends to hurry what I believe in the end to be inevitable, our American Risorgimento, is dear to me. That awakening will make the Italian Renaissance look like a tempest in a teapot."

If there is any one unbroken strand in Pound's experience, it is the one that begins with this statement and continues on to what is durable in his work today. Of all the contrarieties and polarities in Pound, none is more striking than that of the enemy broadcaster, the partisan of Mussolini, as American patriot. The courts may never be able to see this; it is perhaps proper that they should not. To be betrayed by a daft patriot is not much better than to be betrayed by a sanely calculating Iscariot. Nevertheless, the fact cannot be denied that Pound, as a writer and as a man, has had an immense and touching faith in the culture he appeared to be ready to abandon as a youth. He believed with Whitman that American experience was fit and glorious material for poetry, and what he was at war with when he left this country was the spirit that denied this and tried only for "Attic grace" and the "classics in paraphrase". "Make it new," Pound kept saying, from his colloquial rendering of Confucius, and "Make it American", as if he were a booster of home manufacturers at a trade fair. "Are you for American poetry or for poetry?" he wrote Miss Monroe, when she was setting up her magazine. "The latter is more important, but it is important that America should boost (*sic!*) the former, provided it don't (*sic!*) mean a blindness to the art. The glory of any nation is to produce art that can be exported without disgrace to its origin. . . . The force we have, and the impulse, but the guiding sense, the discrimination in applying the force, we must wait and strive for." He believed, and was to persuade many others to believe, that the American language as well as the American experience was fit for poetry: the speech of our people, the garment of their consciousness, was vigorous and supple and tender enough "to be spoken by the gods".

And this has been the point of his curious and often debated work as a translator: he has made everything new and everything American. Edwin Arlington Robinson, the last poet to work effectively in the tradition Pound rejected and sought to crush, once wrote of how Shakespeare

> . . . *out of his*
> *Miraculous inviolable increase*
> *Fills Ilion, Rome, or any town you like*
> *Of olden time with timeless Englishmen.*

Shakespeare sent his imagination travelling in time and space and was never anything but English to the core. Pound expatriated himself for four decades in Europe and went back over the years to Cathay millennia before Christ—and was never, in any time or place, other than American to the marrow and gristle. He filled Rome and Crete and the France of the troubadours and China and Japan with timeless Americans. This is no defence against treason. Yet it is a fact. In his version of *Trachiniæ*, or *Women of Trachis*, a product of his labours at St. Elizabeth's, he has Hyllos say of Herakles

> *They say he's in Euboea,*
> *besieging Eurytusville*
> *or on the way to it.*

Eurytus*ville*, indeed! It is as if Shakespeare had written *The Merchant of Veniceshire* or *Timon of Athensford*.

One must return, sooner or later, to the denial that always follows hard on the affirmation. It could, of course, be no more than a cheap trick to call Eurytus Eurytusville, whereas it was, for an American, a foul one to broadcast, as Ezra Pound did, on 26th May 1942, when our forces were beleaguered in almost every quarter of the globe, that every rare and occasional decency of the United States Government, "every reform . . . is an act of homage toward Mussolini and Hitler. They are your leaders . . ." Unless our monitors had faulty hearing, that is what the man said. In the nineteen presumably treasonable utterances cited in the indictment, that is the one that, on the face of it, is the clearest and most shameful. More often, the broadcasts were a loony garble—so much so that the Italians for a time thought he was broadcasting secrets in code. But there it stands—"Mussolini and Hitler. They are your leaders".

It is possible to take the psychiatrists' way out and say that by then Pound was a nut not to be held responsible. But the matter will not rest there. Some sort of accommodation must be reached between Pound-the-glorious-American-poet and Pound-the-loony-ideologue. Various possibilities suggest themselves. It has often been argued that there is an affinity between American populism and brutal American reaction. But this will not do for Pound the sweet singer; except for his hatred of bankers and his funny money, he was never fetched by the Populist fallacies. Quite the contrary. "It is the function of the public to prevent the artist's expression, by hook or by crook," he wrote, a few years after his embarkation in England. And, "I know the man who translated *Jean Christophe*, and moreover it's a popular craze, so I suppose there must be something wrong with it." And, "I should like the name 'Imagism' to retain some sort of meaning. . . . I cannot trust any democratized committee to maintain that standard." He was armoured against undue respect for the mass of mankind.

A more promising hypothesis is that he was beguiled—eventually into insanity—by a predilection for conspiracy theories of life and history. The man thus beguiled sees society as a kind of machine in which things are always going wrong. This machine is hurting him. He himself is not part of it. He feels he has no control over its workings, and therefore no responsibility for it. He sees a human comedy and a human tragedy, and he may be deeply moved by the spectacles, but they are *spectacles*—things to be seen, from somewhere offstage. Eventually, if he is clever, he discerns ways of improving the spectacles, removing their flaws. The spectacles resist improvement; the stupid players strike back. ("I've got a right to be severe," the young Pound wrote. "For one man I strike, there are ten to strike back at me. I stand exposed.") Going to work on the problem, the intellectual hunts out a general principle—a theory of society's malfunctioning. Young men who pursued this line of thought thirty years after Pound clutched, for obvious enough historic reasons, at the proposition that the fault lay in the fact that the means of production and distribution were in private hands when in fact, for virtue's sake, they should be in public hands, as in the Soviet Union. Some of them, delighted to have got at the root of the problem, betrayed their heritage as foolishly and in many cases far more effectively than Pound did. And some, too, were driven out of their minds.

It was no doubt always in the cards that Pound would reach for the purely mechanical device—currency reform—for righting social wrongs. Loving America, as in truth plenty of the young Communists did, he saw 'society' as something else altogether—something hateful and machine-like. There were not many social vogues in his day. Marxism was little heard of in the circles in which he moved. Somehow he was reached by the Social Credit people, who promised order in society. Then he came upon Silvio Gesell, an erratic German who had observed that interest rates bore no logical relation to economic expansion. Usurers set rates according to what the traffic would bear. Who were the usurers? The principal ones, obviously, were the great international bankers. From this point Pound made the classic leap to anti-Semitism. Somewhat earlier, he had made the leap to the Corporate State in Italy. Pound clearly liked the grandiosity of it—and he liked the most comical of Mussolini's thrashings about in the name of 'order', or meaningful time-tables; it appeared a genuine effort to take the frustrations out of life, to organise society according to a principle, as Pound was trying to organise poetry according to a principle.

We can never know when the cord at last snapped. Nothing we can find in Pound's poetry or his life prepares us for the excessiveness or the sheer franticness of his social concerns. An infatuation with Mussolini would be understandable; Pound was given to infatuations. But the mind boggles when this great critical spirit is heard claiming for Mussolini the perfection he never found in others and so seldom found even in himself. "The more one examines the Milan speech," he wrote apropos of a run-of-the-mine bit of rhetoric by Mussolini, "the more one is reminded of Brancusi, the stone blocks from which no error emerges, from whatever angle one looks at them." A quotation from *Jefferson and/or Mussolini*, published in 1935.

By then the cord was certainly badly frayed.

In his years in St. Elizabeth's, Pound has steadily maintained that he had no wish to oppose his country during the war. He points out, in lucid moments, that he could have saved himself all his misery by the simple device of accepting Italian citizenship in 1939. He clung to his American passport. It is a matter of record that he tried in 1942 to get aboard the last diplomatic train that took Americans from Rome to Lisbon. He was refused permission to board it. He had no choice but to stay in Rapallo. After a while the Italians asked him to broadcast. He accepted. He has said that "no scripts were prepared for me by anybody, and I spoke only when I wanted to". And he goes on, not at all lucidly, "I was only trying to tell the people of Europe and America how they could avoid war by learning the facts about money". The war was itself then an unavoidable fact, and it was not about money—though it does happen to be true that most of Pound's broadcasts did deal with his currency obsessions. It also happens to be true that he lent himself, on whatever terms, to the enemy. He now forgets the terms: "I'd die for an idea all right, but to die for an idea I've forgotten is too much."

He lived out the war in Rapallo, writing and making his occasional broadcasts, and in November 1945, hearing that units of the American occupation forces were looking for him, he delivered himself to the proper military authorities. They placed him under arrest and kept him in an encampment—or Disciplinary Training Centre—near Pisa. Someone in the Army goofed; the word went out that Pound was violent and also that the Fascists thought so highly of him that armed bands might seek to free him. A special cage was built for him out of the heavy mesh steel used for temporary runways. "They thought I was a dangerous wild man and were scared of me. I had a guard night and day. . . . Soldiers used to come up to the cage and look at me. Some of them brought me food. Old Ez was a prize exhibit." For months he lived caged, sleeping on the ground, shielded from the sun and rain only by some tar paper a kindly G.I. found for him. In the cage he wrote furiously, madly, poignantly. The fruit of the imprisonment was *The Pisan Cantos*, for which a distinguished group of American scholars, appointed by the Librarian of Congress, voted him the Bollingen–Library of Congress Award of one thousand dollars for "the highest achievement of American poetry" in the year they were published, 1948. (The howls that went up after this put an end to the committee and the award.) By 1948 he had transferred his residence to St. Elizabeth's, had suffered out eighteen months in a 'maximum-security' ward, and was enjoying the limited freedom he now has—freedom to roam the asylum grounds as long as he stays in sight of the building in which he lives and freedom to chat with such as Kasper and freedom to write

> *The States have passed thru a*
> *dam'd supercilious era*
> *Down, Derry-down*
> *Oh, let an old-man rest.*

He will very likely die there. There has been a clamour of sorts for his release over the last few years, but nothing ever comes of it. The indictment still stands; there is no statute of limitations on treason. The psychiatrists' opinion that he is incompetent to take part in his own defence still stands. Since he is not dangerous and since he receives no therapy at the hospital, he might be released—still under indictment, still adjudged incompetent to state his own case—in the custody of his wife and his friends, who are numerous and long-suffering. Would this mean encouraging intrigues with the likes of young John Kasper? He is free for these intrigues now, and if they are to be taken seriously—if, that is, anyone is really to believe that Ezra Pound is a force in our political life—his status as martyr and prisoner gives an extra cutting-edge of hate and resentment to him and to his frowsier associates. Actually, there is no reason to believe that he is any sort of a force. He made some broadcasts for the Fascists years ago. They were reprehensible. But, as he asked, "Does anyone have the faintest idea what I said?" No one does, unless he looks it up in the indictment. In the language he might be admiring if his contact with American life was restored, we won the war, and anyway no one ever listened to that crazy jazz. The government, if it wished, could act not on grounds of justice but on grounds of largesse. It has sat by while some pretty low characters have been sprung in Germany, Italy, and Japan—real war criminals, now given positions of trust. The war-criminal side of Pound is as trivial in terms of history as his poetry is great. As Hayden Carruth wrote in *Perspectives USA*, the publication distributed to the intelligentsia abroad in bundle lots, "It is hard to think of a good reason why Pound should not have his freedom immediately."

ARTHUR MILLER

The Misfits

Arthur Miller visited Nevada for some weeks in 1956 and wrote this Western shortly after. Although he had written some earlier short stories (one of them, 'A Regular Death Call', appeared in *Esquire* for August 1949), it is interesting to see him interrupting a busy and successful career as a playwright to return to that form. It is obvious that the subject and situation of 'The Misfits' is not easily adaptable to the spatial limitations of the theatre: the compulsion of the subject matter must have been very great. Less sure, perhaps, of his techniques in a non-dramatic medium, Miller allowed his manuscript to be cut considerably for its appearance in *Esquire* for October 1957. The version which appears here, however, is the original uncut one; the long, essentially dramatic and visual opening sequence and several other passages were omitted in the magazine version.

I

WIND blew down from the mountains all night. A wild river of air swept and swirled across the dark sky and struck down against the blue desert and hissed back into the hills. The three cowboys slept under their blankets, their backs against the first upward curve of the circling mountains, their faces towards the desert of sage. The wind and its tidal washing seethed through their dreams and when it stopped there was a lunar silence that caused Gay Langland to open his eyes. For the first time in three nights he could hear his own breathing and in the new hush he looked up at the stars and saw how clear and bright they were. He felt happy and slid himself out of his blankets and stood up fully dressed.

On the silent plateau between the two mountain ranges Gay

Langland was the only moving thing. He turned his head and then his body in a full circle, looking into the deep blue sky for sign of storm. He saw that it would be a good day and a quiet one. He walked a few yards from the two other sleepers and wet the sandy ground. The excitement of the stillness was awakening his body. He returned and lit the bundle of dry sage he had gathered last night, dropped some heavier wood on the quick flames, perched the blackened coffee pot on the stones surrounding the fire-bed, and sat on one heel staring at the fresh orange embers.

Gay Langland was forty-five years old, but as limber as he had ever been in his life. The light of his face brightened when there were things to do, a nail to straighten, an animal to size-up, and it dimmed when there was nothing in his hands, and his eyes then went sleepy. When there was something to be done in a place he stayed there, and when there was nothing to be done he went from it. He had a wife and two children less than a hundred miles from here whom he had not seen in more than three years. She had betrayed him and did not want him, but the children were naturally better off with their mother. When he felt lonely for them all he thought of them longingly, and when the feeling passed it went unsettled, without leaving him with any question as to what he might do to bring them all back together again. He had been born and raised on rangeland and he did not know that anything could be undone that was done, any more than falling rain could be stopped in mid-air. And he had a smile and a look in his face that was in accordance. His forehead was evenly tracked with deep ridges, as though his brows were always raised a little expectantly, slightly surprised, a little amused, and his mouth friendly. His ears stuck out as they often do with little boys or young calves and he had a boy's turned-up snub nose. But his skin was browned by the wind and his small eyes looked and saw, and above all were trained against showing fear.

Gay Langland looked up from the fire at the sky and saw the first delicate stain of pink. He went over to the sleepers and shook Guido Racanelli's arm. A grunt of salutation sounded in Guido's head but he remained on his side with his eyes shut. "The sumbitch died off," Gay said to him. Guido listened, motionless, his eyes shut against the firelight, his bones warm in his fat. Gay wanted to shake him again and wake him but in the last two days he had come to wonder whether Guido was not secretly considering not flying at all. The plane's engine was rattling its valves and one shock absorber was weak. Gay had known the pilot for years and he knew and respected his moods. Flying up and down these mountain gorges within feet of the rock walls was nothing you could pressure a man to do. But now that the wind had died Gay hoped very much that Guido would take off this morning and let them begin their work. He got to his feet and again glanced skywards. Then he stood there thinking of Roslyn. And he had a strong desire to have money in his pocket that he had earned himself when he came to her tonight. The feeling had been returning again and again that he had somehow passed the kidding point, and that he had to work again and earn his way as he always had before he met her. Not that he didn't work for her, but it wasn't the same. Driving her car, repairing her house, running errands—all that stuff wasn't what you would call work. Still, he thought, it was too. Yet, it wasn't either.

He stepped over to the other sleeper and shook him. Perce Howland opened his eyes.

"The sumbitch died, Perce," Gay said.

Perce's eyes looked towards the heavens and he nodded. Then he slid out of his blankets and walked past Gay and stood wetting the sand, breathing deeply as in sleep. Gay always found him humorous to watch when he woke up. Perce walked into things and sometimes stood wetting his own boots. He was a little like a child waking up, and his eyes now were still dreamy and soft.

Gay called over to him, "Better'n wages, huh, Perce?"

"Damn right," Perce muttered, and returned to the fire rubbing his skin against his clothes.

Gay kneeled by the fire again, scraping hot coals into a pile and setting the frying-pan over them on stones. He could pick up hot things without feeling pain. Now he moved an ember with his finger.

"You make me nervous doing that," Perce said, looking down over his shoulder.

"Nothin' but fire," Gay said, pleased.

They were in silence for a moment, both of them enjoying the brightening air. "Guido goin' up?" Perce asked.

"Didn't say. I guess he's thinkin' about it."

"Be light pretty soon," Perce warned.

He glanced off to the closest range, and saw the purple rocks rising in their mystery toward the faintly glowing stars. Perce Howland was twenty-two, hipless and tall, and he stood there as effortlessly as the mountains he was looking at, as though he had been created there in his dungarees, with the tight plaid shirt and the three-button cuffs, the broad-brimmed beige hat set back on his blonde head, and his thumbs tucked into his belt so his fingers could touch the engraved belt buckle with his name spelled out under the raised figure of the bucking horse. It was his first bucking horse prize and he loved to touch it when he stood waiting, and he liked to wait.

Perce had only known Gay Langland for five weeks, and Guido for three days. He had met Gay in a Bowie bar, and Gay had asked him where he was from and what he was doing and he had told Gay his story, which was the usual for most of the rodeo riders. He had come on down from Nevada, as he had done since he was sixteen, to follow the local rodeos and win some money riding bucking horses, but this trip had been different, because he had lost the desire to go back home again.

They had become good friends that night when Gay took him to Roslyn's house to sleep, and when he woke in the morning he had been surprised that an educated Eastern woman should have been so regular and humorous and interested in his opinions. So he had been floating around with Roslyn and Gay Langland, and they were comfortable to him. Gay mostly, because Gay never thought to say he ought to be making something of his life. Gay made him feel it was all right to go from day to day and week to week. Perce Howland did not trust anybody too far and it was not necessary to trust Gay because Gay did not want anything of him or try to manipulate him. He just wanted a partner to go mustanging, and Perce had never done anything like that and he wanted to see how it was. And now he was here, sixty miles from the nearest town, seven thousand feet up in the air, and for two days waiting for the wind to die so the pilot could take off into the mountains where the wild horses lived.

Perce looked out toward the desert, which was beginning to show its silent horizon. "Bet the moon looks like this if anybody could get there."

Gay Langland did not answer. In his mind he could feel the wild horses grazing and moving about in the near-by mountains and he wanted to get to them. Indicating Guido Racanelli, he said, "Give him a shake, Perce. The sun's about up."

Perce started over to Guido, who moved before Perce reached him. "Gettin' light, Guido," Perce said.

Guido Racanelli rolled upright on his great behind, his belly slung over his belt, and he inspected the brightening sky in the distance as though some personal message were out there for him. The pink reflected light brightened his face. The flesh around his eyes was white where the goggles protected his face, and the rest of his skin was burned brown by wind. His silences were more profound than the silences of others because his cheeks were so deep, like the melon-half cheeks of a baboon which curve forward from the mouth. Yet they were hard cheeks, as hard as his great belly. He looked like a jungle bird now, slowly turning his head to inspect the far-away sky, a serious bird with a brown face and white eyes. His head was entirely bald. He took off his khaki army cap and rubbed his fingers into his scalp.

Gay Langland stood up and walked to him and gave him his eggs and thick bacon on a tin plate. "Wind died, Guido," Gay said, standing there and looking down at the pilot.

"It doesn't mean much what it did down here." Guido pointed skyward with his thumb. "Up there's where it counts."

"Ain't no sign of wind up there," Gay said. Gay's eyes seemed amused. He did not want to seem committed to a real argument. "We got no more eggs, Guido," he warned.

Guido ate.

Now the sky flared with true dawn like damp paper suddenly catching fire. Perce and Gay sat down on the ground facing Guido and they all ate their eggs.

The shroud of darkness quickly slipped off the red truck which stood a few yards away. Then, behind it, the little plane showed itself. Guido Racanelli ate and sipped his coffee, and Gay Langland watched him with a weak smile and without speaking. Perce blinked contentedly at the brightening sky, slightly detached from the other two. He finished his coffee and slipped a chew of tobacco into his mouth and sucked on it.

It was a pink day now all around the sky.

Gay Langland made a line in the sand between his thighs and said, "You goin' up, Guido?" He looked at Guido directly and he was still smiling.

Guido thought for a moment. He was older, about fifty. His pronunciation was unaccountably Eastern, with sharp R's. He sounded educated sometimes. He stared off towards the squat little plane. "Every once in a while I wonder what the hell it's all about," he said.

"What is?" Gay asked.

Perce watched Guido's face, thoroughly listening.

Guido felt their attention and spoke with ease and comfort. He still stared past them at the plane. "I got a lousy valve. I know it, Gay."

"Been that way a long time, Guido," Gay said, with sympathy.

"I know," Guido said. They were not arguing but searching now. "And we won't hardly get twenty dollars a piece out of it—there's only four or five horses back in there."

"We knew that, Guido," Gay said. They were in sympathy for one another.

"I might just get myself killed, for twenty dollars."

"Hell, you know them mountains," Gay said.

"You can't see wind, Gay," the pilot said. (Gay knew now that he was going up right away. He saw that Guido had just wanted to get all the dangers straight in his mind so he could see them and count them; then he would go out against them.) "You're flying along in and out of those passes and then you dive for the sons of bitches and just when you're pulling up some goddam gust presses you down and there you are."

"I know," Gay said.

There was silence. Guido sipped his coffee, staring off at the plane. "I just wonder about it every once in a while," the pilot said.

"Well, hell," Perce Howland said, "it's better than wages."

"You damn right it is, Perce," the pilot said thoughtfully.

"I seen guys get killed who never left the ground," Perce said. The two older men knew that his father had been killed by a bull long ago and that he had seen his father die. He had had his own arms broken in rodeos and a Brahma bull had stepped on his chest. "One rodeo near Salinas I see a fella get his head snapped right clear off his chest by a cable busted. They had this cable drawin' horses up on to a truck. I seen his head rolling away like a bowlin' ball. Must've roll twenty-five yards before it hit a fence post and stopped." He spat tobacco juice and turned back to look at Guido. "It had a moustache. Funny thing, I never knowed that guy had a moustache. Never noticed it. Till I see it stop rolling and there it was, dust all over the moustache."

"That was a dusty moustache," Gay said, grinning. They all smiled. Then time hung for a moment as they waited. And at last Guido shifted on to one buttock and said, "Well, let's get gassed up."

Guido leaned himself to one side with his palm on the ground, then got to his feet by moving in a circle around this palm, and stood up. Gay and Perce Howland were already moving off toward the truck, Perce histing up his dungarees over his breakfast-full stomach, and the older Gay more sprightly and intent. Guido stood holding one hand open over the fire, watching them loading the six enormous truck tyres on to the bed of the truck. Each tyre had a twenty-foot length of rope wired to it, and at the end of each rope was a loop. Before they swung the tyres on to the truck, Gay inspected the ropes to be sure they were securely knotted to the tyres, and the loops open and ready for throwing.

Guido blinked against the warming sun, watching the other two, then he looked off to his right where the passes were, and the fingers of his mind felt around beyond those passes into the bowls and hollows of the mountains where last week he had spotted the small herd of wild horses grazing. Now he felt the lightness he had been hoping to feel for three days, the good sense of wanting to fly. For three days he had kept away from the plane because the careless feeling had been itching at him, the feeling which he always thought would lead him to his death. About five weeks ago he had come up to this desert with Gay Langland and he had chased seven mustangs out of the mountains. But that time he had dived to within a foot of the mountain side, and afterwards, as they sat around the fire eating dinner, Guido had had the feeling that he had made that deep dive so he could die. And the thought of his dead wife had come to him again, and the other thought that always came into his mind with her dead face. It was the wonderment, the quiet pressing-in of the awareness that he had never wanted a woman after she had been

buried with the still-born baby beside her in the graveyard outside
Bowie. Seven years now he had waited for some real yearning for
woman, and nothing at all had come to him. It pleasured him to
know that he was free of that, and it sometimes made him careless in
the plane, as though some great bang and a wreckage would make
him again what he had been. By now he could go a week through
Bowie and in an odd moment recall that he hadn't even looked at a
girl walking by, and the feeling of carelessness would come on him, a
kind of loose gaiety, as though everything was comical. Until he had
made that dive and pulled out with his nose almost scraping the
grass, and he had climbed upward with his mouth hanging open and
his body in a sweat. So that through these past three days up here he
had refused to let himself take off until the wind had utterly died,
and he had clung to moroseness. He wanted to take off in the
absolute grip of his own wits, leaving nothing to chance, and now
there was no wind at all, and he felt he had pressed the lightness and
the gaiety out of his mind. He left the dying fire and walked past
Gay and Perce and down the gentle slope to the plane looking like a
stout, serious football coach before the kick-off.

He glanced over the fuselage and at the bald doughnut tyres and
he loved the plane. Again, as always, he looked at the weakened
starboard shock absorber which no longer held its spread and let the
plane stand tilted a little to one side, and told himself that it was not
serious. He heard the truck motor starting, and he unfastened the
knots of the ropes holding the plane to the spikes driven into the
desert floor. Then the truck pulled up, and young Perce Howland
dropped off and went over to the tail handle, gripped it, lifted the
tail off the ground and swung her around so she faced out across the
endless desert and away from the mountains. Then they unwound
the rubber hose from the gas drum on the truck and stuck the
nozzle into the gas tank behind the engine, and Perce turned the
pump crank.

Guido then walked around the wing and over to the cockpit,
whose right door was folded down, leaving the inside open to the air.
He reached in and took out his ripped leather flight jacket and
got into it. Perce stood leaning against the truck mudguard now,
grinning. "That sure is a ventilated-type jacket, Guido," he said.

Then Guido said, "I can't get my size any more." The jacket had one sleeve off at the elbow, and the dried leather was split open down the back, showing the lamb's-wool lining. He had bombed Germany in this jacket long ago. He reached in behind the seat and took out a goggle case, slipped his goggles out, replaced the case, set his goggles securely on his face, and reached in again and took out a shotgun pistol and three shells from a little wooden box beside his seat. He loaded the pistol and laid it carefully under his seat. Then he got into the cockpit, sat in his seat, drew the strap over his belly and buckled it. Meantime Gay had taken his position before the propeller.

Guido called through the open doorway of the cockpit, "Turn her over, Gay-boy!"

Gay stepped up to the propeller, glanced down behind his heels to be sure no stone waited to trip him when he stepped back, and pulled down on the blade and hopped back watchfully.

"Give her another!" Guido called in the silence.

Gay stepped up again, again glancing around his heels, and pulled the blade down. The engine inhaled and exhaled and they could all hear the oil clank of her inner shafts turning loosely.

"Ignition on, Gay-boy!" Guido called, and threw the switch.

This time Gay inspected the ground around him even more carefully, and pulled his hat-brim down tighter on his head. Perce stood leaning on the truck's front mudguard, spitting and chewing, his eyes softly squinted against the brazen sun. Gay reached up and pulled the propeller down and jumped back. A puff of smoke floated up from the engine ports.

"Goddam car gas," Guido said. "Ignition on. Go again, Gay-boy!" They were buying low octane to save money.

Gay again stepped up to the propeller, swung the blade down, and the engine said its 'Chaaahh!' and the ports breathed white smoke into the morning air. Gay walked over to Perce and stood beside him watching. The fuselage shuddered and the propeller turned into a wheel, and the dust blew pleasantly from behind the plane and towards the mountains. Guido gunned her and she tumbled toward the open desert, bumping along over the sage clumps and crunching whitened skeletons of cattle killed by the winter. The stiff-backed plane grew smaller, shouldering its way over the broken ground, and then its nose turned upward and there was space between the

doughnut tyres and the desert, and lazily it climbed, turning back
the way it had come. It flew over the heads of Perce and Gay, who
stood still as they always did, and Guido waved down, a stranger
now and fiercely goggled and wrapped in leather, and they could see
him exposed to the waist, turning from them to look through the
windshield at the mountains ahead of him. The plane flew away,
climbing smoothly, losing itself against the orange and purple
walls which vaulted up from the desert to hide from the cowboys'
eyes the wild animals they wanted for themselves.

II

They would have at least two hours before the plane flew out of
the mountains driving the horses before it, so they washed the three
tin plates and the cups and stored them in the aluminium grub box.
If Guido did find horses they would break camp and return to Bowie
tonight, so they packed up their bedrolls with sailors' tidiness and
laid them neatly side by side on the ground. The six great truck
tyres, each with its looped rope coiled within, lay in two piles on the
bed of the truck. Gay Langland looked them over and touched
them with his hand and stood for a moment trying to think if there
was anything they were leaving behind. He jumped up on the truck
to see that the cap was screwed tight on the gas drum which was
lashed to the back of the cab up front, and it was. Then he hopped
down to the ground and got into the cab and started the engine.
Perce was already sitting there with his hat tipped forward against
the yellow sunlight pouring through the windshield. A thin and
concerned border collie came trotting up as Gay started to close his
door and he invited her into the cab. She leaped up and he snugged
her into the space between the clutch and the left wall of the cab.
"Damn near forgot Belle," he said, and they started off.
    Gay owned the truck and he wanted to preserve the front end,
which he knew could be twisted out of line on broken ground. So he
started off slowly. They could hear the gas sloshing in the drum
behind them outside. It was getting warm now. They rode in
silence staring ahead at the two-track trail they were following
across the bone-cluttered sagebrush. Thirty miles ahead stood the

lava mountains which were the northern border of this desert, the bed of a bowl seven thousand feet up, a place no one ever saw excepting the few cowboys searching for stray cattle every few months. People in Bowie, sixty miles away, did not know of this place. There were the two of them and the truck and the dog, and now that they were on the move they felt between them the comfort of purpose and their isolation, and Perce slumped in his seat blinking as though he would go to sleep again, and Gay smoked a cigarette and let his body flow from side to side with the pitching of the truck. There was a moving cloud of dust in the distance toward the left, and Gay said, "Antelope," and Perce tipped his hat back and looked. "Must be doin' sixty," he said, and Gay said, "More. I chased one once and I was doin' more than sixty and he lost me." Perce shook his head in wonder and they turned to look ahead again.

After he had thought a while Perce said, "We better get over to Largo by tomorrow if we're gonna get into that rodeo. They's gonna be a crowd trying to sign up for that one."

"We'll drive down in the morning," Gay said.

"I'll have to see about gettin' me some stock."

"We'll get there early tomorrow; you'll get stock if you come in early."

"Like to win some money," Perce said. "I just wish I get me a good horse down there."

"They be glad to fix you up, Perce. You're known pretty good around there now. They'll fix you up with some good stock," Gay said. Perce was one of the best bronc riders and the rodeos liked to have it known he would appear.

Then there was silence. Gay had to hold the gear-shift lever in high or it would slip out into neutral when they hit bumps. The transmission fork was worn out, he knew, and the front tyres were going too. He dropped one hand to his pants pocket and felt the four silver dollars he had from the ten Roslyn had given him when they had left her days ago.

As though he had read Gay's mind, Perce said, "Roslyn would've liked it up here. She'd liked to have seen that antelope, I bet." Perce grinned as both of them usually did at Roslyn's Eastern surprise at everything they did and saw and said.

"Yeah," Gay said, "she likes to see things."

Through the corner of his eye he watched the younger man, who was looking ahead with a little grin on his face. "She's a damned good sport, old Roslyn," Gay said.

"Sure is," Perce Howland said. And Gay watched him for any sign of guile, but there was only a look of glad appreciation. "First woman like that I ever met," the younger man said.

"They's more," Gay said. "Some of them Eastern women fool you sometimes. They got education but they're good sports. And damn good *women* too, some of them."

There was a silence. Then the younger man asked, "You get to know a lot of them? Eastern women?"

"Ah, I get one once in a while," Gay said.

"Only educated women I ever know they was back home near Teachers College. Students. Y'know," he said, warming to the memory, "I used to think, hell, education's everything. But when I saw the husbands some of them got married to—schoolteachers and everything, why, I don't give them much credit. And they just as soon climb on a man as tell him good morning. I was teachin' them to ride for a while near home."

"Just because a woman's educated don't mean much. Woman's a woman," Gay said. The image of his wife came into his mind. For a moment he wondered if she were still living with the same man he had beaten up when he discovered them together in a parked car six years ago.

"You divorced?" Perce asked.

"No. I never bothered with it," Gay said. It always surprised him how Perce said just what was on his mind sometimes. "How'd you know I was thinkin' of that?" he asked, grinning with embarrassment. But he was too curious to keep silent.

"Hell, I didn't know," Perce said.

"You're always doin' that. I think of somethin' and you go ahead and say it."

"That's funny," Perce said.

They rode on in silence. They were nearing the middle of the desert, where they would turn east. Gay was driving faster now because he wanted to get to the rendezvous and sit quietly waiting for the plane to appear. He held on to the gear-shift lever and felt it trying to spring out of high and into neutral. It would have to be fixed. The time was coming fast when he would need about fifty dollars or sell the truck, because it would be useless without repairs. Without a truck and without a horse he would be down to what was in his pocket.

Perce spoke out of the silence. "If I don't win Saturday I'm gonna have to do something for money."

"Goddam, you always say what's in my mind."

Perce laughed. His face looked very young and pink. "Why?"

"I was just now thinkin'," Gay said, "what I'm gonna do for money."

"Well, Roslyn give you some," Perce said.

He said it innocently, and Gay knew it was innocent, and yet he felt angry blood moving into his neck. Something had happened in these five weeks and Gay did not know for sure what it was. Roslyn had taken to calling Perce cute and now and again she would bend over and kiss him on the back of the neck when he was sitting in the living-room chair, drinking with them.

Not that that meant anything in itself because he'd known Eastern women before who'd do something like that and it was just their way. Especially college graduate divorced women. What he wondered at was Perce's way of hardly even noticing what she did to him. Sometimes it was like he'd already had her and could ignore her the way a man will who knows he's boss. But then Gay thought it might just be that he really wasn't interested, or maybe that he was keeping cool in deference to Gay.

Again Gay felt a terrible longing to earn money working. He sensed the bottom of his life falling if it turned out Roslyn had really been loving this boy beside him. It had happened to him once before with his wife but this frightened him more and he did not know exactly why. Not that he couldn't do without Roslyn. There wasn't anybody or anything he couldn't do without. She was about his age and full of laughter that was not laughter and gaiety that was not gaiety and adventurousness that was laboured, and he knew all this perfectly well even as he laughed with her and was high with her in the bars and rodeos. He had only lived once, and that was when he had had his house and his wife and his children. He knew the difference, but you never kept anything and he had never particularly thought about keeping anything or losing anything. He had been all his life like Perce Howland sitting beside him now, a man moving on or ready to. It was only when he discovered his wife with a stranger that he knew he had had a stake to which he had been pleasurably tethered. He had not seen her or his children for years, and only rarely thought about any of them. Any more than his father had thought of him very much after the day he had gotten on his pony, when he was fourteen, to go to town from the ranch, and had kept going into Montana and stayed there for three years. He lived in his country as his father did and it was the same endless range wherever he went and it connected him sufficiently with his father and his wife and his children. All might turn up sometime in some town or at some rodeo where he might happen to look over his shoulder and see his daughter or one of his sons, or they might never turn up. He had neither left anyone nor not-left as long as they were all alive on these ranges, for everything here was always beyond the furthest shot of vision and far away, and mostly he had worked alone or with one or two men between distant mountains anyway.

He drove steadily across the grand plateau in the truck with Perce Howland beside him, and he felt he was going to be afraid soon. He was not afraid now, but something new was opening up inside him. He wanted very much to earn money by working and he kept turning over in his mind the idea of handling money he had earned by his work instead of money Roslyn had given him. He grew tired of thinking about it.

In the distance now he could see the shimmering wall of the heat waves rising from the clay flatland they wanted to get to. Now they were approaching closer and it opened to them beyond the heat waves, and they could see once again how vast it was, a prehistoric lake-bed thirty miles long by seventeen miles wide, couched between the two mountain ranges. It was a flat, beige waste without grass or bush or stone where a man might drive a car at a hundred miles an hour with his hands off the wheel and never hit anything at all. They drove in silence. The truck stopped bouncing as the tyres rolled over harder ground where there were fewer sage clumps. The waves of heat were dense before them and they drove through them as through dreams of watery cascades. Now the truck rolled smoothly and they were on the clay lake-bed, and when they had gone a few hundred yards on to it Gay pulled up and shut off the engine. The air was still in a dead, sunlit silence. When he opened his door he could hear a squeak in the hinge he had never noticed before. When they walked around out here they could hear their shirts rasping against their backs and the brush of a sleeve against their trousers.

They stood on the clay ground, which was as hard as concrete, and turned to look the way they had come. They looked back toward the mountains at whose feet they had camped and slept, and scanned their ridges for Guido's plane. It was too early for him and they made themselves busy taking the gas drum off the truck and setting it a few yards away on the ground because they would want the truck bed clear when the time came to run the horses down. Then they climbed up and sat inside the tyres with their necks against the tyre beads and their legs hanging over.

Perce said, "I sure hope they's five up in there."

"Guido saw five," he said.

"He said he wasn't sure if one wasn't only a colt," Perce said.

Gay let himself keep silence. He felt he was going to argue with Perce. He watched Perce through the corner of his eye, saw the flat, blonde cheeks and the strong, lean neck and there was something tricky about Perce now. "How long you think you'll be stayin' around here, Perce?" he asked.

They were both watching the distant ridges for a sign of the plane.

"Don't know," Perce said, and spat over the side of the truck. "I'm gettin' a little tired of this, though."

"Well, it's better than wages, Perce."

"Hell yes. Anything's better than wages."

Gay's eyes crinkled. "You're a real misfit, boy."

"That suits me fine," Perce said. They often had this conversation and savoured it. "Better than workin' for some goddam cow outfit buckarooin' so somebody else can buy gas for his Cadillac."

"Damn right," Gay said.

"Hell, Gay, you are the most misfitted man I ever saw and you done all right."

"I got no complaints," Gay said.

"I don't want nothin' and I don't want to want nothin'."

"That's the way, boy."

Gay felt closer to him again and he was glad for it. He kept his eyes on the ridges far away. The sun felt good on his shoulders. "I think he's havin' trouble with them sumbitches up in there."

Perce stared out at the ridges. "Ain't two hours yet." Then he turned to Gay. "These mountains must be cleaned out by now, ain't they?"

"Just about," Gay said. "Just a couple small herds left. Can't do much more around here."

"What you goin' to do when you got these cleaned out?"

"Might go North, I think. Supposed to be some big herds in around Thighbone Mountain and that range up in there."

"How far's that?"

"North about a hundred miles. If I can get Guido interested."

Perce smiled. "He don't like movin' around much, does he?"

"He's just misfitted like the rest of us," Gay said. "He don't want nothin'." Then he added, "They wanted him for an airline pilot flyin' up into Montana and back. Good pay too."

"Wouldn't do it, huh?"

"Not Guido," Gay said, grinning. "Might not like some of the passengers, he told them."

Both men laughed and Perce shook his head in admiration for Guido. Then he said, "They wanted me take over the riding academy up home. I thought about that. Two hundred a month and board. Easy work too. You don't hardly have to ride at all. Just stand around and see the customers get satisfied and put them girls off and on."

He felt silent. Gay knew the rest. It was the same story always. It brought him closer to Perce and it was what he had liked about Perce in the first place. Perce didn't like wages either. He had come on Perce in a bar where the boy was buying drinks for everybody with his rodeo winnings, and his hair still clotted with blood from a bucking horse's kick an hour earlier. Roslyn had offered to get a doctor for him and he had said, "Thank you kindly. But I ain't bad hurt. If you're bad hurt you gonna die and the doctor can't do nothin', and if you ain't bad hurt you get better anyway without no doctor."

"Now it suddenly came upon Gay that Perce had known Roslyn before they had met in the bar. He stared at the boy's profile. "Want to come up North with me if I go?" he asked.

Perce thought a moment. "Think I'll stay around here. Not much rodeoin' up North."

"I might find a pilot up there, maybe. And Roslyn drive us up in her car."

Perce turned to him, a little surprised. "Would she go up there?"

"Sure. She's a damn good sport," Gay said. He watched Perce's eyes, which had turned interested and warm.

Perce said, "Well, maybe; except, to tell you the truth, Gay, I never feel comfortable takin' these horses for chicken feed."

"Somebody's goin' to take them if we don't."

"I know," Perce said. He turned to watch the far ridges again. "Just seems to me they belong up there."

"They ain't doin' nothin' up there but eatin' out good cattle range. The cow outfits shoot them down if they see them."

"I know," Perce said.

"They don't even bother takin' them to slaughter. They just rot up there if the cow outfits get to them."

"I know," Perce said.

There was silence. Neither bug nor lizard nor rabbit moved on the great basin around them and the sun warmed their necks and their thighs. Gay said, "I'd a soon sell them for riding horses but they ain't big enough, except for a kid. And the freight on them's more than they're worth. You saw them—they ain't nothin' but skinny horses."

"I just don't know if I'd want to see like a hundred of them goin' for chicken feed, though. I don't mind like five or six, but a hundred's a lot of horses. I don't know."

Gay thought. "Well, if it ain't this it's wages. Around here anyway." He was speaking of himself and explaining himself.

"I'd just as soon ride buckin' horses and make out that way, Gay." Perce turned to him. "Although I might go up North with you. I don't know."

"Roslyn wouldn't come out here at first," Gay said, "but soon as she saw what they looked like she stopped complainin' about it. You didn't hear her complainin' about it."

"I ain't complainin', Gay. I just don't know. Seems to me God put them up there and they belong up there. But I'm doin' it and I guess I'd go on doin' it. I don't know."

"Sounds to me like the newspapers. They want their steaks, them people in town, but they don't want castration or branding or cleanin' wild horses off the ranges."

"Hell, man, I castrated more bulls than I got hairs on my head," Perce said.

"I better get the glasses," Gay said, and slid out of the tyre in which he had been lounging and off the truck. He went to the cab and reached in and brought out a pair of binoculars, blew on the lenses, mounted the truck, and sat on a tyre with his elbows resting on his knees. He put the glasses to his eyes and focused them. The mountains came up close with their pocked, blue hides. He found the pass through which he believed the plane would come and studied its slopes and scanned the air above it. Anger was still warming him. "God put them up there!" Why, Christ, God put everything everywhere. Did that mean you couldn't eat chickens, for instance, or beef? His dislike for Perce was flowing into him again.

They heard the shotgun off in the sky somewhere and they stopped moving. Gay narrowed his eyes and held the binoculars perfectly still.

"See anything?" Perce asked.

"He's still in the pass, I guess," Gay said.

They sat still, watching the sky over the pass. The moments went by. The sun was making them perspire now and Gay wiped his wet eyebrows with the back of one hand. They heard the shotgun again from the general sky. Gay spoke without lowering the glasses, "He's probably blasting them out of some corner."

Perce quickly arched out of his tyre. "I see him," he said quickly. "I see him glintin', I see the plane."

It angered Gay that Perce had seen him first without glasses. In the glasses Gay could see the plane clearly now. It was flying out of the pass, circling back and disappearing into the pass again. "He's got them in the pass now. Just goin' back in for them."

"Can you see them?" Perce asked.

"He ain't got them in the clear yet. He just went back in for them.

Now through his glasses he could see moving specks on the ground where the pass opened on to the desert table. "I see them," he said.

He counted, moving his lips. "One, two, three, four. Four and a colt."

"We gonna take the colt?" Perce asked.

"Hell, can't take the mare without the colt."

Perce said nothing. Then Gay handed him the glasses. "Take a look."

Gay slid off the truck bed and went forward to the cab and opened its door. His dog lay shivering on the floor under the pedals. He snapped his fingers and she warily got up and leaped down to the ground and stood there quivering as she always did when wild horses were coming. He watched her sit and wet the ground, and how she moved with such care and concern and fear, sniffing the ground and moving her head in slow motion and setting her paws down as though the ground had hidden explosives everywhere. He left her there and climbed on to the truck and sat on a tyre beside Perce, who was still looking through the glasses.

"He's divin' down on them. God, they sure can run."

"Let's have a look," Gay said and reached out, and Perce handed him the glasses, saying, "They're comin' on fast."

Gay watched the horses in the glasses. The plane was starting down towards them from the arc of its climb. They swerved as the roaring motor came down over them, lifted their heads, and galloped faster. They had been running now for over an hour and would slow down when the plane had to climb after a dive and the motor's noise grew quieter. As Guido climbed again Gay and Perce heard a shot, distant and harmless, and the shot sped the horses on again as the plane took time to bank and turn. Then as they slowed the plane returned over them, diving down over their backs, and their heads shot up again and they galloped until the engine's roar receded over them. The sky was clear and lightly blue and only the little plane swung back and forth across the desert like the glinting tip of a magic wand, and the horses came on toward the vast stripped clay bed where the truck was parked.

The two men on the truck exchanged the glasses from time to time. Now they sat upright on the tyres waiting for the horses to reach the edge of the lake-bed, when Guido would land the plane and they would take off with the truck. And now the horses stopped.

"They see the heat waves," Gay said, looking through the glasses. He could see the horses trotting with raised, alarmed heads along the edge of the barren lake-bed, which they feared because the heat waves rose from it like liquid in the air, and yet their nostrils did not smell water and they dared not move ahead on to unknowable territory. The plane dived down on them and they scattered but would not go forward on to the lake-bed from the cooler, sage-dotted desert behind them. Now the plane banked high in the air and circled out behind them over the desert and banked again and came down within yards of the ground and roared in behind them almost at the height of their heads, and as it passed over them, rising, the men on the truck could hear the shotgun. Now the horses leaped forward on to the lake-bed all scattered and heading in different directions, and they were only trotting, exploring the ground under their feet and the strange, superheated air in their nostrils. Gradually, as the plane wound around the sky to dive again they closed ranks and slowly galloped shoulder to shoulder out on to the borderless lake-bed. The colt galloped a length behind with its nose nearly touching the mare's long silky tail.

"That's a big mare," Perce said. His eyes were still dreamy and his face was calm, but his skin had reddened.

"She's a bigger mare than usual up there, ya," Gay said. Both men watched the little herd now, even as they got to their feet on the truck. There was the big mare, as large as any full-grown horse, and both of them downed their surprise at the sight of her. They knew the mustang herds lived in total isolation and that inbreeding had reduced them to the size of large ponies. The herd swerved now and they saw the stallion. He was smaller than the mare but still larger than any they had brought down before. The other two horses were small, the way mustangs ought to be.

The plane was coming down for a landing now. Gay and Perce Howland moved to the forward edge of the truck's bed where a strap of white webbing was strung at hip height between two stanchions protruding upward from sockets at the corners of the truck. They drew another web strap from one stanchion to the other and stood inside the two. Perce tied the back strap to his stanchion. Then they turned around inside their harness and each reached into a tyre behind him and drew out a coil of rope whose ends hung in a loop. They glanced out on the lake-bed and saw Guido taxi-ing toward them and they stood waiting for him. He cut the engine twenty

yards from the truck and leaped out of the open cockpit before the
plane had halted. He lashed the tail of the plane to a rope which
was attached to a spike driven into the clay, and trotted over to the
truck lifting his goggles off and stuffing them into his torn jacket
pocket. Perce and Gay called out laughingly to him but he seemed
hardly to have seen them. His face was puffed with preoccupation.
He jumped into the cab of the truck and the collie dog jumped in
after him and sat on the floor, quivering. He started the truck and
roared ahead across the flat clay into the watery waves of heat.

They could see the herd standing still in a small clot of dots more
than two miles off. The truck rolled smoothly and in the cab Guido
glanced at the speedometer and saw it was past sixty. He had to be
careful not to turn over and he dropped back to fifty-five. Gay on
the right front corner of the truck bed and Perce Howland on the
left, pulled their hats down to their eyebrows and hefted the looped
ropes, which the wind was threatening to coil and foul in their palms.
Guido knew that Gay Langland was a good roper and that Perce
was unsure, so he headed for the herd's left in order to come up to
them on Gay's side of the truck if he could. This whole method, the
truck, the tyres, the ropes and the plane were Guido's invention and
once again he felt the joy of having thought of it all. He drove with
both heavy hands on the wheel and his left foot ready over the brake
pedal. He reached for the shift lever to feel if it were going to spring
out of gear and into neutral, but it felt tight and if they did not hit a
bump he could rely on it. The herd had started to walk, but it
stopped again now and the horses were looking at the truck, ears
raised, necks stretched up and forwards. Guido smiled a little. They
looked silly to him standing there, but he knew and pitied them their
ignorance.

The wind smashed against the faces of Perce and Gay standing on
the truck bed. The brims of their hats flowed up and back from a
low point in front and their faces were dark red. They saw the horses
watching their approach at a standstill. And as they roared closer
and closer they saw that this herd was beautiful.

Perce Howland turned his head to Gay, who glanced at him at the
same time. There had been much rain this spring and this herd must
have found good pasture. They were well-rounded and shining.
The mare was almost black and the stallion and the two others were

K

deeply brown. The colt was curly-coated and had a grey sheen. The stallion dipped his head suddenly and turned his back on the truck and galloped. The others turned and clattered after him with the colt running alongside the mare. Guido pressed down on the gas and the truck surged forward, whining. They were a few yards behind the animals now and they could see the bottoms of their hoofs, fresh hoofs that had never been shod. They could see the full manes flying and the thick and long black tails that would hang down to their fetlocks when they were still. The truck was coming abreast of the mare now and beside her the others galloped with only a loud ticking noise on the clay. It was a gentle tacking clatter, for they were light-footed and unshod. They were slim-legged and wet after running almost two hours in this alarm, but as the truck drew alongside the mare and Gay began twirling his loop above his head, the whole herd wheeled away to the right and Guido jammed the gas pedal down and swung with them, but they kept galloping in a circle and he did not have the speed to keep abreast of them, so he slowed down and fell behind them a few yards until they would straighten out and move ahead again. And they wheeled like circus horses, slower now, for they were at the edge of their strength, and suddenly Guido saw a breadth between the stallion and the two browns and he sped in between, cutting the mare off at the left with her colt. Now the horses stretched, the clatter quickened. Their hind legs flew straight back and their necks stretched low and forward. Gay whirled his loop over his head and the truck came up alongside the stallion, whose lungs were hoarsely screaming with exhaustion, and Gay flung the noose. It fell on the stallion's head and with a whipping of the lead Gay made it fall over his neck. The horse swerved away to the right and stretched the rope until the tyre was pulled off the truck bed and dragged along the hard clay. The three men watched from the slowing truck as the stallion, with startled eyes, pulled the giant tyre for a few yards, then leaped up with his forelegs in the air and came down facing the tyre and trying to back away from it. Then he stood still, heaving, his hind legs dancing in an arc from right to left and back again as he shook his head in the remorseless noose.

As soon as he was sure the stallion was secure, Guido scanned the lake-bed and without stopping turned sharply left toward the mare and the colt, which were trotting idly together by themselves. The two browns were already disappearing toward the north but Guido knew they would halt soon because they were tired, while the mare might continue to the edge of the lake-bed and back into her familiar hills where the truck could not follow. He straightened the truck and jammed down the gas pedal. In a minute he was straight on behind her and he drew up on her left side because the colt was was running on her right. She was very heavy, he saw, and he wondered now if she were a mustang at all. As he drove alongside her his eye ran across her flanks seeking out a brand, but she seemed unmarked. Then through his right window he saw the loop flying out and down over her head, and he saw her head fly up and then she fell back. He turned to the right, braking with his left boot, and he saw her dragging a tyre and coming to a halt with the free colt watching her and trotting beside her very close. Then he headed straight ahead across the flat toward two specks which rapidly enlarged until they became the two browns, which were at a stand-still and watching the oncoming truck. He came in between them and, as they galloped, Perce on the left roped one and Gay roped the other almost at the same time. And Guido leaned his head out of his window and yelled up at Perce, who was on the truck bed on his side: "Good boy!" he hollered, and Perce let himself return an excited grin, although there seemed to be some trouble in his eyes.

Guido made an easy half circle and headed back to the mare and the colt, and in a few minutes he slowed to a halt some twenty yards away and got out of the cab. The dog remained sitting on the floor of the cab, shaking all over her body.

The three men approached the mare. She had never seen a man and her eyes were wide in fear. Her rib cage stretched and collapsed very rapidly and there was a trickle of blood coming out of her nostrils. She had a heavy, dark brown mane and her tail nearly touched the ground. The colt with dumb eyes shifted about on its silly bent legs trying to keep the mare between itself and the men and the mare kept shifting her rump to shield the colt from them.

They wanted now to move the noose higher up on the mare's neck because it had fallen on her from the rear and was tight around the middle of her neck where it could choke her if she kept pulling against the weight of the tyre. They had learned from previous forays that they could not leave a horse tied that way without the danger of suffocation and they wanted them alive until they could bring a larger truck from Bowie and load them on it.

Gay was the best roper, so Perce and Guido stood by as he twirled a noose over his head, then let it fall open softly, just behind the forefeet of the mare. They waited for a moment, then approached her and she backed a step. Then Gay pulled sharply on the rope and her forefeet were tied together. Then with another rope Gay lass'd her hind feet and she swayed and fell to the ground on her side. Her body swelled and contracted, but she seemed resigned. The colt stretched its nose to her tail and stood there as the men came to the mare and spoke quietly to her, and Guido bent down and opened the noose and slipped it up under her jaw. They inspected her for a brand but she was clean.

"Never see a horse that size up here," Gay said to Guido.

Guido stood there looking down at the great mare.

Perce said, "Maybe wild horses was all big once," and he looked to Guido for confirmation.

Guido bent and sat on his heels and opened the mare's mouth and the other two looked in with him. "She's fifteen if she's a day," Gay said, and to Perce he said, "She wouldn't be around much longer anyway."

"Ya, she's old," Perce agreed, and his eyes were filled with thought.

Guido stood up and the three went back to the truck. Perce hopped up and sat on the truck bed with his legs dangling, and Gay sat in the cab with Guido. They drove across the lake-bed to the stallion and stopped, and the three of them approached him.

"Ain't a bad-lookin' horse," Perce said.

They stood inspecting the horse for a moment. He was standing still now, heaving for breath and bleeding from the nostrils. His head was down, holding the rope taut, and he was looking at them with his deep brown eyes that were like the lenses of enormous binoculars. Gay got his rope ready in his hand. "He ain't nothin' but a misfit," he said, "except for some kid. You couldn't run cattle with him and he's too small for a riding horse."

"He is small," Perce conceded. "Got a nice neck, though."

"Oh, they're nice-*lookin'* horses, some of them," Guido said.

"What the hell you goin' to do with them, though? Cost more to ship them anywhere than they'd bring."

Gay twirled the loop over his head and they spread out around the stallion. "They're just old misfit horses, that's all," he said, and he flung the rope behind the stallion's forelegs and the horse backed a step and he drew the rope and the noose bit into the horse's lower legs drawing them together, and he swayed but he would not fall.

"Take hold," Gay called to Perce, who ran around the horse and grabbed on to the rope and held it taut. Then Gay went back to the truck, got another rope, returned to the rear of the horse and looped his hind legs. But the stallion would not fall. Guido stepped closer to push him over but he swung his head and showed his teeth and Guido stepped back. "Pull on it!" Guido yelled to Gay and Perce, and they pulled on their ropes to trip the stallion, but he righted himself and stood there bound by the head to the tyre and his feet by the two ropes which the men held. Then Guido hurried over to Perce and took the rope from him and walked with it toward the rear of the horse and pulled hard. The stallion's forefeet slipped back and he came down on his knees and his nose struck the clay ground and he snorted as he struck, but he would not topple over and stayed there on his knees as though he were bowing to something with his nose propping up his head against the ground and his sharp bursts of breath blowing up dust in little clouds under his nostrils. Now Guido gave the rope back to young Perce Howland, who held it taut, and he came up alongside the stallion's neck and laid his hands on the side of the neck and pushed, and the horse fell over on to his flank and lay there and, like the mare, when he felt the ground against his body he seemed to let himself out and for the first time his eyes blinked and his breath came now in sighs and no longer fiercely. Guido shifted the noose up under his jaw, and they opened the ropes around his hooves and when he felt his legs free he first raised his head curiously and then clattered up and stood there looking at them, from one to the other, blood dripping from his nostrils and a stain of deep red on both dusty knees. For a moment the three men stood watching him to be sure he was tightly noosed around the neck. Only the clacking of the truck's engine sounded on the enormous floor between the mountains and the wheezing inhale of the horse and his blowing out of air. Then the men moved without hurrying to the truck and Gay stored his two extra ropes between the seat of the cab and got behind the wheel with Guido beside him, and Perce climbed on to the back of the truck and lay down facing the sky and made a pillow with his palms.

Gay headed the truck south towards where they knew the plane was, although it was beyond their vision yet. Guido was slowly catching his breath and now he lighted a cigarette, puffed it, and rubbed his left hand into his bare scalp. He sat gazing out the windshield and the side window. "I'm sleepy," he said.

"What you reckon?" Gay asked.

"What you?" Guido said. He had dust in his throat and his voice sounded high and almost girlish.

"That mare might be six hundred pounds."

"I'd say about that, Gay," Guido agreed.

"About four hundred apiece for the browns and a little more for the stallion."

"That's about the way I figured."

"What's that come to?"

Guido thought. "Nineteen hundred, maybe two thousand," he said.

They fell silent figuring the money. Two thousand pounds at six cents a pound came to a hundred and twenty dollars. The colt might make it a few dollars more, but not much. Figuring the gas for the plane and the truck, and twelve dollars for their groceries, they came to the figure of a hundred dollars for the three of them. Guido would get forty-five dollars, since he had used his plane, and Gay would get thirty-five including the use of his truck, and Perce Howland, if he agreed, as he undoubtedly would, had the remaining twenty.

They fell silent after they had said the figures, and Gay drove in thought. Then he said, "We should've watered them the last time. They can pick up a lot of weight if you let them water."

"Yeah, let's be sure to do that," Guido said.

They knew they would as likely as not forget to water the horses before they unloaded them at the dealer's lot in Bowie. They would be in a hurry to unload and to be free of the horses and only later, as they were doing now, would they remind themselves that by letting the horses drink their fill they could pick up another fifteen or twenty dollars in added weight. They were not thinking of the money any more, once they had figured it, and if Perce were to object to his smaller share they would both hand him a five or ten dollar bill or more if he wanted it. They were only abiding by a custom alien to them of dividing money with any self-interest or guile. They had not come here for the money, not that they were above wanting money, but because they would soon be rid of it and there wasn't enough to matter anyway. They had no belief in money and it was not real to them any more than it is real to children, who do not understand price and the value of things. They believed in the range and they had an abiding faith that one way or another they would never really come to want, even if they had to hire out to a cow outfit and work cattle for a while, and they rarely had to do that. There was always something, a friend to borrow from or a truck to sell, or running mustangs. They wanted only to *be* and now, as they rolled on towards the plane which Guido would fly off to Bowie in the distant valley where people were, they knew that it was over for a while, that they had done what they had planned to do. Now, for a while, they would pitch and roll with time on their hands, wondering what to do next, and then that next thing would come along and they would do it and be interested in it while it was going on, and then time would return and they would sit it out in bars or sleeping or in Gay's case going around with Roslyn or even building a new addition to her cabin for her, and in Perce's case riding a bucking horse some Saturday in a local rodeo.

Gay stopped the truck beside the plane at the edge of the lake-bed. The tethered horses were far away now, excepting for the mare and her colt, which stood in clear view less than half a mile off. Guido opened his door and said to Gay, "See you in town. Let's get the other truck tomorrow morning."

"Perce wants to go over to Largo and sign up for the rodeo to-morrow," Gay said. "Tell ya—we'll go in and get the truck and come back here this afternoon maybe. Maybe we bring them in tonight."

"All right, if you want to. I'll see you boys tomorrow," Guido said, and he got out and stopped for a moment to talk to Perce. "Perce?" he said.

Perce propped himself up on one elbow and looked down at him. He looked very sleepy. Guido smiled. "You sleeping?"

Perce's eyelids almost seemed swollen and his face was indrawn and troubled. "I was about to," he said.

Guido let the reprimand pass. "We figure about a hundred dollars clear. Twenty all right for you?"

"Ya, twenty's all right," Perce said, blinking heavily. He hardly seemed to be listening.

"See you in town," Guido said, and turned and waddled off to the plane, where Gay was already standing with his hands on the propeller blade. Guido got in and Gay swung the blade down and the engine started immediately. Guido waved to Gay and Perce, who raised one hand slightly from the truck bed. Guido gunned the plane and she trundled off and into the sky and the two men on the ground watched her as she flew toward the mountains and away.

Now Gay returned to the truck and as he started to climb in behind the wheel he looked at Perce, who was still propped up on one elbow, and he said, "Twenty all right?" And he said this because he thought Perce looked hurt.

"Heh? Ya, twenty's all right," Perce answered. Then he let himself down from the truck bed and Gay got behind the wheel. Perce stood beside the truck and wet the ground while Gay waited for him. Then Perce got into the cab and they drove off.

Perce agreed to come back this afternoon with Gay in the other truck and load the horses, although both of them knew that once they got into town they might have a drink and time would go by and they would wait until morning before making the trip back. As they drove across the lake-bed in silence they both knew, gradually, that they would wait until morning because they were tired now and would be more tired later. The mare and her colt stood between them and the sage desert toward which they were heading. Perce stared out the window at the mare and he saw that she was watching them apprehensively but not in real alarm, and the colt was lying upright on the clay, its head nodding slightly as though it would soon fall asleep. Perce looked long at the colt as they approached and he thought about it waiting there beside the mare, unbound and free to go off, and he said to Gay, "Ever hear of a colt leave a mare?"

"Not that young a colt," Gay said. "He ain't goin' nowhere." And he glanced to look at Perce.

They passed the mare and colt and left them behind and Perce laid his head back and closed his eyes. His tobacco swelled out his left cheek and he let it soak there.

Now the truck left the clay lake-bed and it pitched and rolled on the sage desert. They would return to their camp and pick up their bedrolls and cooking implements, and then drive to the road, which was almost fifteen miles beyond the camp across the desert.

"Think I'll go back to Roslyn's tonight," Gay said.

"Okay," Perce said and did not open his eyes.

"We can pick them up in the morning and then take you down to Largo."

"Okay," Perce said.

Gay thought about Roslyn. She would probably razz them about all the work they had done for a few dollars, saying they were too dumb to figure in their labour time and other hidden expenses. To hear her sometimes they hadn't made any profit at all. "Roslyn going to feel sorry for the colt," Gay said, "so might as well not mention it."

Perce opened his eyes, and with his head resting on the back of the seat he looked out the window at the mountains. "Hell, she feeds that dog of hers canned dogfood, doesn't she?"

Gay felt closer to Perce again and he smiled. "Sure does."

"Well, what's she think is in the can?"

"She knows what's in the can."

"There's wild horses in the can," Perce said.

They drove in silence for a while. Then Perce said, "That's what beats me."

After a few moments Gay said, "You comin' back to Roslyn's with me or you gonna stay in town?"

"I'd just as soon go back with you."

"Okay," Gay said. He felt good about going into her cabin now. There would be her books on the shelves he had built for her, and they would have some drinks, and Perce would fall asleep on the couch and they would go into the bedroom together. He liked to come back to her after he had worked, more than when he had only driven her here and there or just stayed around her place. He liked his own money in his pocket. And he tried harder to visualise how it would be with her and he thought of himself being forty-six soon, and the nearing fifty. She would go back East one day, he knew, maybe this year maybe next. He wondered again when he would begin turning grey and how he would look with grey hair and he set his jaw against the idea of himself grey and an old man and the picture of it in his mind.

Perce spoke, sitting up in his seat. "I want to phone my mother. Damn, I haven't called her all year." He stared out the window at the mountains. He had the memory of how the colt looked and he wished it would be gone when they returned in the morning. Then he said, "I got to get to Largo tomorrow and register."

"We'll go," Gay said.

"I could use a good win," he said. He thought of five hundred dollars now, and of the many times he had won five hundred dollars. "You know something, Gay?" he said.

"Huh?"

"I'm never goin' to amount to a damn thing." Then he laughed. He was hungry and he laughed without restraint for a moment and then laid his head back and closed his eyes.

"I told you that first time I met you, didn't I?" Gay grinned. He felt a bravery between them now, and he saw that Perce was grinning with a certain gaiety. He felt the mood coming on for some drinks at Roslyn's. Then Perce spoke.

"That colt won't bring two dollars anyway. What you say we just left him there?"

"Why, you know what he'd do?" Gay said. "He'd just follow the truck right into town."

"I guess he would at that," Perce said. He spat a stream of juice out the window.

They reached the camp in twenty minutes and loaded the three bedrolls and the aluminium grub-box in the truck and drove on toward Bowie. After they had driven for fifteen minutes without speaking, Gay said he wanted to go North very soon for the hundreds of horses that were supposed to be in the mountains there. But Perce Howland had fallen fast asleep beside him. Gay wanted to talk about that expedition because as they neared Bowie he began to visualise Roslyn razzing them again, and it was clear to him that he

had somehow failed to settle anything for himself; he had put in
three days for thirty-five dollars and there would be no way to
explain it so it made sense and it would be embarrassing. And yet
he knew that it had all been the way it ought to be even if he could
never explain it to her or anyone else. He reached out and nudged
Perce, who opened his eyes and lolled his head over to face him.
"You comin' up to Thighbone with me, ain't you?"

"Okay," Perce said, and went back to sleep.

Gay felt more peaceful now that the younger man would not be
leaving him. He drove in contentment.

The sun shone hot on the beige plain all day. Neither fly nor bug
nor snake ventured out on the waste to molest the four horses
tethered there, or the colt. They had run nearly two hours at a
gallop and as the afternoon settled upon them they pawed the hard
ground for water, but there was none. Toward evening the wind
came up and they backed into it and faced the mountains from
which they had come. From time to time the stallion caught the
smell of the pastures up there and he started to walk toward the
vaulted fields in which he had grazed, but the tyre bent his neck
around and after a few steps he would turn to face it and leap into
the air with his forelegs striking at the sky and then he would come
down and be still again. With the deep blue darkness the wind blew
faster, tossing their manes and flinging their long tails in between
their legs. The cold of night raised the colt on to its legs and it stood
close to the mare for warmth. Facing the southern range five horses
blinked under the green glow of the risen moon and they closed their
eyes and slept. The colt settled again on the hard ground and lay
under the mare. In the high hollows of the mountains the grass they
had cropped this morning straightened in the darkness. On the
lusher swards which were still damp with the rains of spring their
hoof-prints had begun to disappear. When the first pink glow of
another morning lit the sky, the colt stood up and as it had always
done at dawn it walked waywardly for water. The mare shifted and
her bone hoofs ticked the clay. The colt turned its head and
returned to her and stood at her side with vacant eye, its nostrils
sniffing the warming air.

SAUL BELLOW

Leaving the Yellow House

Although he has published only a very few books, Saul Bellow is generally considered one of America's most important writers of fiction. His first two novels, *The Dangling Man* (1944) and *The Victim* (1947), had an admiring but small audience; and it was not until his third novel, *The Adventures of Augie March* (1953), received the National Book Award as 'the most distinguished work of fiction published in 1953' that Bellow found a readership consonant with his reputation. In 1956 his celebrated short novella *Seize the Day* appeared, first in *Partisan Review* and then in a collection of his short stories.

'Leaving the Yellow House' was his first major piece of fiction to appear after *Seize the Day*, which it much resembles in length and theme. Saul Bellow had spent some months in the West at the same time Arthur Miller was there (see page 261). Both writers (who knew each other) reacted to the experience by writing their first Western—unusual Westerns, to say the least—and *Esquire*, which hadn't bought a Western in years, published them both: Miller's 'The Misfits' in October 1957, and Bellow's 'Leaving the Yellow House' three months later, in January of 1958. The stories differ interestingly, each being very characteristic of its author's methods and preoccupations in form and content.

THE NEIGHBOURS—there were in all six white people who lived at Sego Desert Lake—told one another that old Hattie could no longer make it alone. The desert life, even with a forced-air furnace in the house and butane gas brought from town in a truck, was still too difficult for her. There were older women in the county. Twenty miles away was Amy Walters, the gold miner's widow. But she was a hardier old girl. Every day of the year she took a bath in the lake.

And Amy was crazy about money and knew how to manage it, as Hattie did not. Hattie was not exactly a drunkard, but she hit the bottle pretty hard, and now she was in trouble and there was a limit to the help she could expect from even the best of neighbours.

They were fond of her, though. You couldn't help being fond of Hattie. She was big and cheerful, puffy, comic, boastful, with a big round back and stiff, rather long legs. Before the century began she had graduated from finishing school and studied the organ in Paris. But now she didn't know a note from a skillet; she had tantrums when she played canasta. And all that remained of her fine fair hair was frizzled along her forehead in small grey curls. Her forehead was not much wrinkled, but the skin was bluish, the colour of skim milk. She walked with long strides in spite of the heaviness of her hips, pushing on, round-backed, with her shoulders and showing the flat rubber bottoms of her shoes.

Once a week, in the same cheerful, plugging but absent way, she took off her short skirt and the dirty aviator's jacket with the wool collar and put on a girdle, a dress and high-heeled shoes. When she stood on these heels her fat old body trembled. She wore a big brown Rembrandt-like tam with a ten-cent-store brooch, eyelike, carefully centred. She drew a straight line with lipstick on her mouth, leaving part of the upper lip pale. At the wheel of her old turret-shaped car, she drove, seemingly methodical but speeding dangerously, across forty miles of mountainous desert to buy frozen meat pies and whisky. She went to the Laundromat and the hairdresser, and then had lunch with two Martinis at the Arlington. Afterwards she would often visit Marian Nabot's Silvermine Hotel at Miller Street near skid row and pass the rest of the day gossiping and drinking with her cronies, old divorcées like herself who had settled in the West. Hattie never gambled any more and she didn't care for the movies, and at five o'clock she drove back at the same speed, calmly, partly blinded by the smoke of her cigarette. She was a tough-looking smoker. The fixed cigarette gave her a watering eye.

The Rolfes and the Paces were her only white neighbours at Sego Desert Lake. There was Sam Jervis too, but he was only an old gandy walker who did odd jobs in her garden, and she did not count him. Nor did she count among her neighbours Darly, the dudes' cowboy who worked for the Paces, nor Swede, the telegrapher. Pace had a guest ranch, and Rolfe and his wife were rich and had retired. Thus there were three good houses at the lake, Hattie's yellow house, Pace's and the Rolfes'. All the rest of the population—Sam, Swede, Watchtah the section foreman, and the Mexicans and Indians and Negroes—lived in shacks and boxcars. You could count all the trees in a minute's time: cottonwoods and box elders. All the rest, down to the shores, was sagebrush and juniper. The lake was what remained of an old sea that had covered the volcanic mountains. To the north there were some tungsten mines; to the south, fifteen miles, was an Indian village built of railroad sleepers.

In this barren place Hattie had lived for more than twenty years. Her first summer was spent not in a house but in an Indian wikiup on the shore. She used to say that she had watched the stars from this almost roofless shelter. After her divorce she took up with a cowboy named Wicks. Neither of them had any money—it was the Depression—and they had lived on the range, trapping coyotes for a living. Once a month they would come into town and rent a room and go on a bender. Hattie told this sadly, but also gloatingly, and with many trimmings. A thing no sooner happened to her than it was transformed into something else. "We were caught in a storm," she said, "and we rode hard, down to the lake and knocked on the door of the yellow house"—now her house. "Alice Parmenter took us in and let us sleep on the floor." What had actually happened was that the wind was blowing—there had been no storm—and they were not far away from the house anyway; and Alice Parmenter, who knew that Hattie and Wicks were not married, offered them separate beds; but Hattie, swaggering, had said in a loud voice, "Why get two sets of sheets dirty?" And she and her cowboy had slept in Alice's double bed while Alice had taken the sofa.

Now Wicks was gone. There was never anybody like him in the sack; he was brought up in a whorehouse and the girls taught him everything, said Hattie. She didn't really understand what she was saying, but believed that she was being Western, and more than anything else she wanted to be thought of as a rough, experienced woman of the West. Still, she was a lady, too. She had good silver and good china and engraved stationery, but she kept canned beans and A-1 sauce and tunafish and bottles of catsup and fruit salad on the library shelves of her living-room. On the night table was the Bible her pious brother Angus—her other brother was a heller—had given her; but behind the little cabinet door was a bottle of bourbon. When she awoke in the night she tippled herself back to sleep. In the glove compartment of her old car she kept little sample bottles for emergencies on the road. Old Darly found them after her accident.

The accident did not happen far out in the desert as she had always feared, but near her home. She had had a few Martinis with the Rolfes one evening and as she was driving home over the railroad crossing she lost control of the car and drove off the crossing on to the tracks. The explanation she gave was that she had sneezed, and the sneeze had blinded her and made her twist the wheel. The motor was killed and all four wheels of the car sat smack on the rails. Hattie crept down from the door, high off the roadbed. A great fear took hold of her—for the car, for the future, and not only for the future but for the past—and she began to hurry on stiff legs through the sagebrush to Pace's ranch.

Now the Paces were away on a hunting trip and had left old Darly in charge; he was tending bar in the old cabin that went back to the days of the pony express when Hattie burst in. There were two customers, a tungsten miner and his girl.

"Darly, I'm in trouble. Help me. I've had an accident," said Hattie.

How the face of a man will alter when a woman has bad news to tell him! It happened now to lean old Darly; his eyes went flat and looked unwilling, his jaw moved in and out, his wrinkled cheeks began to flush, and he said, "What's the matter—what's happened to you now?"

"I'm stuck on the tracks. I sneezed. I lost control of the car. Tow me off, Darly, with the pick-up before the train comes."

Darly threw down his towel and stamped his high-heeled boots with anger. "Now what have you gone and done?" he said. "I told you to stay home after dark."

"Where's Pace? Ring the fire bell and fetch Pace."

"There's nobody on the property but me," said the lean old man. "And I'm not supposed to close the bar and you know it as well as I do."

"Please, Darly. I can't leave my car on the tracks."

"Too bad!" he said. Nevertheless he moved from behind the bar. "How did you say it happened?"

"I told you, I sneezed," said Hattie.

Everyone, as she later told it, was as drunk as sixteen thousand dollars: Darly, the miner and the miner's girl.

Darly was limping as he locked the door of the bar. A year before, a kick from one of Pace's mares had broken his ribs as he was loading her into the trailer, and he hadn't recovered from it. He was too old. But he dissembled the pain. The high-heeled narrow boots helped, and his painful bending looked like the ordinary stooping posture of a cowboy on the ground. However, Darly was not a genuine cowboy, like Pace, who had grown up in the saddle. He was a latecomer from the East and until the age of forty had never been on horseback. In this respect he and Hattie were alike. They were not the Westerners they seemed to be.

Hattie hurried after him through the ranch yard.

"Damn you!" he said to her. "I got thirty bucks out of that sucker and I would have skinned him out of his whole pay cheque if you minded your business. Pace is going to be sore as hell."

"You've got to help me. We're neighbours," said Hattie.

"You're not fit to be living out here. You can't do it any more. Besides, you're swacked all the time."

Hattie couldn't afford to talk back to him. The thought of her car on the tracks made her frantic. If a freight came now and smashed it, her life at Sego Desert Lake would be finished. And where would she go then? She was not fit to live in this place. She had never made the grade at all; she only seemed to have made it. And Darly —why did he say such hurtful things to her? Because he himself was sixty-eight years old, and he had no other place to go, either; he took bad treatment from Pace besides. Darly stayed because his only alternative was to go to the soldiers' home. Moreover, the dude women would crawl into his sack. They wanted a cowboy and they thought he was one. Why, he couldn't even raise himself out of his bunk in the morning. And where else would he get women? "After the season," she wanted to say to him, "you always have to go to the Veterans' Hospital to get yourself fixed up again." But she didn't dare offend him now.

The moon was due to rise. It appeared as they drove over the ungraded dirt road towards the crossing where Hattie's turret-shaped car was sitting on the rails. At great speed Darly wheeled the pick-up around, spraying dirt on the miner and his girl, who had followed in their car.

"You get behind the wheel and steer," Darly told Hattie.

She climbed into the seat. Waiting at the wheel she lifted up her face and said, "Please, God, I didn't bend the axle or crack the oil pan."

When Darly crawled under the bumper of Hattie's car the pain in his ribs suddenly cut off his breath, so instead of doubling the tow chain he fastened it at full length. He rose and trotted back to the truck on the narrow boots. Motion seemed the only remedy for the pain; not even booze did the trick any more. He put the pick-up into towing gear and began to pull. One side of Hattie's car dropped into the roadbed with a heave of springs. She sat with a stormy, frightened, conscience-stricken face, racing the motor until she flooded it.

The tungsten miner yelled, "Your chain's too long."

Hattie was raised high in the air by the pitch of the wheels. She had to roll down the window to let herself out because the door handle had been jammed from the inside for years. Hattie struggled out on the uplifted side crying, "I better call the Swede. I better have him signal. There's a train due."

"Go on, then," said Darly. "You're no good here."

"Darly, be careful with my car. Be careful."

The ancient sea bed at this place was flat and low and the lights of her car and of the truck and of the tungsten miner's Chevrolet were bright and big at twenty miles. Hattie was too frightened to think of this. All she could think was that she was a procrastinating old woman; she had lived by delays; she had meant to stop drinking, she had put off the time, and now she had smashed her car—a terrible end, a terrible judgment on her. She got to the ground and, drawing up her skirt, she started to get over the tow chain. To prove that the chain didn't have to be shortened, and to get the whole thing over with, Darly threw the pick-up forward again. The chain jerked up and struck Hattie in the knee and she fell forward and broke her arm.

She cried, "Darly, Darly, I'm hurt. I fell."

"The old lady tripped on the chain," said the miner. "Back up here and I'll double it for you. You're getting nowheres."

Drunkenly the miner lay down on his back in the dark, soft red cinders of the roadbed. Darly had backed up to slacken the chain.

Darly hurt the miner, too. He tore some skin from his fingers by racing ahead before the chain was secure. Uncomplainingly the miner wrapped his hand in his shirt-tail saying, "She'll do it now." The old car came down from the tracks and stood on the shoulder of the road.

"There's your goddam car," said Darly to Hattie.

"Is it all right?" she said. Her left side was covered with dirt, but she managed to pick herself up and stand, round-backed and heavy, on her stiff legs. "I'm hurt, Darly." She tried to convince him of it.

"Hell if you are," he said. He believed she was putting on an act to escape blame. The pain in his ribs made him especially impatient with her. "Christ, if you can't look after yourself any more you've got no business out here."

"You're old yourself," she said. "Look what you did to me. You can't hold your liquor."

This offended him greatly. He said, "I'll take you to the Rolfes. They let you tie this on in the first place, so let them worry about you. I'm tired of your bunk, Hattie."

He speeded up. Chains, spade and crowbar clashed on the sides of the truck. She was frightened and held her arm and cried. Rolfe's dogs jumped at her to lick her when she went through the gate. She shrank from them crying, "Down, down."

"Darly," she cried in the darkness, "take care of my car. Don't leave it standing there on the road. Darly, take care of it, please."

But Darly in his ten-gallon hat, his chin-bent face wrinkled, small and angry, a furious pain in his ribs, tore away at high speed.

"Oh, God, what will I do!" she said.

The Rolfes were having a last drink before dinner, sitting at their fire of pitchy railroad sleepers, when Hattie opened the door. Her knee was bleeding, her eyes were tiny with shock, her face grey with dust.

"I'm hurt," she said desperately. "I had an accident. I sneezed and lost control of the wheel. Jerry, look after the car. It's on the road."

They bandaged her knee and took her home and put her to bed. Helen Rolfe wrapped a heating pad around her arm.

"I can't have the pad," Hattie complained. "The switch goes on and off and every time it does it starts my generator and uses up the gas."

"Ah, now, Hattie," Rolfe said, "this is not the time to be stingy. We'll take you to town in the morning and have you looked over. Helen will phone Doctor Stroud."

Hattie wanted to say, "Stingy! Why, you're the stingy ones. I just haven't got anything. You and Helen are ready to hit each other over two bits in canasta." But the Rolfes were good to her; they were her only real friends here. Darly would have let her lie in the yard all night, and Pace would sell her to the bone man if he had an offer.

So she didn't talk back to the Rolfes, but as soon as they left the yellow house and walked through the super-clear moonlight under the great skirt of branch shadows to their new car, Hattie turned off the switch and the heavy swirling and battering of the generator stopped. Presently she began to have her first real taste of the pain in her arm, and she sat rigid and warmed the injured place with her hand. It seemed to her that she could feel the bone. Before leaving, Helen Rolfe had thrown over her an eiderdown that had belonged to Hattie's dead friend India, from whom she had inherited the small house and everything in it. Had the eiderdown lain on India's bed the night she died? Hattie tried to remember, but her thoughts were mixed up. She was fairly sure the death-bed pillow was in the loft, and she believed she had put the rest of the bedding in a trunk. Then how had this eiderdown got out? She couldn't do anything about it now but draw it away from contact with her skin. It kept her legs warm; this she accepted, but she didn't want it any nearer.

More and more Hattie saw her own life as though from birth to the present every moment had been filmed. Her fancy was that when she died she would see the film shown. Then she would know how she appeared from the back, watering the plants, in the bathroom, asleep, playing the organ, embracing—everything, even tonight, in pain, almost the last pain, perhaps, for she couldn't take much more. How many more turns had life to show her yet? There couldn't be a lot. To lie awake and think such thoughts was the worst thing in the world. Better death than insomnia. Hattie not only loved sleep, she believed in it.

The first attempt to set the bone was not successful. "Look what they've done to me," said Hattie and showed the discoloured skin on her breast. After the second operation her mind wandered. The sides of her bed had to be raised, for in her delirium she roamed the wards. She cried at the nurses when they shut her in, "You can't make people prisoners in a democracy without a trial." She cursed them fiercely.

For several weeks her mind was not clear. Asleep, her face was lifeless; her cheeks were puffed out and her mouth, no longer wide and grinning, was drawn round and small. Helen sighed when she saw her.

"Shall we get in touch with her family?" she asked the doctor. "She has a brother in Maine who is very strait-laced. And another one down in Mexico, even older than Hattie."

"No younger relations?" asked the doctor. His skin was white and thick. He had chestnut hair, abundant but very dry. He sometimes explained to his patients, "I had a tropical disease during the war."

"Cousins' children," said Helen. She tried to think who would be called to her own bedside. Rolfe would see that she was cared for. He would hire a nurse. Hattie could not afford one. She had already gone beyond her means. A trust company in Philadelphia paid her eighty dollars a month. She had a small bank account.

"I suppose it will be up to us to get her out of hock," said Rolfe. "Unless the brother down in Mexico comes across."

In the end, no relations had to be called. Hattie began to recover. At last she could recognise some of her friends, though her mind was still in disorder; much that had happened she couldn't recall.

"How much blood did they have to give me?" she kept asking. "I seem to remember five, six, eight different times. Daylight, electric light. . . ." She tried to smile, but she couldn't make a pleasant face as yet. "How am I going to pay?" she said. "At twenty-five bucks a quart. My little bit of money is just about wiped out."

Blood became her constant topic, her preoccupation. She told everyone who came to see her, "—have to replace all that blood. They poured gallons of the stuff into me. I hope it was all good."

And, though very weak. she began to grin and laugh again. There was more of a hiss in her laughter than formerly; the illness had affected her chest.

"No cigarettes, no booze," the doctor told Helen.

"Doctor," Helen asked him, "do you expect her to change?"

"All the same, I am obliged to say it."

"Life may not be much of a temptation to her," said Helen.

Her husband laughed. When his laughter was intense it blinded one of his eyes and his short Irish face turned red except for the bridge of his small, sharp nose where the skin grew white. "Hattie's like me," he said. "She'll be in business till she's cleaned out. And if Sego Lake was all whisky she'd use her last strength to knock her old yellow house down and build a raft of it. So why talk temperance to her now?"

Hattie recognised the similarity between them. When he came to see her she said, "Jerry, you're the only one I can really talk to about my troubles. What am I going to do for money? I have Hotchkiss Insurance. I paid eight dollars a month."

"That won't do you much good, Hat. No Blue Cross?"

"I let it drop ten years ago. Maybe I could sell some of my valuables."

"What have you got?" he said. His eye began to droop with laughter.

"Why," she said defiantly, "there's plenty. First there's the beautiful, precious Persian rug that India left me."

"Coals from the fireplace have been burning it for years, Hat!"

"The rug is in perfect condition," she said with an angry sway of her shoulders. "A beautiful object like that never loses its value. And the oak table from the Spanish monastery is three hundred years old."

"With luck you could get twenty bucks for it. It would cost fifty to haul it out of here. It's the house you ought to sell."

"The house?" she said. Yes, that had been in her mind. "I'd have to get twenty thousand for it."

"Eight is a fair price."

"Fifteen. . . ." She was offended, and her voice recovered its strength. "India put eight into it in two years. And don't forget that Sego Lake is one of the most beautiful places in the world."

"But where is it? Five hundred and some miles to San Francisco and two hundred to Salt Lake City. Who wants to live way out here in Utah but a few eccentrics like you and India and me?"

"There are things you can't put a price tag on. Beautiful things."

"Oh, bull, Hattie! You don't know what they are any more than I do. I live here because it figures for me, and you because India left you the house. And just in the nick of time, too. Without it you wouldn't have had a pot of your own."

His words offended Hattie; more than that, they frightened her. She was silent and then grew thoughtful, for she was fond of Jerry Rolfe and he of her. He had good sense and moreover he only spoke her own thoughts. He spoke no more than the truth about India's death and the house. But she told herself, *He doesn't know everything. You'd have to pay a San Francisco architect ten thousand just to* think *of such a house. Before he drew a line.*

"Jerry," the old woman said, "what am I going to do about replacing the blood in the blood bank?"

"Do you want a quart from me, Hat?" His eye began to fall shut.

"You won't do. You had that tumour, two years ago. I think Darly ought to give some."

"The old man?" Rolfe laughed at her. "You want to kill him?"

"Why," said Hattie with anger, lifting up her massive face with its fringe of curls which had become frayed by fever and perspiration; at the back of her head the hair had knotted and matted so that it had to be shaved, "he almost killed me. It's his fault that I'm in this condition. He must have blood in him. He runs after all the chicks —all of them—young and old."

"Come, you were drunk, too," said Rolfe.

"I've driven drunk for forty years. It was the sneeze. Oh, Jerry, I feel wrung out," said Hattie, haggard, sitting forward in bed. But her face was cleft by her nonsensically happy grin. She was not one to be miserable for long; she had the expression of a perennial survivor.

Every other day she went to the therapist. The young woman worked her arm for her; it was a pleasure and a comfort to Hattie, who would have been glad to leave the whole cure to her. However, she was given other exercises to do, and these were not so easy. They rigged a pulley for her and Hattie had to hold both ends of a rope and saw it back and forth through the scraping little wheel. She bent heavily from the hips and coughed over her cigarette. But the most important exercise of all she shirked. This required her to put the flat of her hand to the wall at the level of her hips and, by working her finger-tips slowly, to make the hand ascend to the height of her shoulder. That was painful; she often forgot to do it, although the doctor warned her, "Hattie, you don't want adhesions, do you?"

A light of despair crossed Hattie's eyes. Then she said, "Oh, Dr. Stroud, buy my house from me."

"I'm a bachelor. What would I do with a house?"

"I know just the girl for you—my cousin's daughter. Perfectly charming and very brainy. Just about got her Ph.D."

"You must get quite a few proposals yourself," said the doctor.

"From crazy desert rats. They chase me. But," she said, "after I pay my bills I'll be in pretty punk shape. If at least I could replace that blood in the blood bank I'd feel easier."

"If you don't do as the therapist tells you, Hattie, you'll need another operation. Do you know what adhesions are?"

She knew. But Hattie thought, *How long must I go on taking care of myself?* It made her angry to hear him speak of another operation. She had a moment of panic, but she veiled it from him. With him, this young man whose skin was already as thick as buttermilk and whose chestnut hair was as dry as death, she always assumed the part of a small child. She said, "Yes, doctor." But her heart was in a fury.

Night and day, however, she repeated, "I was in the Valley of the Shadow. But I'm alive." She was weak, she was old, she couldn't follow a train of thought very easily, she felt faint in the head. But she was still here; here was her body, it filled space, a great body. And though she had worries and perplexities, and once in a while her arm felt as though it was about to give her the last stab of all; and though her hair was scrappy and old, like onion roots, and scattered like nothing under the comb, yet she sat and amused herself with visitors; her great grin split her face; her heart warmed with every kind word.

And she thought, 'People will help me out. It never did me any good to worry. At the last minute something turned up, when I wasn't looking for it. Marian loves me. Helen and Jerry love me.

Half Pint loves me. They would never let me go to the ground. And I love them. If it were the other way around, I'd never let them go down.'

Above a horizon in a baggy vastness which Hattie by herself occasionally visited, the features of India, or her shade, sometimes rose. She was indignant and scolding. Not mean. Not really mean. Few people had ever been really mean to Hattie. But India was annoyed with her. "The garden is going to hell, Hattie," she said. "Those lilac bushes are all shrivelled."

"But what can I do? The hose is rotten. It broke. It won't reach."

"Then dig a trench," said the phantom of India. "Have old Sam dig a trench. But save the bushes."

Am I thy servant still? said Hattie to herself. *No*, she thought, *let the dead bury their dead.*

But she didn't defy India now any more than she had done when they lived together. Hattie was supposed to keep India off the bottle, but often both of them began to get drunk after breakfast. They forgot to dress, and in their slips the two of them wandered drunkenly around the house and blundered into each other, and they were in despair at having been so weak. Late in the afternoon they would be sitting in the living-room, waiting for the sun to set. It shrank, burning itself out on the crumbling edges of the mountains. When the sun passed, the fury of the daylight ended and the mountain surfaces were more blue, broken, like cliffs of coal. They no longer suggested faces. The east began to look simple, and the lake less inhuman and haughty. At last India would say, "Hattie—it's time for the lights." And Hattie would pull the switch chains of the lamps, several of them, to give the generator a good shove. She would turn on some of the wobbling eighteenth-century-style lamps whose shades stood out from their slender bodies like dragonflies' wings. The little engine in the shed would shuffle, then spit, then charge and bang, and the first weak light would rise unevenly in the bulbs.

"*Hettie!*" cried India. After she drank she was penitent, but her penitence too was a hardship to Hattie, and the worse her temper the more English her accent became. "*Where the hell ah you, Hettie!*" After India's death Hattie found some poems she had written in which she, Hattie, was affectionately and even touchingly mentioned. But Hattie's interest in ideas was very small, whereas India had been all over the world and was used to brilliant society. India wanted her to discuss Eastern religion, Bergson and Proust, and Hattie had no head for this, and so India blamed her drinking on Hattie. "I can't talk to you," she would say. "And I'm here because I'm not fit to be anywhere else. I can't live in New York any more. It's too dangerous for a woman my age to be drunk in the street at night."

And Hattie, talking to her Western friends about India, would say, "She is a lady" (implying that they made a pair). "She is a creative person" (this was why they found each other so congenial). "But helpless? Completely. Why, she can't even get her own girdle on."

"Hettie! come here. Het-tie! Do you know what sloth is?"

Undressed, India sat on her bed and with the cigarette in her drunken, wrinkled, ringed hand she burned holes in the blankets. On Hattie's pride she left many small scars, too. She treated her like a servant.

Weeping, India begged her afterwards to forgive her. *"Hattie, please, don't condemn me in your heart. Forgive me, dear, I know I am bad. But I hurt myself more in my evil than I hurt you."*

Hattie would keep a stiff bearing. She would lift up her face with its incurved nose and puffy eyes, and say, "I am a Christian person. I never bear a grudge." And by repeating this she actually brought herself to forgive India.

But of course she had no husband, no child, no skill, no savings. And what she would have done if India had not died and left her the yellow house, nobody knows.

Jerry Rolfe said privately to Marian, "Hattie can't do anything for herself. If I hadn't been around during the '44 blizzard she and India both would have starved. She's always been careless and lazy and now she can't even chase a cow out of her yard. She's too feeble. The thing for her to do is go East to her brother. Hattie would have ended at the poor farm if it hadn't been for India. But India should have left her something besides the house. Some dough. India didn't use her head."

When Hattie returned to the lake she stayed with the Rolfes.

"Well, old shellback," said Jerry, "there's a little more life in you now."

Indeed, with joyous eyes, the cigarette in her mouth and her hair newly frizzed and overhanging her forehead, she seemed to have triumphed again. She was pale, but she grinned, she chuckled, and she held a bourbon Old-Fashioned with a cherry and a slice of orange in it. She was on rations; the Rolfes allowed her two a day. Her back, Helen noted, was more bent than before. Her knees went outward a little weakly; her feet, however, came close together at the ankles.

"Oh, Helen dear and Jerry dear, I am so thankful, so glad to be back at the lake. I can look after my place again, and I'm here to see the spring. It's more gorgeous than ever."

Heavy rains had fallen while Hattie was away. The sego lilies, which bloomed only after a wet winter, came up from the loose dust, especially around the marl pit; but even on the burnt granite they seemed to grow. Desert peach was beginning to appear and in Hattie's yard the rose-bushes were filling out. The roses were yellow and abundant, and the odour they gave off was like that of damp tea leaves.

"Before it gets hot enough for the rattlesnakes," said Hattie to Helen, "we ought to drive up to Marky's ranch to cut watercress."

Hattie was going to attend to lots of things, but the heat came early that year and, as there was no television to keep her awake, she slept most of the day. She was now able to dress herself, though there was little more that she could do. Sam Jervis rigged the pulley for her on the porch and she remembered once in a while to use it. Mornings when she had her strength she rambled over to her own house, examining things, behaving importantly and giving orders to Sam Jervis and Wanda Gingham. At ninety, Wanda, a Shoshone, was still an excellent seamstress and house cleaner.

Hattie looked over the car, which was parked under a cottonwood tree. She tested the engine. Yes, the old pot would still go. Proudly, happily, she listened to the noise of tappets; the dry old pipe shook as the smoke went out at the rear. She tried to work the shift, turn the wheel. That, as yet, she couldn't do. But it would come soon, she was confident.

At the back of the house the soil had caved in a little over the cesspool and a few of the old railroad sleepers over the top had rotted. Otherwise things were in good shape. Sam had looked after the garden. He had fixed a new catch for the gate after Pace's horses—maybe because he never could afford to keep them in hay—had broken in and Sam found them grazing and drove them out. Luckily they hadn't damaged many of her plants. Hattie felt a moment of wild rage against Pace. He had brought the horses into her garden, she was sure. But her anger didn't last long. It was reabsorbed into the feeling of golden pleasure that enveloped her. She had little strength, but all that she had was a pleasure to her. So she forgave even Pace, who would have liked to do her out of the house, who had always used her, embarrassed her, cheated her at cards, passed the buck whenever he could. He was a fool about horses. They were ruining him. Breeding horses was a millionaire's amusement.

She saw the animals in the distance, feeding. Unsaddled, the mares appeared undressed; they reminded her of naked women, walking with their glossy flanks in the sego lilies which curled on the ground. The flowers were yellowish, like winter wool, but fragrant; the mares, naked and gentle, walked through them. Their strolling, their perfect beauty, the sound of their hoofs on stone touched a deep place in Hattie's nature. Her love for horses, birds and dogs was well-known. Dogs led the list. And now a piece cut from a green blanket reminded her of Richie. The blanket was one he had torn, and she had cut it into strips and placed them under the doors to keep out the draughts. In the house she found more traces of him: hair he had shed on the furniture. Hattie was going to borrow Helen's vacuum cleaner, but there wasn't really enough current to make it pull as it should. On the doorknob of India's room hung the dog collar.

Hattie had decided to have herself moved into India's bed when she lay dying. Why use two beds? A perilous look came into her eyes while her lips pressed together forbiddingly. 'I follow,' she said, speaking to India with an inner voice, 'so never mind.' Presently—before long—she would have to leave the yellow house in her turn. And as she went into the parlour thinking of the will, she sighed. Pretty soon she would have to attend to it. India's lawyer, Claiborne, helped her with such things. She had phoned him in town, while she was staying with Marian, and talked matters over

with him. He had promised to try to see the house for her. Fifteen
thousand was her bottom price, she said. If he couldn't find a
buyer, perhaps he could find a tenant. Two hundred dollars a month
was the rental she set. Rolfe laughed. But Hattie turned toward
him one of those proud, dulled looks she always took on when he
angered her and said haughtily, "For summer on Sego Lake?"

"You're competing with Pace's ranch."

"Why, the food is stinking down there. He cheats the dudes," said
Hattie. "He really cheats them at cards. You'll never catch me
playing blackjack with him again."

And what would she do, thought Hattie, if Claiborne could
neither rent nor sell the house? This question she shook off as
regularly as it returned. *I don't have to be a burden on anybody*, thought
Hattie. *It's looked bad many a time before, but when push came to shove, I
made it. Somehow I got by.* But she argued with herself. *How many
times? How long, O God—an old thing, feeble, no use to anyone?* Who said
she had any right to hold a piece of property?

She was sitting on her sofa, which was very old, India's sofa, eight
feet long, kidney-shaped, puffy and bald. An underlying pink shone
through the green; the upholstered tufts were like the pads of dogs'
paws; between them rose bunches of hair. Here Hattie slouched,
resting, with her knees wide apart and a cigarette in her mouth, eyes
half shut but far-seeing. The mountains seemed not fifteen miles but
fifteen hundred yards away, the lake a blue band; the tea-like odour
of the roses, though they were still unopened, was already in the air,
for Sam was watering them in the heat. Gratefully Hattie yelled,
"Sam!"

Sam was very old, and all shanks. His feet looked big. His old
railroad jacket was made tight across his back by his stoop. A
crooked finger with its great broad nail over the mouth of the hose
made the water spray and sparkle. Happy to see Hattie he turned
his long jaw, empty of teeth, and his blue eyes, which seemed to
penetrate his temples with their length (it was his face that turned,
not his body), and he said, "Oh, there, Hattie. You've made it back
today? Welcome, Hattie."

"Have a beer, Sam. Come around the back and I'll give you a
beer."

She never had Sam come in, owing to his skin disease. There were raw patches on his chin and the back of his ears. Hattie feared in-fection from his touch. She gave him the beer can, never a glass, and she put on gloves before she used the garden tools. Since he would take no money from her—she had to pay Wanda Gingham a dollar a day—she got Marian to find old clothes for him in town and she left food for him at the door of the damp-wood-smelling boxcar where he lived.

"How's the old wing, Hat?" he said.

"It's coming. I'll be driving again before you know it," she told him. "By the first of May I'll be driving again." Every week she moved the date forward. "By Decoration Day I expect to be on my own again," she said. In mid-June however she was still unable to drive. Helen Rolfe said to her, "Hattie, Jerry and I are due in Seattle the first week of July."

"Why, you never told me that," said Hattie.

"You don't mean to tell me this is the first you heard of it," said Helen. "You've known about it from the first—since Christmas."

It wasn't easy for Hattie to meet her eyes. She presently put her head down. Her face became very dry, especially the lips. "Well, don't you worry about me. I'll be all right here," she said.

"Who's going to look after you?" said Jerry. He evaded nothing himself and tolerated very little evasion in others. Except, as Hattie knew, he always indulged her. She couldn't count on her friend Half Pint, she couldn't really count on Marian either. Until now, this very moment, she had only the Rolfes to turn to. Helen, trying to be steady, gazed at her and made sad, involuntary movements with her head, sometimes nodding, sometimes seeming as if she dis-agreed. Hattie, with her inner voice, swore at her: *Bitch-eyes. I can't win because I'm old. Is that fair?* And yet she admired Helen's eyes. Even the skin about them, slightly wrinkled underneath, was touch-ing, beautiful. There was a heaviness in her bust that went, as if by attachment, with the heaviness of her eyes. Her head, her hands and feet should have taken a more slender body. Helen, said Hattie, was the nearest thing she had on this earth to a sister. But there was no reason to go to Seattle—no genuine business. It was only idleness, only a holiday. The only reason was Hattie herself; this was their way of telling her that there was a limit to what she could expect them to do. Helen's head wavered, but her thoughts were steady;

she knew what was passing through Hattie's mind. Like Hattie, she was an idle woman. Why was her right to idleness better?

Because of money? thought Hattie. Because of age? Because she has a husband? Because she had a daughter in Swarthmore College? But a funny thing occurred to her. Helen disliked being idle, whereas she herself never made any bones that an idle life was all she was ever good for. But for her it was uphill, all the way, because when Waggoner divorced her she didn't have a cent. She even had to support Wicks for seven or eight years. Except with horses, he had no sense. And then she had had to take a ton of dirt from India. *I am the one*, Hattie asserted to herself. *I would know what to do with Helen's advantages. She only suffers from them. And if she wants to stop being an idle woman why can't she start with me, her neighbour?* Her skin, for all its puffiness, burned with anger. She said to Rolfe and Helen, "Don't worry. I'll make out by myself. But if I have to leave the lake you'll be ten times more lonely than before. Now I'm going back to my house."

She lifted up her broad old face and her lips were childlike with suffering. She would never take back what she had said.

But the trouble was no ordinary trouble. Hattie was herself aware that she rambled, forgot names, and answered when no one spoke.

"We can't just take charge of her," Rolfe said. "What's more, she ought to be near a doctor. She keeps her shotgun loaded so she can fire it if anything happens to her in the house. But who knows what she'll do? I don't believe it was Jacamares who killed that Doberman of hers."

He drove into her yard the day after she returned to her house and said, "I'm going into town. I can bring you some chow if you like."

She couldn't afford to refuse his offer, angry though she was, and she said, "Yes, bring me some stuff from the Mountain Street Market. Charge it." She only had some frozen shrimp and a few cans of beer in the ice-box. When Rolfe had gone she put out the shrimp to thaw.

People really used to stick by one another in the West. Hattie now saw herself as one of the pioneers. This modern race had come later. After all, she had lived on the range like an old-timer. Wicks had had to shoot their Christmas dinner and she had cooked it—

venison. He killed it on the reservation, and if the Paiutes had caught them there would have been hell to pay.

The weather was hot, the clouds were heavy and calm in a large sky. The horizon was so huge that in it the lake must have seemed like a saucer of milk. *Some milk!* Hattie thought. Two thousand feet deep in the middle, so deep no body could ever be recovered. It went around with the currents, and there were rocks like eye-teeth, and hot springs, and colourless fish at the bottom which were never caught. Now that the white pelicans were nesting they patrolled the rocks for snakes and other egg thieves. They were so big and flew so slow you might imagine they were angels. Hattie no longer visited the lake shore; the walk exhausted her. She saved her strength to go to Pace's bar in the afternoon.

She took off her shoes and stockings and walked on bare feet from one end of her house to the other. On the land side she saw Wanda Gingham sitting near the tracks while her great-grandson played in the soft red gravel. Wanda wore a large purple shawl and her black head was bare. All about her was—was nothing, Hattie thought; for she had taken a drink, breaking her rule. Nothing but mountains, thrust out like men's bodies; the sagebrush was the hair on their chests.

The warm wind blew dust from the marl pit. This white powder made her sky less blue. On the water side were the pelicans, pure as spirits, slow as angels, blessing the air as they flew with great wings.

Should she or should she not have Sam do something about the vine on the chimney? Sparrows nested in it, and she was glad of that. But all summer long the king snakes were after them and she was afraid to walk in the garden. When the sparrows scratched the ground for seed they took a funny bound; they held their legs stiff and flung back the dust with both feet. Hattie sat down at her old Spanish table, watching them in the cloudy warmth of the day, clasping her hands, chuckling and sad. The bushes were crowded with yellow roses, half of them now rotted. The lizards scrambled from shadow to shadow. The water was smooth as air, gaudy as silk. The mountains succumbed, falling asleep in the heat. Drowsy, Hattie lay down on her sofa; its pads were like dogs' paws. She gave in to sleep and when she woke it was midnight; she did not want to

alarm the Rolfes by putting on her lights, so took advantage of the
moon to eat a few thawed shrimps and go to the bathroom. She undressed and lifted herself into bed and lay there feeling her sore arm.
Now she knew how much she missed her dog. The whole matter of
the dog weighed heavily on her soul; she came close to tears in
thinking about him and she went to sleep, oppressed by her secret.

I suppose I had better try to pull myself together a little, thought Hattie
nervously in the morning. *I can't just sleep my way through.* She knew
what her difficulty was. Before any serious question her mind gave
way; it became diffused. She said to herself, *I can see bright, but I feel
dim. I guess I'm not so lively any more. Maybe I'm becoming a little
touched in the head, as mother was.* But she was not so old as her mother
was when she did those strange things. At eighty-five her mother had
to be kept from going naked in the street. *I'm not as bad as that yet,*
thought Hattie. *Thank God. I walked into the men's wards, but that was
when I had a fever, and my nightie was on.*

She drank a cup of Nescafé and it strengthened her determination
to do something for herself. In all the world she had only her brother
Angus to go to. Her brother Will had led a rough life; he was an old
heller, and now he drove everyone away. He was too crabby,
thought Hattie. Besides he was angry because she had lived so long
with Wicks. Angus would forgive her. But then he and his wife were
not her kind. With them she couldn't drink, she couldn't smoke, she
had to make herself small-mouthed, and she would have to wait
while they read a chapter of the Bible before breakfast. Hattie could
not bear to wait for meals. Besides, she had a house of her own at
last; why should she have to leave it? She had never owned a thing
before. And now she was not allowed to enjoy her yellow house. *But
I'll keep it,* she said to herself rebelliously. *I swear to God I'll keep it.
Why, I barely just got it. I haven't had time.* And she went out on the
porch to work the pulley and do something about the adhesions in
her arm. She was sure now that they were there. *And what will I do?*
she cried to herself. *What will I do? Why did I ever go to Rolfe's that
night—and why did I lose control on the crossing!* She couldn't say now "I
sneezed". She couldn't even remember what had happened, except
that she saw the boulders and the twisting blue rails and Darly. It
was Darly's fault. He was sick and old himself, and couldn't make it.
He envied her the house, and her woman's peaceful life. Since she

returned from the hospital he hadn't even come to visit her. He only said, "Hell, I'm sorry for her, but it was her fault." What hurt him most was that she said he couldn't hold his liquor.

Her resolve to pull herself together did not last; she remained the same procrastinating old woman. She had a letter to answer from Hotchkiss Insurance, and it drifted out of sight. She was going to phone Claiborne the lawyer, and it slipped her mind. One morning she announced to Helen that she believed she would apply to an institution in Los Angeles that took over the property of old people and managed it for them. They gave you an apartment right on the ocean, and your meals and medical care. You had to sign over half of your estate. "It's fair enough," said Hattie. "They take a gamble I may live to be a hundred."

"I wouldn't be surprised," said Helen.

However, Hattie never got around to sending to Los Angeles for the brochure. But Jerry Rolfe took it on himself to write a letter to her brother Angus about her condition. And he drove over also to have a talk with Amy Walters, the gold miner's widow at Fort Walters—as the ancient woman called it. One old tar-paper building was what she owned, plus the mine shafts, no longer in use since the death of her second husband. On a heap of stones near the road a crimson sign *Fort Walters* was placed, and over it a flagpole. The American flag was raised every day. Amy was working in the garden in one of dead Bill's shirts. He had brought water down from the mountains for her in a home-made aqueduct so she could raise her own peaches and vegetables.

"Amy," Rolfe said, "Hattie's back from the hospital and living all alone. You have no folks and neither has she. Not to beat around the bush about it, why don't you live together?"

Amy's face had great delicacy. Her winter baths in the lake and her soups and the waltzes she played for herself alone on the grand piano that stood beside her wood stove and the murder stories she read till darkness made her go to bed had made her remote. She looked delicate, yet her composure couldn't be touched. It was very strange.

"Hattie and me have different habits, Jerry," said Amy. "And Hattie wouldn't like my company. I can't drink with her."

L

"That's true," said Rolfe, recalling that Hattie referred to Amy as though she were a ghost. He couldn't speak to Amy of the solitary death that was in store for her. There was not a cloud in the arid sky today, and there was not a shadow of death on Amy. She was tranquil, she seemed to be supplied with a sort of pure fluid that would feed her life slowly for years to come.

He said, "All kinds of things could happen to a woman like Hattie in that yellow house, and nobody would know."

"That's a fact. She doesn't know how to take care of herself."

"She can't. Her arm hasn't healed."

Amy didn't say that she was sorry to hear it. In the place of those words came a silence which could have meant that. Then she said, "I might go for a few hours a day, but she would have to pay me."

"Now, Amy, you must know as well as I do that Hattie has never had any money—not much more than her pension. Just the house."

At once Amy said, no pause coming between his words and hers, "I would take care of her if she'd agree to leave the house to me."

"Leave it in your hands, you mean?" said Rolfe. "To manage?"

"In her will. To belong to me."

"Why, Amy, what would you do with Hattie's house?" he said.

"It would be my property, that's all. I'd have it."

"Maybe you would leave Fort Walters to her in your will," he said.

"Oh no," she answered quickly. "Why should I do that? I'm not asking Hattie for her help. I don't need it. Hattie is a city woman."

Rolfe could not carry this proposal back to Hattie. He was too wise ever to mention her will to her.

But Pace was not so careful of her feelings. By mid-June Hattie had begun to visit the bar regularly. She had so many things to think about she couldn't keep herself at home. When Pace came in from the yard one day—he had been packing the axles of his horse-trailer and was wiping grease from his fingers—he said with his usual bluntness, "How would you like it if I paid you fifty bucks a month for the rest of your life, Hat?"

Hattie was holding her second Old-Fashioned of the day. At the bar she made it appear that she observed the limit; but she had started drinking at home after lunch. She began to grin, expecting Pace to make one of his jokes. But he was wearing his scoop-shaped Western hat as level as a Quaker, and he had drawn down his chin, a sign that he was not fooling. She said, "That would be nice, but what's the catch?"

"No catch," he said. "This is what we'd do. I'd give you five hundred dollars cash, and fifty bucks a month for life, and you'd let me put some dudes in the yellow house, and you'd leave the house to me in your will."

"What kind of a deal is that?" said Hattie, her look changing. "I thought we were friends."

"It's the best deal you'll ever get," he said.

That day was sultry, but Hattie till now had thought that it was nice, that she was dreamy, but comfortable, about to begin to enjoy the cool of the day; but now she felt that such cruelty and injustice had been waiting to attack her that it would have been better to die in the hospital than be so disillusioned.

She cried, "Everybody wants to push me out. You're a cheater, Pace. God! I know you. Pick on somebody else. Why do you have to pick on me? Just because I happen to be around?"

"Why, no, Hattie," he said, trying now to be careful. "It was just a business offer."

"Why don't you give me some blood for the bank if you're such a friend of mine?"

"Well, Hattie, you drink too much, and you oughtn't have been driving anyway."

"The whole thing happened because I sneezed. Everybody knows it. I wouldn't sell you my house. I'd give it away to the lepers first. You'd let me go and then never send me a cent. You never pay anybody. You can't even buy wholesale in town any more because nobody trusts you. It looks as though I'm stuck, that's all, just stuck. I keep on saying that this is my only home in all the world, this is where my friends are, and the weather is always perfect and the lake is beautiful. I wish the whole damn empty old place were in Hell. It's not human and neither are you. But I'll be here the day the sheriff takes your horses—you never mind."

He told her then that she was drunk again, and so she was, but she was more than that, and though her head was spinning she decided to go back to the house at once and take care of some things she had been putting off. This very day she was going to write to the lawyer, Claiborne, and make sure that Pace never got her property. She wouldn't put it past him to swear in court that India had promised him the yellow house.

She sat at the table with pen and paper, trying to think how to put it.

"I want this on record," she wrote. "I could kick myself in the head when I think how he's led me on. I have been his patsy ten thousand times. As when that drunk crashed his Cub plane on the lake shore. At the coroner's jury he let me take the whole blame. He had instructed me when I was working for him never to take in any drunks. And this flier was drunk. He had nothing on but a T shirt and Bermuda shorts and he was flying from Sacramento to Salt Lake City. At the inquest Pace denied he had ever given me such instructions. The same was true when the cook went haywire. She was a tramp. He never hires decent help. He cheated her on the bar bill and blamed me and she went after me with a meat cleaver. She disliked me because I criticised her for drinking at the bar in her one-piece white bathing suit with the dude guests. But he turned her loose on me. He hints that he did certain things for India. She would never have let him. He was too common for her. It can never be said about India that she was not a lady in every way. He thinks he is the greatest sack-artist in the world. He only loves horses, as a fact. He has no claims at all, oral or written, on this yellow house. I want you to have this over my signature. He was cruel to Pickle-Tits who was his first wife, and he's no better to the charming woman who is his present one. I don't know why she takes it. It must be despair." She said to herself, *I don't suppose I'd better send that.*

She was still angry. Her heart was knocking from within: the deep pulses, as after a hot bath, beat at the back of her thighs. The air outside was dotted with transparent particles. The mountains were red as clinkers. The iris leaves were fan sticks—they stuck out like Jiggs' hair.

She always ended by looking out of the window at the desert and the lake. *They drew you from yourself. But after they had drawn you, what did they do with you? It was too late to find out. I'll never know. I wasn't meant to. I'm not the type,* Hattie reflected. *Maybe something too cruel for women or for any woman, young or old.*

So she stood up and, rising, she had the sensation that she had gradually become a container for herself. *You get old, your heart, your liver, your lungs seem to expand in size, and the walls of the body give way outward,* she thought, *and you take the shape of an old jug, wider and wider towards the top. You swell up with tears and fat.* She no longer even smelled to herself like a woman. Her face with its much-slept-upon skin was only faintly like her own—like a cloud that has changed. It was a face. It became a ball of yarn. It had drifted open. It had scattered.

I was never one single thing anyway, she thought. *Never my own. I was only loaned to myself.*

But the thing wasn't over yet. And in fact she didn't know for certain that it was ever going to be over; she had only had other people's word for it that death was such and such. *How do I know?* she asked herself challengingly. Her anger had sobered her for a little while. Now she was again drunk. *It was strange. It is strange. It may continue being strange.* She further thought, *I used to wish for death more than I do now. Because I didn't have anything at all. I changed when I got a roof of my own over me. And now? Do I have to go? I thought Marian loved me, but she has a sister. And I never thought Helen and Jerry would desert me. And now Pace insulted me. They think I'm not going to make it.*

She went to the cupboard—she kept the bourbon bottle there; she drank less if, each time, she had to rise and open the cupboard door. And, as if she were being watched, she poured a drink and swallowed it.

The notion that in this emptiness someone saw her was connected with the other fancy that she was being filmed from birth to death. That this was done for everyone. And afterwards you could view your life.

Hattie wanted to see some of it now, and she sat down on the dogs'-paw cushions of her sofa and, with her knees far apart and a smile of yearning and of fright, she bent her round back, burned a cigarette at the corner of her mouth and saw—the Church of Saint-Sulpice in Paris where her organ teacher used to bring her. It looked like country walls of stone, but rising high and leaning outwards were towers. She was very young. She knew music. The sky was grey. After this she saw some entertaining things she liked to tell people about. She was a young wife. She was in Aix-les-Bains with her mother-in-law, and they played bridge in a mud bath with a British general and his aide. There were artificial waves in the swimming pool. She lost her bathing suit because it was a size too big. How did she get out? Ah, you got out of everything.

She saw her husband, James John Waggoner IV. They were snowbound together in New Hampshire. "Jimmy, Jimmy, how can you fling a wife away?" she asked him. "Have you forgotten love? Did I drink too much—did I bore you?" He had married again and had two children. He had gotten tired of her. And though he was a vain man with nothing to be vain about—no looks, not too much intelligence, nothing but an old Philadelphia family—she had loved him. She too had been a snob about her Philadelphia connections. Give up the name of Waggoner? How could she? For this reason she had never married Wicks. "How dare you," she had said to Wicks, "come without a shave in a dirty shirt and muck on you, come and ask me to marry! If you want to propose, go and clean up first." But his dirt was only a pretext. *Trade Waggoner for Wicks?* she asked herself again with a swing of her shoulders. She wouldn't think of it. Wicks was an excellent man. But he was a cowboy. He couldn't even read. But she saw this on her film. They were in Athens Canyon, in a crate-like house, and she was reading aloud to him from *The Count of Monte Cristo*. He wouldn't let her stop. While walking to stretch her legs, she read, and he followed her about to catch each word. After all, he was very dear to her. Such a man! Now she saw him jump from his horse. They were living on the range, trapping coyotes. It was just the second grey of evening, cloudy, moments after the sun had gone down. There was an animal in the trap, and he went toward it to kill it. He wouldn't waste a bullet on the creatures, but killed them with a kick of his boot. And then Hattie saw that this coyote was all white—snarling teeth, white cruff. "Wicks, he's white! White as a polar bear. You're not going to kill him, are you?" The animal flattened to the ground. He snarled and cried. He couldn't pull away because of the heavy trap. And Wicks killed him. What else could he have done? The white beast lay dead. The dust of Wicks' boots hardly showed on its head and jaws. Blood ran from the muzzle.

And now came something on Hattie's film she tried to shun. It was she herself who had killed her dog, Richie. Just as Rolfe and Pace had warned her, he was vicious, his brain was turned. She, because she was on the side of all dumb creatures, defended him when he bit the trashy woman Jacamares was living with. Perhaps if she had had Richie from a puppy he wouldn't have turned on her. When she got him he was already a year and a half old and she couldn't break him of his habits. But she thought only she understood him. And Rolfe had warned her, "You'll be sued, do you know it? The dog will take out after somebody smarter than that Jacamares' woman and you'll be in for it."

Hattie saw herself as she swayed her shoulders and said, "Nonsense."

But what fear she had felt when the dog went for her on the porch. Suddenly she could see by his skull, by his eyes, that he was evil. She screamed at him, "Richie!" And what had she done to him? He had lain under the gas range all day growling and wouldn't come out. She tried to urge him out with the broom, and he snatched it in his teeth. She pulled him out and he left the stick and tore at her. Now, as the spectator of this, her eyes opened, beyond the pregnant curtain and the air wave of marl dust, summer's snow, drifting over the water. "Oh, my God! Richie!" Her thigh was snatched by his jaws. His teeth went through her skirt. She felt she would fall. Would she go down? Then the dog would rush at her throat—then black night, bad-odoured mouth, the blood pouring from her torn veins. Her heart shrivelled as the teeth went in her thigh, and she couldn't delay another second but took her kindling hatchet from the nail, strengthened her grip on the smooth wood and hit the dog. She saw the blow. She saw him die at once. And then in fear and shame she hid the body. And at night she buried him in the yard. Next day she accused Jacamares. On him she laid the blame for the disappearance of her dog.

She stood up; she spoke to herself in silence, as was her habit. *God, what shall I do? I have taken life. I have lied. I have borne false witness. I have stalled. And now what shall I do? Nobody will help me.*

And suddenly she made up her mind that she should go and do what she had been putting off for weeks, namely, test herself with the car, and she slipped on her shoes and went out. Lizards ran before her in the thirsty dust. She opened the hot, broad door of the car. She lifted her lame hand on to the wheel. Her right hand she reached far to the left and turned the wheel with all her might. Then she started the motor and tried to drive out of the yard. But she could not release the emergency brake with its rasp-like rod. She reached with her good hand, the right, under the steering wheel and pressed her bosom on it and strained. No, she could not shift the gears and steer. She couldn't even reach the hand brake. The sweat broke out on her skin. Her efforts were too much. She was deeply wounded by the pain in her arm. The door of the car fell open again and she turned from the wheel and, with her stiff legs outside the door, she wept. What could she do now? And when she had wept over the ruin of her life she got out of the old car and went back to the house. She took the bottle of bourbon from the cupboard and picked up the ink bottle and a pad of paper and sat down to write her will.

My Will, she wrote, and sobbed to herself.

Since the death of India she had numberless times asked the question, To Whom? Who will get this when I die? She had unconsciously put people to the test to find out whether they were worthy. It made her more severe than before.

Now she wrote, "I, Harriet Simmons Waggoner, being of sound mind and not knowing what may be in store for me at the age of seventy-two (born 1885), living alone at Sego Desert Lake, instruct my lawyer, Harold Claiborne, Paiute County Court Building, to draw my last will and testament upon the following terms."

She sat perfectly still now to hear from within who would be the lucky one, who would inherit the yellow house. For which she had waited. Yes, waited for India's death, choking on her bread because she was a rich woman's servant and whipping girl. But who had done for her, Hattie, what she had done for India? And who, apart from India, had ever held out a hand to her? Kindness, yes. Here and there people had been kind. But the word in her head was not kindness, it was succour. And who had given her that? Only India. If at least, next best after succour, someone had given her a shake and said, "Stop stalling. Don't be such a slow, old, procrastinating sit-stiller." Again, it was only India who had done her good. She had offered her succour. *"Het-tie!"* said that drunken mask. *"Do you know what sloth is? Damn your poky old life!"*

But I was waiting, Hattie realised. *I was waiting, thinking, "Youth is terrible, frightening. I will wait it out. And men? Men are cruel and strong. They want things I haven't got to give." There were no kids in me*, thought Hattie. *Not that I wouldn't have loved them, but such my nature was. And who can blame me for having it? My nature?*

She drank from an Old-Fashioned glass. There was no orange in it, no ice, no bitters or sugar, only the stinging, clear bourbon.

So then, she continued, looking at the dry sun-stamped dust and the last freckled flowers of red wild peach, *to live with Angus and his wife, and have to hear a chapter from the Bible before breakfast; once more in the house—not of a stranger, perhaps, but not far from it either*. In other houses, in someone else's house, to wait for mealtimes was her lifelong punishment. She always felt it in the throat and stomach. And so she would again, and to the very end. However, she must think of someone to leave the house to.

And first of all she wanted to do right by her family. None of them had ever dreamed that she, Hattie, would ever have something to bequeath. Until a few years ago it had certainly looked as if she would die a pauper. So now she could keep her head up with the proudest of them. And, as this occurred to her, she actually lifted up her face with its broad nose and victorious eyes; if her hair had become shabby as onion roots, if at the back her head was round and bald as a newel post, what did that matter? Her heart experienced a childish glory, not yet tired of it after seventy-two years. She, too, had amounted to something. *I'll do some good by going*, she thought. *Now I believe I should leave it to, to.* . . . She returned to the old point of struggle. She had decided many times and many times changed her mind. She tried to think. *Who would get the most out of it?* It was a tearing thing to go through. If it had not been the yellow house but instead some brittle thing she could hold in her hand, then the last thing she would do would be to throw and smash it, and so the thing and she herself would be demolished together. But it was vain to think such thoughts. To whom should she leave it? Her brothers? Not they. Nephews? One was a submarine commander. The other was a bachelor in the State Department. Then began the roll call of cousins. Merton? He owned an estate in Connecticut. Anna? She

had a face like a hot-water bottle. That left Joyce, the orphaned
daughter of her cousin Wilfred. Joyce was the most likely heiress.
Hattie had already written to her and had her out to the lake at
Thanksgiving, two years ago. But this Joyce was another odd one;
over thirty, good, yes, but placid, running to fat, a scholar—ten
years in Eugene, Oregon, working for her degree. In Hattie's
opinion this was only another form of sloth. Nevertheless, Joyce yet
hoped to marry. Whom? Not Dr. Stroud. He wouldn't. And still
she had vague hope. Hattie knew how that could be. At least have
a man she could argue with.

She was now more drunk than at any time since her accident.
Again she filled her glass. *Have ye eyes and see not? Sleepers, awake!*

Knees wide apart she sat in the twilight, thinking. Marian?
Marian didn't need another house. Half Pint? She wouldn't know
what to do with it. Brother Louis came up for consideration next.
He was an old actor who had a church for the Indians at Athens
Canyon. Hollywood stars of the silent days sent him their negligées;
he altered them and wore them in the pulpit. The Indians loved his
show. But when Billy Shawah blew his brains out after his two-
week bender, they still tore his shack down and turned it inside out
to get rid of his ghost. They had their old religion. No, not Brother
Louis. He'd show movies in the yellow house to the tribe or make a
nursery of it.

And now she began to consider Wicks. When last heard from he
was south of Bishop, California, a handy man in a saloon off towards
Death Valley. It wasn't she who heard from him, but Pace. Herself,
she hadn't actually seen Wicks since—how low she had sunk then!—
she had kept the hamburger stand on Route 158. The little lunch-
room had supported them both. Wicks hung around on the end
stool, rolling cigarettes (she saw it on the film). Then there was a
quarrel. Things had been going from bad to worse. He'd begun to
grouse now about this and now about that. He complained about
the food, at last. She saw and heard him. "Hat," he said, "I'm
good and tired of hamburger." "Well, what do you think I eat?"
she said with that round, defiant movement of her shoulders which
she herself recognised as characteristic (*me all over*, she thought). But
he opened the cash register and took out thirty cents and crossed
the street to the butcher's and brought back a steak. He threw

it on the griddle. "Fry it," he said. She did and watched him eat. And when he was through she could bear her rage no longer. "Now," she said, "you've had your meat. Get out. Never come back." She kept a pistol under the counter. She picked it up, cocked it, pointed it at his heart. "If you ever come in that door again, I'll kill you," she said.

She saw it all. *I couldn't bear to fall so low*, she thought, *to be slave to a shiftless cowboy*.

Wicks said, "Don't do that, Hat. Guess I went too far. You're right."

"You'll never have a chance to make it up," she cried. "Get out!"

On that cry he disappeared, and since then she had never seen him.

"Wicks, dear," she said. "Please! I'm sorry. Don't condemn me in your heart. Forgive me. I hurt myself in my evil. I always had a thick idiot head. I was born with a thick head."

Again she wept, for Wicks. She was too proud. A snob. Now they might have lived together in this house, old friends, simple and plain. She thought, *He really was my good friend*.

But what would Wicks do with a house like this, alone, if he was alive and survived her? He was too wiry for soft beds or easy chairs.

And she was the one who had said stiffly to India, "I'm a Christian person. I do not bear a grudge."

Ah, yes, she said to herself. *I have caught myself out too often. How long can this go on?* And she began to think, or try to think, of Joyce, her cousin's daughter. Joyce was like herself, a woman alone, getting on, clumsy. She would have given much, now, to succour Joyce.

But it seemed to her now that that too had been a story. First you heard the pure story. Then you heard the impure story. Both stories. She had paid out years, now to one shadow, now to another shadow.

Joyce would come here to the house. She had a little income and could manage. She would live as Hattie had lived, alone. Here she would rot, start to drink, maybe, and day after day read, day after day sleep. See how beautiful it was here? It burned you out. How empty? It turned you into ash.

"How can I doom a young person to the same life?" asked Hattie.

"It's for somebody like me. When I was younger it wasn't right. But now it is. Only I fit in here. It was made for my old age, to spend my last years peacefully. If I hadn't let Jerry make me drunk that night—if I hadn't sneezed! My arm! I'll have to live with Angus. My heart will break there away from my only home."

She now was very drunk, and she said to herself, *Take what God brings. He gives no gifts unmixed. He makes loans.*

She resumed her letter of instructions to lawyer Claiborne, "Upon the following terms," she wrote a second time. "Because I have suffered much. Because I only lately received what I have to give away, I can't bear it." The drunken blood was soaring to her head. But her hand was clear enough. She wrote, "It is too soon! Too soon! Because I do not find it in my heart to care for anyone as I would wish. Being cast off and lonely, and doing no harm where I am. Why should it be? This breaks my heart. In addition to everything else, why must I worry about this, which I must leave? I am tormented out of my mind. Even though by my own fault I have put myself into this position. And am not ready to give up on this. No, not yet. And so I'll tell you what, I leave this property, land, house, garden and water rights, to Hattie Simmons Waggoner. Me! I realise this is bad and wrong. It cannot happen. Yet it is the only thing I really wish to do, so may God have mercy on my soul."

"How can that be?" She studied what she had written and finally she acknowledged that she was drunk. "I'm drunk," she said, "and don't know what I'm doing. I'll die, and end. Like India. Dead as that lilac bush. Only tonight I can't give the house away. I'm drunk and so I need it. But I won't be selfish from the grave. I'll think again tomorrow," she promised herself. She went to sleep then.

BERNARD SHAW

Letters to Alice Lockett

These previously unpublished letters of George Bernard Shaw appeared in the April 1958 'Special British Issue' with the following note:

"When GBS first fell in love, he was twenty-seven years old, the impoverished young author of four novels which no publisher would touch, working on a fifth, and living with (and off) his mother on the second floor at 36 Osnaburgh Street, N.W., London.

"The object of his first—and most desperately romantic—passion was a beautiful young hospital nurse, Alice Lockett, who came to the flat evenings to study singing with his mother. It was Shaw's habit to escort her after the lesson to Liverpool Street, where she caught a train back to Walthamstow. When the correspondence opens, Shaw had known her for more than a year and, for the first time, had persuaded Miss Lockett to miss her train.

"GBS had been in London almost eight years, had had his fling at formal employment and had given it up in favor of the reading room at the British Museum, where he was writing novels, reading Marx and studying Wagner scores. He joined debating groups in order to conquer a painful self-consciousness about speaking in public. With his brilliant red beard, pallid skin, and a suit he had worn almost since the day of his arrival from Ireland, the GBS who penned this polished prose seemed an indescribably strange and shabby young man.

"During the twenty-five months spanned in these excerpts, Shaw completed the fifth novel, *An Unsocial Socialist*, and while it was rejected by book publishers, it did run in serialized form (without pay) through all of 1884, in *To-day*. It was during this period, too, that he joined the new Fabian Society, beginning a lifetime of political agitation that would direct his energies and influence his art.

"There is a twelve-month hiatus between the next-to-last and the final letter, unaccounted for in Shaw's relationship with Miss Lockett, but critical to his career. Through his new friend, William Archer, GBS began writing book reviews for *The Pall Mall Gazette*, music criticism for *The Dramatic Review* and art criticism for Annie Besant's *Our Corner*. He also made his debut as an orator, presenting the first formal declarations of the new Fabian Society. His father died in Ireland, and out of his life insurance came the only new suit GBS had owned in many years. By the end of 1885, he had found people who interested him, earned enough to support himself (£112) and soon he would move, with his mother, to a house on Fitzroy Square. But beyond that, and more important to the fate of his romance with Alice Lockett, Shaw embarked on his first affair—having been seduced on his twenty-ninth birthday by Jenny Patterson, a widow twelve years his senior, just two and a half months before the final letter to Miss Lockett was composed.

"Alice Lockett continued to study music with Shaw's mother and retained enough sentimental feeling toward GBS to keep his letters. She later married a doctor, Salisbury Sharpe, raised two children and, with her husband, continued to visit Mrs. Shaw socially. These letters, recently purchased from her estate by New York book dealer John Fleming and sold to Guillermo Tamayo of Caracas, Venezuela, are here made public for the first time."

9TH SEPTEMBER 1883: forgive me. . . . In playing on my own thoughts for the entertainment of the most charming of companions last night, I unskilfully struck a note that pained her—unless she greatly deceived me. I have felt remorseful ever since, and she has been reproaching herself all day for wilfully missing a train. Heavens! to regret having dared at last to be frank and kind! Did you not see at that moment a set of leading strings fall from you and hang themselves upon me in the form of golden chains? The heart of any other man would have stopped during those seconds after you had slowly turned your back upon the barrier and yet were still in doubt. Mine is a machine and did not stop; but it did something strange. It put me in *suspense*, which is the essence of woman's power over man, and which you had never made me feel before—I was always certain of what you would do until that question of the train arose. And I repaid you for the luxury by paining you. I did not intend to do so any more than you intended to please me, so forgive forgive forgive forgive forgive me.

I cannot (or perhaps will not) resist the impulse to write to you. Believe nothing that I say—I have a wicked tongue, a deadly pen, and a cold heart—I shall be angry with myself tomorrow for sending you this, and yet, when I next meet you, I shall plunge headlong into fresh cause for anger.

Farewell, dear Alice. There! is it not outrageous? Burn it. Do not read it. Alas! it is too late: you *have* read it.

11TH SEPTEMBER: Come! if you meant all you said, you would not have written to me at all. When you are with me, you have flashes of generosity. You strive to keep it down, you have tried to prove that it does not exist by a wicked letter, and yet the letter—most ungenerous of letters—owes its very existence to that generosity. . . . You strive to be an unapproachable grown up person of the world, worldly. It is that grown up person, Miss Lockett to wit, who reproaches me for my weakness, fearing that weakness instinctively because it is my strength. Well, let Miss Lockett beware, for she is the dragon that preys upon Alice, and I will rescue Alice from her. I hate her with a mortal hatred. . . I will shew Alice what she is, and Alice will abandon her forever. Miss Lockett says she cannot help despising me. It is false; Miss Lockett fears me, and is piqued when I dispraise her. She says that unless I have a very bad memory, I will recollect the ungenerous things she has said to me. Wrong again: I do not recollect one of them, and yet my memory is good, for I recollect everything that Alice has said to me. . . . Alice is the sweetest of companions, and for her sake I have sworn war against foolish Miss Lockett, who is ashamed of her and suppresses and snubs her as the false and artificial always suppresses, snubs and is ashamed of the natural, simple, humble, and truthful. But Miss Lockett, proud as she is of her strength, is a weakling; and her complaints, her pains, her bitter letters beginning with that vile phrase "May I ask," and going on to ask without waiting for the permission that she was not sincere in begging, are the throes of her dissolution.

Have I not also a dual self—an enemy within my gates—an egotistical George Shaw upon those neck I have to keep a grinding foot—a first cousin of Miss Lockett? And such a model of a righteous man as that George Shaw was in the days of his dominion! How resolved he was to be an example to others, to tread the path of duty, to respect himself, to walk with the ears of his conscience strained on the alert, to do everything as perfectly as it could be done, and—oh —monstrous!—to improve all those with whom he came in contact.

Here was a castle of strength and rectitude for you! And here was a foundation of measureless ignorance, conceit, and weakness! Verily, until he became as a little child again and was not ashamed to fall in love with Alice (then greatly under the thumb of Miss Lockett, who was, however, much flattered by the attention of a person of superior talent) he was in a bad way. . . . She thinks it is due to herself to pretend that love is an infringement of her claims to respect.

But her claim refutes itself. Respectability is a quality, not a right. The lily does not claim whiteness—it *is* white. Alice does not claim respectability—she *is* respectable.

Farewell, dear Alice—do not show this letter to Miss Lockett; it will only enrage her. Do not let her write to me again—write yourself. . . . Pray hide our correspondence from her, hide our interviews from her, and be tranquil, she will not trouble you long. . . .

8TH OCTOBER: I am sorry that I offend you by now being serious. I am sorrier that I please you still less when I am serious. I am glad that I can read between the lines of your reproaches, and make all your unmeant resentment matter for fresh meaning. And do you not think yourself an ungrateful wretch to accuse me of want of seriousness? . . . If you have made me feel, have I not made you think? Have I been altogether unto you as a liar, and as waters that fail? (This is Scripture, and I hope you will not profanely doubt the seriousness of *that*.) I am, as I have private reasons for knowing, opinionated, vain, weak, ignorant, lazy and so forth, and the glimpses you get of these failings do not deceive you in the least. But dare any man or woman profess themselves impartial, modest, strong, wise, and diligent? Let any such cast the first stone. Such failings are instructive to witness sometimes, and you may learn a little from them alone, not to mention the abysses of folly of which I do not know myself to be guilty any more than I know the taste of water. (We do not know the taste of water because our palates live in water. For an analogous reason, thoroughly false people are never conscious of their falsehood.) You must not expect perfection from me. By the bye, I have observed that the people who hold the abominable doctrine of oringinal sin are those who seem most surprised when they meet with people who fall short of absolute virtue. (They don't know that there is no such thing as absolute virtue.)

. . . Farewell, and study Figaro diligently. Mozart's music and your *beaux yeux*—what need I more to be happy after my day's work. Ah, if our business here were merely to be happy! (I confess I shouldn't really enjoy such a state of things, I despise happiness.)

5TH NOVEMBER: . . . Wretch that you were to catch that train, and fool that I am to put myself in the way of caring whether you caught it or not! I will be your slave no longer: you used me vilely when we met before, and you disappointed me horribly tonight. I recant every word I have ever said to you, and plead temporary insanity as my excuse for having uttered them. I am exceedingly glad that I had not to wait another half hour at that waiting room. I detest the entire universe. I did nothing but tell you monstrous lies—I wonder you can be so credulous as to believe my transparent flatteries. I say the same things to everybody. I believe in my soul that you never meant to catch that train—that you were as much disappointed as I when you found it had not gone. As much disappointed, that is, as I pretended to have been. In reality, I was overjoyed. You told me I was in an unamiable humour. Behold the fruits of it. Must I eternally flatter flatter flatter flatter? If ever woman was undeservedly beloved (supposing any man could be found mad enough to love you a little at odd moments when your complexion is unusually beautiful) you are she.

Yours with the most profound Indifference and in the most entire Freedom from any attraction on the part of Any Woman Living.

6TH NOVEMBER: Aha! I thought a new sort of letter would make you answer me. . . . So I must not love you for your good looks and complexion (fancy the vanity of a woman praising herself in that fashion. For shame!) but for what you are. Well, what are you? Come, tell me what all these great qualities are for which I am to love you. You say you are generous and manly (which latter is nonsense). Is it generous to tell me that I consider myself irresistible (which you spell improperly)? You say you cannot respect me because I am your slave. How can you be so conceited as to believe that I am your slave? You say the writing of your letter afforded you the greatest delight, and then you go on through six pages boasting intolerably of your insight, your superiority to flattery, your 'true generousness' (generosity), your scorn of servility, your 'good looks', your 'beautiful complexion', the extent to which your spiritual nature surpasses both, the nobility of women in general, your 'heart and fancy', and your scrupulous justice and gratitude even to such worms as myself so far as I deserve it. Then comes a lecture to me on the sin of vanity. I believe such a monstrous outburst of egotism never was penned. And, after being called base, clumsy (oh fury!), impatient and ignorant, I am told that I am very entertaining and instructive. Am I a dancing bear or a learned pig that I should be insulted thus? I have sometimes blamed you for being morbidly afraid lest people should suppose that you were praising yourself, and I have effected a frightfully complete cure. 'Beautiful complexion!' 'True generousness!'—did any man ever read or woman write such things before? But it is all my fault for telling you of them. Why don't you date your letters, and write legibly, and write on paper unblemished by vain shows of insincere grief?

Alas, my dear Alice, all this folly goes against the grain with me tonight. . . . We are a pair of children, and petulant children should be petted and kissed into good humour. I am too big to be petted; but you are not too big to be kissed, and your 'beautiful complexion' has tempted me often. Enough, midnight strikes, and my head is in a tumult with matters about which you do not care twopence. But your corner is an adorable place in which to pass the evening of a busy day. You will find all about it and about your dual entity (if you understand that) made the foundation of the most sentimental part of my book.

Oh ye, to whom she shows this letter, consider whether you have not been as great fools as I, before ye blame me. Is it my fault if she does not deserve all the hours I have given to her?

19TH NOVEMBER: This is a silly letter to replace the sensible one you tore up and threw out of the window. Or else it is a sensible letter to replace the silly one you destroyed. I do not know which—I only know that when we were at the piano this evening, and you— No, I will not tell you. . . .

I am full of remorse for saying these things to you. If I had your heart, I know I should break it, and yet I wish I had it. Is not this monstrous? Take your lesson in the morning, so that I may never see you again, I implore you; and when you have done so, and I presently beg you to come in the evening, do not listen to me.

Oh, the infinite mischief that a woman may do by stooping forward to turn over a sheet of music!

I am alone, and yet there is a detestable, hardheaded, heartless, cynical, cool devil seated in my chair telling me that all this is insincere, lying affection. But I defy him—it is he who is. I have only sold my working hours to him. Hate and mistrust him as much as you will; but believe me too, and help me to snatch a few moments from his withering power. . . .

29TH NOVEMBER: I think our acquaintance had better cease at once, and for ever. I will not go into particulars, as I have no desire to wound your feelings, which I have always scrupulously respected. I will merely say that though I despise falsehood and treachery, yet I wish you well and forgive you. When we next meet, let it be as strangers. . . .

. . . Never again will I believe the professions of people with whom religion and an affectation of conscientiousness is only a cloak for the most heartless coquetry. I apply this observation to no particular individual: it is impersonal and general. My circumstances provoke it, and I leave its application to your conscience.

I relinquish an acquaintance which was never more than the amusement of an idle hour, without regret, save for having ever formed it.

Yours truly,
Whom?

Not I, on my soul, oh tyrannical but irresistible Alice. . . .

19TH AUGUST 1884: So you have no time for thought. Poor Alice! Shall I write you a letter in return for your three sheets of reticences? A year ago I would have written copiously. But now I begin to reflect. For the last fourteen years I have been writing letters— some thousands of them—a couple of hundred perhaps to women— and what has come of it all? Only that it is growing harder and harder to write, easier and easier to be written to. You are a novice at letter writing, I an expert. I am a novice at love-making, you an expert. Let us then improve ourselves by practice. Write to me, and I will make love to you—to relieve the enormous solitude which I carry about with me. I do not like myself, and sometimes I do not like you; but there are moments when our two unfortunate souls seem to cling to the same spar in a gleam of sunshine, free of the other wreckage for a moment.

Well, let us make the most of the days of our vanity. Do you ever read Shakespeare, or Swift, or Koheleth (popularly known as Ecclesiastes)?

Why have you become so abandonedly reckless of the impropriety of corresponding with me?

16TH OCTOBER: Demon! Demon! Demon! Not a statement in your letter is true except the wicked and heartless one that you went home by the 8.32 train, which was the act of a fiend. You did want to answer my letter. You did not consider it unfair. There *was* occasion to write. A decided arrangement *was* made. I am never wanting in decision. Mistrust did not creep into your heart after my letter: you have no heart; and you have mistrusted me (and, with more reason, yourself also) ever since we first met. You are neither imaginative nor impulsive, and I believe you went home in a rage. I do not try my best to make anything: if I were capable of trying my best I should be a better man, and not suffer you to make a fool of me. . . .

I am not offended: I am only furious. You were quite right to go by the 8.32. Had you waited, I should have despised you (or tried to, on principle); for I respect people who always act sensibly and are devoid of the weaknesses known as 'feelings'. You behaved like a prudent woman, like a lady, and like a flint-hearted wretch.

. . . Thank God (if there was any such person) I have perfect control of my temper, and, when I am hurt, can conceal my indignation. . . . Adieu, dear demon.

P.S. Heavens! I nearly put this by mistake into the envelope of the other one, which is to Elinor Huddart! It happens that we had an appointment the other day which she was unable to keep, and I have not seen her since. Fancy her feelings if she had received this and took all the abuse to herself. I should have been lectured, too; Elinor is a serious friend, and not a trifler like Miss Lockett.

8TH OCTOBER 1885: No, not for the smallest fraction of a second.
My season is commencing: my nights are filling up one by one: I am
booked for half a dozen lectures within the next month. I shall be
out tonight with Stepniak and the underdone. My DR copy must be
done today. Tomorrow an article is due for the *Magazine of Music*.
On Saturday my contribution to *Our Corner* must be written. On
Sunday there is a lecture, not one idea for which have I yet arranged.
Meanwhile, *To-day* is howling for more copy. See you this week!
Avaunt, sorceress: not this month—not until next July. Not, in any
case, until I am again in the detestable humour which is the only one
to which you minister. Remember: I am not always a savage. My
pleasures are music, conversation, the grapple of my intelligence
with fresher ones. All this I can sweeten with a kiss; but I cannot
saturate and spoil it with fifty thousand. Love-making grows tedious
to me—the emotion has evaporated from it. This is your fault: since
your return I have seen you twice, and both times you have been
lazy and unintelligently luxurious. I will not spend such evenings
except when I am for a moment tired and brutish. Even then I will
turn with relief and gratitude from moral death with you to moral
life and activity with other women—with men—with the Fabians
even—with my work—anywhere where all my faculties and sym-
pathies are awake and active. I only value friends for what they can
give me: if you can only give me one thing, I shall value you only for
that. It is useless for you to protest—the matter is not within my will
—you will be valued as you deserve, not as you wish to be valued.
You have said that the most beautiful woman can give no more than
she has. Do not forget that I cannot esteem the most beautiful
woman for more than she is. I want as much as I can get: there is no
need to force it upon me if it exists; I am only too thirsty for companionship. Beware. When all the love has gone out of me, I am
remorseless: I hurl the truth about like destroying lightning.—
GBS

GEORGE JEAN NATHAN

Memoirs of Mencken and Fitzgerald

In September 1957, at the beginning of George Jean Nathan's fatal illness, *Esquire's* Publisher's Page carried what Arnold Gingrich called "less a formal tribute than a sort of informal get-well note." It was subtitled 'The Last of the Boulevardiers' and said, in part:

"Mencken and Nathan were two of the best friends that *Esquire* ever had, particularly in the formative years of its first decade. Both contributed to the magazine in its early days, before Nathan began writing about the theatre for us on a regular monthly basis, and both were enormously helpful to it. Nathan obtained such contributors for us as Sinclair Lewis and Edgar Lee Masters, while Mencken was influential in getting both Theodore Dreiser and Scott Fitzgerald into our pages."

In October 1936 the dean of drama critics had begun the first of his monthly series of theatre reviews under the heading 'First Nights and Passing Judgments'. The series continued through September 1946, and Nathan regularly revised and incorporated the pieces into his *Theatre Book of the Year*.

Nine years later, in August 1955, Nathan began another column of drama criticism, 'Reflections After the Curtain Falls'. This regular feature, along with essays by Aldous Huxley and Paul Gallico, comprised the opening 'Golden Curtain' in each issue of *Esquire* through the mid-1950s. When Nathan became so ill he could no longer meet monthly deadlines, he was asked to write, at his leisure, his memoirs of Mencken, which appeared in October 1957, and of Sinclair Lewis, F. Scott Fitzgerald, and Theodore Dreiser, all three of which appeared after his death in *Esquire's* 25th Anniversary issue, October 1958.

THE HAPPIEST DAYS OF H. L. MENCKEN

I first laid eyes on the cherub-faced man with the golden hair parted in the middle and slapped down like a barber's on Sunday morning, and in a stiff, starched Herbert Hoover collar on a morning in the early May of 1908. It was in the offices of the old *Smart Set* Magazine where we had been called in to be offered the respective jobs of literary and dramatic critic. The stranger thrust out his hand at me and exclaimed, "I'm H. L. Mencken from Baltimore and I'm the biggest damned fool in Christendom and I don't want to hear any boastful reply that you claim the honour." Fifteen minutes later, after we had completed our business, we were seated together drinking a mutual congratulatory Florestan cocktail in the bar of the old Beaux Arts Café a block and a half away. "What's your attitude toward the world?" he asked, and continued before I had a chance to open my mouth, "I view it as a mess in which the clowns are paid more than they are worth, so I respectfully suggest that, when we get going, we get our full share."

When we subsequently got going we found ourselves in the posts of co-editors of the magazine in whose offices we had first met. "I see a magazine as something to make the idiotic more idiotic and the crazy crazier," was his dictum. "So I hope you will agree with me when we propose, first, to get the proper amount of fun out of our jobs and to pray that the money, if any, will respectfully oblige us by duly coming in afterwards."

The popular belief that friendships and even acquaintances met on shipboard, save possibly in the instances of chorus girls, never last and that one subsequently runs as from the plague if one again encounters them after landing takes a twist worthy of O. Henry and even Horatio Alger at his most imaginative in the break that eventually landed Mencken and me in the post of the *Smart Set's* co-editors and, eventually, co-owners. One day on the return trip of the *Europa* from Europe a stranger approached me on the deck and asked me where I had obtained my exact duplicate of a tweed overcoat that he was wearing. After I imparted the information he requested, he suggested that I join him for a drink in the smoking-room. "What's your name?" he bade me. When I told him, he allowed that I was the only writer he had ever met personally and that he had a proposition for me. "I have just acquired the *Smart Set* Magazine and I offer you the editorship starting as soon as we land." I inquired his name—it was Eltinge F. Warner—and told him that if my recently made friend, Mencken, would serve as co-editor with me I would accept the job. The rest is magazine history.

Mencken said that he would go with me and when, several days later, we arrived at our editorial sanctum, the first thing he did was to cock his shoes up on the handsome mahogany desk to the anguish of our publisher and to inquire of me what I had in mind as our editorial policy. Before I had a chance to answer he interrupted, "After all, that can wait. More magazines are spoiled by the announcement of an editorial policy that their editors soon find they have to abandon if their magazine is to survive than even magazines with too much money in the bank. Much more important is that we go to work setting up a free lunch for poets. Poets," he went on, "can no more be expected to write anything worthwhile in the way of poetry on an empty stomach or the kind of garbage they have to subsist on in Greenwich Village than Shakespeare, as witness the *Sonnets*. We can't afford to pay them enough money if they are good, so the least we can do for them is to content their bellies." The rest of the morning was spent in setting up a delicious lunch on a marble slab that Mecken foresightedly had shipped from Baltimore and that consisted of stacks of liverwurst, pretzels, anchovies, olives, celery and pots of cheese, not to mention ham sandwiches with mustard, Saratoga chips, and a shotgun to frightened off Harry Kemp, the Greenwich Village genius who was destined to be our assiduous customer.

"I have always maintained, along with the discoverer of that miraculous cure-all of a bygone century called 'Peruna'—which contained enough alcohol tonic to make an arthritic kangaroo jump into the air like a Mordkin coached by a Russian chiropractor—that a man without personal peculiarities was either an unimaginative clodhopper or, I say it with becoming modesty, a genius." Mencken certainly had his share of idiosyncrasies. His favourite cigar—which once as a youth he had rolled in his father's cigar factory and which bore the name of 'Uncle Willie' and cost all of five cents—was the priceless gift he bestowed on his carefully chosen acquaintances. These benefactions, each encircled with a handsome cigar band voluptuously engraved with the name of some three-dollar brand, he would bestow with a flourish upon whomever he chose to honour, and always with the words, "I give you this token of my esteem which I have imported from distant parts at a prohibitive cost and with which I beseech you to honour me in return by blowing some of the fragrance in my direction." He insisted that he never felt completely at home and at ease without a cuspidor nearby, and when we set up office at our magazine he brought up from his family's old home in Hollins Street, Baltimore, three brass souvenirs that had once been the proud property of his paternal grandfather. When our fastidious partner caught sight of the ornaments and let out a howl Mencken conciliated him by conceding to drape, at his own expense, the spittoons with cretonne coverings whenever lady authors appeared on the scene. He always said that every man ought to feel rich whether he had a cent or not to his name and to that end had a habit of distributing ten-dollar bills in out-of-the-way corners of his jackets and pants pockets. "When I accidentally come upon one of the bills," he assured me, "I always feel a satisfactory glow come over me and the surprise does me no end of good." Whereupon he would lead me into the nearest drink house and set them up.

One of his pet philosophies was, "Whom the gods would destroy they first make popular." But, though he was not in the least gregarious, he always got along with people, even those whom he disliked, and it is a fact that even when he encountered someone he elected to consider an enemy, he was soon in comradely arm in arm with him and so full of good will and joyous spirits that the imagined foe soon became a loving friend.

He hated New York, which he always referred to in his correspondence as Sodom and Gomorrah, and was always eager to get back to his home in Baltimore. When he was in New York, which was every other week, it was our custom to walk up Fifth Avenue each morning to our offices. "There is nothing like the smell of gasoline odours to invigorate one more than the Adirondacks," he would observe. "The main trouble with this wicked city of yours is that people here judge and esteem every man according to the amount of money he has, which gives me an idea. Let's impress the booboisie with our eminence by piling up some big mazuma, which should be easy for two such remarkable geniuses as we are, not to say crooks." He accordingly, with some eloquent assistance from me, concocted a plan to get out a pulp magazine on the side which would be such an atrocity that we would hide when any of our friends mentioned it in our presence. The magazine which we duly published, and which sold out its first issue completely in a single day and netted us and our partners a tidy small fortune, was called *The Parisienne* and catered to the French-American sentimentalists during the First World War. It was adorned with a cover picturing a saucy French minx and contained frisky tailpieces at the bottom of every page consisting of drawings in the manner of those adorning the Paris boulevard magazines. Mencken insisted it be printed on green paper which, he told the readers in an editorial, like the green grass and billiard tables, was much easier on the eyes than the white paper on which other magazines were printed and which would guarantee to the readers the welfare of their eyes, otherwise risking serious strain and even occasional blindness. The paper, because of the shortage imposed upon publishers by the restrictions of war, was obtained for us by our senior partner, Eugene F. Crowe, the paper tycoon, who was of a humour on a par with Mencken's. The paper he got us was, haplessly, so rough and so full of wood pulp that Mencken allowed that if the readers found fault with it they could at least use it for toothpicks.

Although those who did not know him sometimes mistook Mencken's air of supreme self-confidence for brag, he often said privately that he considered himself a failure. He was personally a modest man about himself, though he said that even if he was not modest to the point of self-embarrassment he fully realised his potentialities and abilities. He was, indeed, so modest that he always—even after he had achieved literary fame and had published, among fifty other books, his monumental *The American Language*—referred to himself as merely a newspaperman. His prankishness, however, never deserted him and among his pet diversions was affectionately autographing photographs to himself of Otto von Bismarck, the German Kaiser and various American Presidents like Calvin Coolidge, Martin Van Buren and Abraham Lincoln. His best-known hoax was the publication of an article that claimed the first bathtub ever to be in use in the White House was installed during the Millard Fillmore administration. This news was solemnly reprinted in the *Congressional Record*, has been included in various encyclopædias and has been popularly accepted as gospel.

During Prohibition he imported a famous brewmaster from the celebrated Pschorrbräu brewery in Munich and installed him in the cellar of his Baltimore house. The beverage, which Mencken dispensed to his delighted cronies, was eight per cent in alcohol content and on one occasion it exploded and the brew flooded the house of the next-door neighbour.

Those were the gala days in our friend's life. He said that never thereafter did he enjoy himself so hugely. This was true. For when, subsequent to our sale of the *Smart Set*, we as co-editors founded *The American Mercury* with our good friend Alfred A. Knopf, a change overcame Mencken and, though he never lost his fondness for waggishness, a much more serious attitude infected him. His relative sobriety took the alarming form of a consuming editorial interest in politics and a dismissal of his previous interest in *belles-lettres*, which had been so great a factor in the prosperity of our former periodical. The newspaperman in Mencken superseded the literary man and he favoured filling the *Mercury* with pieces written by assorted jailbirds, hobos, politicians and riff-raff of all species. The magazine, however, largely because of the novelty of such material, nevertheless promptly caught on, and though it sold for fifty cents and was very expensive to produce (Knopf had a new type face manufactured that was so beautiful we found no one could read it and also imported an especial celery paper from Japan on which to print the magazine), it actually made one dollar profit on its first issue. Knopf, incidentally, who is lavish in everything he undertakes, including unheard-of delicacies at his dinner table and shirts so be-hued that they caused Mencken to remark that "Alfred must think he is an Easter egg", went along with us in complete agreement with whatever course, foolish or otherwise, we chose to follow. We didn't, true, go in for such editorial whimsies as, in the case of *Smart Set*, giving over an entire single issue to a full-length novel about an undertaker and his modern methods of advertising (including reproductions of his imbecile advertisements). Nor did Mencken broadcast a request to agents that they send us any and all manuscripts that had been rejected by the loftily self-called Quality Group of magazines, namely, *The Century*, *Harper's*, *The Atlantic Monthly*, *Scribner's*, etc., which manuscripts gave us our most sensational success, Somerset Maugham's *Miss Thompson*, subsequently dramatised into the mint known by the title *Rain*. Rather, Mencken endorsed such contributions as a graph-filled treatise on the population growth in Mississippi. But, though it seemed to some that a new and unusual gravity had been imposed upon him by his new editorial post, his former ebullience could not be suppressed. As heretofore, he professed, despite his perfect health, to be always dying and he would appear in our office affecting the walk of an old Dixie family retainer suffering from an acute pain in the kidneys. In addition, he would counter everyone else's catalogue of ailments with a lengthy list of his own. (This was a favourite device of his to spare himself the necessity of listening to the others' malaises.)

"As for me," he would always write to me, "I am enjoying my usual decrepitude. A new disease has developed hitherto unknown to the faculty. A dermatitis caused by the plates I wear for my arches. No one seems to know how to cure it. I shall thus go limping to the crematory. My ailments this morning come to the following:

a. A burn on the tongue (healing)
b. A pimple inside the jaw
c. A sour stomach
d. Pain in the prostate
e. Burning in the gospel pipe (always a preliminary of the hay-fever season)
f. A cut finger
g. A small pimple inside the nose (going away)
h. A razor cut, smarting
i. Tired eyes."

He was, in short, a walking compendium of mankind's complaints of all natures. If it wasn't one thing it was another. When he appeared in the office one morning, he loudly lamented that, while he did not mind his Negro cook's filching of almost everything in his ice-box to take home, he objected to having to supply her with a Ford to cart it away. He allowed that he considered it something of an imposition. During Prohibition he complained that his favourite beer hall in Union City, New Jersey, had a sign pasted on its front window reading, "This place closed by the Prohibition Agents", and directly beneath it another adorned with an arrow, "Kindly use rear door", thus necessitating his walking, and in his decrepit condition, at least thirty feet away.

Another grouse was that Julius Klein, the violinist at Luchow's Restaurant in Fourteenth Street, played his favourite Strauss waltzes altogether too quickly and that he accordingly could not keep accurate time with them with his foot.

When anyone complimented him on the sudden prosperity of the *Mercury* he would reply with his pet rejoinder, "Whom the gods would destroy they first make popular."

"We are pretty good," he would concede to me, "but let's not forget that the embalmer may be waiting just around the corner."

Reverting to his regular complaints, one letter from him had this to say, "I have been trying to start my new book, but an infection in the sinuses has got into my larynx and I am uncomfortable. *Immer traubel!* I begin to give up hope." At another time, "My sister is making a really extraordinary recovery; she should recover completely. I assume that I'll be the next to be laid up. I pray, but without hope." And again, "Hay fever has me by the ear and I am making the usual rough weather of it. It seems to be rather more severe than usual. What a world!"

His credo was that we never got a good editorial idea save only over a beer table at night, but that the trouble with it was that when morning came around the idea proved to be no good.

His favourite low burlesque comedian was George Bickel and when he met Ethel Barrymore and discovered that she shared his enthusiasm for the artist he founded a George Bickel Alumni Association on the spot, and presently gathered into the fold such of the literary elect as Theodore Dreiser, Edgar Lee Masters and Joseph Hergesheimer. Having been a dramatic critic in his young newspaper days, and having seen only the performances of a stock company in his native Baltimore, he seemed to think that the theatre in his later period was constituted in its entirety mainly and only of bad imitations of Ibsen plays and steadfastly refused to be lured into it. Reprimanded on one occasion by our friend, John D. Williams, the Harvard brains of the Charles Frohman offices, who insisted that he was a dolt for his attitude and who assured him that he would change his mind if he were to see a play by the great Italian dramatist, Dario Niccodemi, which in truth was a horrible turkey,

Mencken, impressed, was inveigled not only into going to the play but, dressing himself up in evening finery, he sat stoically in a box through the performance without saying a word. But at its end he gave Williams a poke in the eye, with the words, "That was the most dreadful hogwash that ever poisoned my nose!"

He maintained that the wittiest line that the *Smart Set* ever printed was from an anonymous contributor, "When love dies, there is no funeral; the corpse remains in the house." Perhaps his own remark that pleasured him most was, "Hamlet has been played by 5,000 actors; no wonder he is crazy."

He professed to be a disciple of Nietzsche's 'Be hard!' philosophy. But he never failed to spend hours shopping for Christmas toys for his little niece, collecting fancy cigar bands for her, obediently eating turkey on Thanksgiving Day and getting a tear in his eye whenever an orchestra played 'Roses from the South'.

He always referred to himself and me as "two retired porch climbers".

He was proud of the fact that he had an uncle who still drew a pension as a Civil War veteran. He confided that the uncle had patriotically suffered his wounds when Federal draft agents entered a saloon in Baltimore and his uncle slipped on the floor suds and broke a leg in trying to evade them.

Early one afternoon at about this period, our mutual friend, T. R. Smith, then managing editor of the *Century* Magazine, telephoned Mencken and myself at our office and asked us both to come up to his apartment that evening for a drink. When we got there, we found with Smith a tall, skinny, paprika-headed stranger to whom we were introduced as one Lewis. The fellow was known to neither of us save as the author of a negligible serial that had appeared in *The Saturday Evening Post* and that had subsequently been gathered between book covers, and, to me specifically, as the author of a play called *Hobohemia*, produced the year before down in Greenwich Village and exquisitely—if I may be permitted so critically indelicate a word—epizoötic.

Barely had we taken off our hats and coats and before Smith had an opportunity even to fish out his de luxe corkscrew from behind his de luxe sets of the works of the more esoteric Oriental and Polack amorists, when the tall, skinny, paprika-headed stranger simultaneously coiled one long arm around Mencken's neck and the other around mine, well-nigh strangling us and putting resistance out of the question, and—yelling at the top of his lungs—began, "So you guys are critics, are you? Well, let me tell you something. I'm the best writer in this here gottdamn country and if you, Georgie, and you, Hank, don't know it now, you'll know it gottdamn soon. Say, I've just finished a book that'll be published in a week or two and it's the gottdamn best book of its kind that this here gottdamn country has had and don't you guys forget it! I worked a year on the gott-damn thing and it's the goods. I'm a-telling you! Listen, when it comes to writing a novel, I'm so far ahead of most of the men you two think are good that I'll be gottdamned if it doesn't make me sick to think of it! Just wait till you read the gottdamn thing. You've got a treat coming, Georgie and Hank, and don't you boys make no mistake about that!"

Projected from Smith's flat by the self-endorsing uproar—it kept up for fully half an hour longer—Mencken and I jumped into a taxi-cab, directed the driver to speed us post-haste to a tavern where we might in some peace recover our equilibrium and our eardrums, and looked at each other. "Of all the idiots I've ever laid eyes on, that fellow is the worst!" groaned Mencken, gasping for breath. Regaining my own breath some moments later, all that I could add was that if any such numskull could ever write anything worth reading, maybe there was something in Christian Science too.

Three days later I got the following letter from Mencken, who had returned to Baltimore:

"Dear George: Grab hold of the bar rail, steady yourself, for a terrible shock! I've just read the advance sheets of the book of that *Lump* we met at Schmidt's and, by God, he has done the job! It's a genuinely excellent piece of work. Get it as soon as you can and take a look. I begin to believe that perhaps there isn't a God after all. There is no justice in the world.

"Yours in Xt.,

"M."

The book was *Main Street*, the author Sinclair Lewis.

THE GOLDEN BOY OF THE TWENTIES

F. SCOTT FITZGERALD once told me that he planned to write a novel about me. It turned out to be *The Beautiful and Damned.*

Subsequently he came to me somewhat apologetically and explained that he found that he had tried, but could not have lionised me in his novel. He said that he found himself unable to write a heroic character other than himself and that he had to be the hero of any novel he undertook. So I duly discovered that what he started as heroic me resulted in a wholly minor and subsidiary character not distinguished for any perceptibly favourable attributes.

On such occasions, if he suspected he had offended a friend in any way, it was his conciliating gesture to appear at the friend's diggings the very next morning and to present him with one of his used old pocket handkerchiefs, not visibly re-laundered. That the handkerchief was embroidered with his initials did not notably impress the recipient.

Despite his personal vanity, Scott's life was wrapped up in his lovely young wife, who was born Zelda Sayre in Alabama and whom he met as a young Lieutenant in an Army Training Camp in Kentucky. This Zelda, conscious of her beauty, was something of an exhibitionist and was given to such whimsies as disrobing herself in the Grand Central Station.

On one occasion, indeed, she went to the extreme of getting into the bathtub during a house party at the undergraduate club at Princeton to which Scott belonged and inviting the house guests *en masse* to come in and revel in her pulchritude, bringing about her husband's suspension from the club and causing a campus scandal of sizeable proportions.

On an earlier occasion, Scott allowed that she had divested herself of her clothing and had stood in the middle of the railroad tracks in Birmingham, Alabama, and had waved a lantern and brought the startled passengers scurrying out of the stalled express train. Scott loved to recount the episode in a tone of rapturous admiration.

Another incident of Zelda's exhibitionism was one that Scott used to remember with considerably less relish.

One night our friend, John Williams, the noted theatrical producer, gave a small dinner party in his apartment just off Union Square.

During it the fair Zelda abruptly took off for a splash in the Union Square fountain. Followed by Williams and her husband in hot pursuit, she was encountered there in her birthday clothes surrounded by at least a dozen frantically indignant cops.

When Scott sought to intercede with them and to explain to them that it was his wife who was doing the Godiva act, they pushed him aside and informed him that he was on the way to the hoosegow. At this point, Williams ventured to explain to them who their potential jailbird was, whereupon one of the cops, who mistook Scott for Ed Fitzgerald, the popular radio comedian of the time, deemed his pleasure at meeting Scott and allowed that the lady in the fountain must accordingly be the comedian's wife, Pegeen. This managed to assuage the cops' wrath and to spare Scott and his wife the humiliation of arrest for disorderly conduct.

In his biography on Fitzgerald, which is full of distortions of the truth, Arthur Mizner, currently a professor at Cornell, alleges that I once tried to flirt with Zelda and so enraged Scott that he engaged me in a furious fist fight. The facts are far different. While Zelda and I were accustomed to engage publicly in obviously exaggerated endearing terms which Scott appreciated and which were in the accepted vein of Dixie chivalry, our close friendship was never interrupted.

The subject of our intimate explorations was resolutely fastidious. Scott would have it no other way. It was said of him during his undergraduate days that he sent out questionnaires to prospective feminine dates as to (1) whether they had had their hair washed during the day, and (2) how many baths they had taken.

He once aroused the wrathful indignation of the coloured elevator boys in the New York hotel at which he was staying by confining their tips at Christmas-time to fancily wrapped bottles of a well-known deodorant. I can further testify from personal observation that it was his habit, to their consternation, to demand of any female companion in taxi-cabs that they open their mouths so he might determine that the insides of their teeth were free of tartar.

A one-time close friend of his mother has confided to me that, as a baby, he not only cried for Pear's soap but ate it, and with what seemed to be relish.

Once in Paris he burst into my hotel room in the early dawn,

M

pulled me out of bed and proclaimed that he had just read the work of a new to him American writer named Hemingway who promised to be the greatest of his generation.

When in his cups it was his drollery to descend upon my working quarters in company with his friends Edmund (Bunny) Wilson, the now celebrated literary critic, whom he deeply admired for his critical gifts, Donald Ogden Stewart, Ed Paramore and Edna St. Vincent Millay, all in a more or less exalted state, and to occupy his talents in applying matches to the rubber bindings on the pillows on my sofa. Their howls of glee when the rubber started to stench up the place could be heard a block away and were matched by my less gleeful own.

Scotty, as he was familiarly called, visualised himself as the banner-carrier of the youth of his generation and was such an admirer and celebrant of youth for its own sake that, although he was polite and even deferential to his elders, whom he usually addressed as 'sir', it was clearly evident that he privately considered them all and sundry on the way to an Old Man's Home or ready for the embalmer.

The only evidence of his being interested—and then strictly platonically—in any female of the species apart from his wife was an absurdly young, personable actress named Lois Moran. She was a lovely kid of such tender years that it was rumoured she still wore the kind of flannel nightie that bound around her ankles with ribbons and Scott never visited her save when her mother was present.

Once, while I was spending a week-end with him and Zelda in their Connecticut house, the racket made by the house party lasted so long into the night that I had to get up at dawn and, seeking quiet, went down into the cellar. Rummaging about, I came upon some notebooks marked 'Zelda's Diary' and looked through them. They interested me so greatly that in my then capacity as a magazine editor I later made her an offer for them. When I informed her husband, he said that he could not permit me to publish them since he had gained a lot of inspiration from them and wanted to use parts of them in his own novels and short stories, as, for example, 'The Jelly Bean'.

There was just one important occasion on which Fitzgerald consulted me in the matter of research on subjects which he was writing about.

It was during that fantastic era known as Prohibition, when he was beginning work on his highly regarded novel, *The Great Gatsby*.

Fitzgerald's plan was to be a novel about a fabulously rich Prohibition operator who lived luxuriously on Long Island and he asked me to introduce him to such persons I happened to know who might supply him with proper patterns and the necessary atmospheric details.

When I duly made him known to one such, Nicky Bates, who, except for an habitual spruce and natty shirt, closely resembled the present Yogi Berra, he protested that it was not at all what he was looking for and that he hoped I would put him into touch with a glossier specimen closer to the type upon which he sought to model his character.

On a subsequent week-end I accordingly took him to a house party on Long Island at which were gathered some of the more notorious speakeasy operators and their decorative girl friends. When we departed the scene, Fitzgerald objected that this, again, was not what he wanted and that I was guilty of playing a joke on him and introducing him to a party of Wellesley girls and their Rutgers boy friends.

Fitzgerald was spoiled by too early success. His first novel, *This Side of Paradise*, which he wrote when he flunked out of Princeton, was an immediate success and netted him in excess of forty-odd thousand dollars. He afterwards expected every other one of his books to be a like success and lived up to what he imagined would be his subsequent income. He could not understand why everything that followed was not as financially rosy and, though he never lost confidence in himself, one could readily detect his disappointment and even indignation.

"I am writing better than ever before," he once said to me, "and, though they seem still to like my stuff, public taste would appear to be not so good as it once had been."

Fitzgerald so regarded his popular acceptance as the logical thing that when he entered a smart restaurant or even a roadside hot dog stand he was ruffled if the waiter or counterman did not greet him in terms otherwise befitting a candidate for the Presidency. He was, however, in the habit of soothing the offender's embarrassment over his delinquency by slipping him a gratuity, which paid off in terms of the embarrassed servitor's additional protestations that he had committed a dreadful *faux pas* in having failed to recognise Fitzgerald as the eminento which he was.

If any man may be said to have died of a broken heart Scott was that one.

He himself was aware of what had befallen him since the incapacity of his dearly beloved wife and his surrender to Hollywood, and he described it without reserve in a series of utterly frank confessions which he wrote for one of the popular magazines. Zelda's death left Scott in a state from which he never fully recovered. He himself died ultimately forsaken, save for a feminine friend (now a noted Hollywood columnist) who had befriended him and consoled him in his dying moments.

Yet here was a writer who adorned his period with some lastingly lovely writing, with a very true romance in a time of so much questionable realism and, not least of all, with his own warm and friendly company.

What will be the final estimate of him I do not know, but, far from being what has been described as "someone who once kissed a Gibson Girl and told", he left his mark on a generation that will long remember him with deep and tender affection.

APPENDIX

A Check-List of
Contributions of Literary Import
to Esquire Magazine
1933-1958

Compiled by E. R. HAGEMANN and JAMES E. MARSH
of the English Department, University of California at Los Angeles

A FEW COMMENTS on our methodology are in order. In addition, to listing contributions alphabetically and individual contributions chronologically, the compilers have also attempted to locate subsequent reprintings. The search was as thorough as possible, but it did not lead into the bewildering jumble of paper-backs or allied ephemera. The selection of contributors was based on (1) contemporary importance and (2) continued importance to literature. However unbiased such a list may be deemed, it inevitably becomes personal, and thus the reader is advised that undoubtedly some names of importance were omitted.

References and abbreviations, numbered in reading sequence

1. Authors listed alphabetically, with years of birth and death immediately following in parentheses.
2. Title of the selection within quotation marks; titles listed

chronologically, in order of date of appearance in the magazine.
3. Magazine's volume number, a large Roman numeral. Each number represents one half-year of the magazine's issues.
4. Date of issue, month and year, within parentheses.
5. Page numbers in magazine on which selection appears.
6. If the selection has never been reprinted or collected since its appearance in the magazine, the word 'uncollected' appears. If selection was reprinted, perhaps in a volume collection of the author's short stories, or perhaps in some other anthology, this fact is mentioned—naming the title of book and, in parentheses, place of publication, name of publishing company (usually in abridged form), year of publication.
7. In many cases, interesting variations between the version that appeared in *Esquire* and the version that appeared in some subsequent book are specified.

Franklin Pierce ADAMS (1881-)
'A Generous Gentleman of Character.'
XVII (March, 1942), 52, 104. Article; on John Kieran of 'Information Please'; uncollected.

'Horatio Alger, Jr.' XXVI (September, 1946), 80, 185-186. Article; uncollected.

George ADE (1866-1944)
'A Treatise on Pie.' I (Autumn, 1933), 20, 86. Article; uncollected.

'The White Ewe.' I (January, 1934), 32, 145, 150, 154. One-act play; uncollected.

Alfred ADLER (1870-1937)
'Love is a Recent Invention.' V (May, 1936), 56, 128. Article; uncollected.

'Training School for Lovers.' VI (September, 1936), 57, 197-198. Article; uncollected.

'Bankrupts of Love.' VI (December, 1936), 109, 321. Article; uncollected.

Mortimer Jerome ADLER (1902-)
'How to Talk Sense in Company.'
XXI (June, 1944), 59, 171-176. Article; uncollected.

Conrad Potter AIKEN (1889-)
'Fly Away Ladybird.' II (November, 1934), 50, 167. Short story; collected in *The Armchair Esquire*

' "Prelude" and "Prospect".' III (June, 1935), 36. Two poems; 'Prelude', without title, collected in Aiken, *Time in the Rock* (N.Y.: Scribner's, 1936), p. 102.

'The Two-a-day.' IV (December, 1935), 62. Three poems; 'Frost and Nye', 'Sterretts', and 'Curtain'; uncollected.

'A Pair of Vikings.' XV (March, 1941), 30, 132-136. Short story; collected in *The Short Stories of Conrad Aiken* (N.Y.: Duell, 1950).

Richard ALDINGTON (1892-)
'Towers of Manhattan.' V (April, 1936), 96. Poem; not collected in *The Complete Poems of Richard Aldington* (London: Wingate, 1948).

'Going Native Nearby.' XIII (February, 1940), 56, 100. Article; uncollected.

ary, 1946), 108, 228-234. Short story; included in 'The Roll of Honor [1946]', Martha Foley, ed., *The Best American Short Stories of 1947* (Boston, 1947); and in Baker, *Worlds Without End* (London: Sylvan, 1945).

Henri BARBUSSE (1874-1935)
'Against the Impending War.' III (January, 1935), 26, 151. Article; uncollected.

John BARTH (1930-)
'The Remobilization of Jacob Horner.' L (July, 1958), 55-59. Chapter from novel: *The End of the Road* (N.Y.: Doubleday, 1958).

Joseph Hamilton BASSO (1904-)
'The Man Who Made Peace.' XVI (August, 1941), 64, 135-136. Short story; uncollected.

'The Other Side of the River.' XVII (May, 1942), 54, 160-164. Short story; uncollected.

Herbert Ernest BATES (1905-)
'A Story Without an End.' I (April, 1934), 68, 144, 148. Short story; collected in Bates, *The Woman Who Had Imagination* (N.Y.: Macmillan, 1934).

'The Spiv's Master.' II (August, 1934), 54-55, 120. Short story; uncollected.

'Jonah and Bruno.' V (January, 1936), 49, 194-195. Short story; collected in Bates, *Cut and Come Again* (London: Cape, 1935).

Ralph BATES (1899-)
'In the Midst of Death We Live.' X (October, 1938), 64-65, 158-160. Short story; collected as 'Guadarrama Ballad' in Bates, *Sirocco* (N.Y.: Random House, 1939).

Lucius Morris BEEBE (1902-)
'The Regal Rolls-Royce.' XLIII (June, 1955), 63, 147-148, 150. Article; uncollected.

Thomas BEER (1889-1940)
'Must Memory Be Reverent?' II (August, 1934), 31. Article; uncollected.

Brendan BEHAN (1924?-)
'The Quare Fellow: Act One.' XLVIII (August, 1957), 24-33. A play (in part); with illustrations; published complete and under same title, N.Y., 1957.

Samuel Nathaniel BEHRMAN (1893-)
'Rest But Not in Peace.' XLIX (February, 1958), 41-42. Short story; uncollected.

Saul BELLOW (1915-)
'Leaving the Yellow House.' XLIX (January, 1958), 112, 114, 116, 119-126. Short story; collected in *The Armchair Esquire*.

Nathaniel BENCHLEY (1915-)
'Surprise Party.' XL (October, 1953), 82-83, 152-155. Short story; uncollected.

'An Hour for Lunch.' XL (December, 1953), 129, 233-235. Short story; uncollected.

'Well Do Whatever You Want.' XLVIII (July, 1957), 69-71. Short story; uncollected.

Stephen Vincent BENÉT (1898-1943)
'We Aren't Superstitious.' VII (May, 1937), 47, 212, 214, 216, 218-219. Article; on the Salem witch trials; collected in H. W. Hintz and B. D. N. Grebanier, eds., *Modern American Vistas* (N.Y.: Dryden, 1940).

William Rose BENÉT (1886-1950)
'Rowdy-Ditty of Horizontal Man.' V (March, 1936), 88. Poem; uncollected.

Konrad BERCOVICI (1882-)
'Pledge of the Dibras.' XVII (March, 1942), 54-55, 176. Short story; uncollected.

Alvah Cecil BESSIE (1904-)
'Profession of Pain.' III (May, 1935), 46, 125. Short story; uncollected.

'Man With Wings.' XIV (July, 1940), 81, 184-186. Short story; uncollected.

Richard Pike BISSELL (1913-   )
'Storm on the Mississippi.' XL (November, 1953), 84, 146. Article; uncollected.

Maxwell BODENHEIM (1893-1954)
'Sincerely Yours, Culture.' VIII (October, 1937), 74. Four untitled sonnets; collected under same general title in Bodenheim, *Lights in the Valley* (N.Y.: Harbinger House, 1942).

'A Sister Writes.' XX (November, 1943), 120. Poem; uncollected.

Anthony BOUCHER [William Anthony Parker White] (1911-   )
'Nine-Finger Jack.' XXXV (May, 1951), 54, 104. Short story; collected in McCloy and Halliday, eds., *Twenty Great Tales of Murder* (N.Y.: Random House, 1951); and in Bleiler and Dikty, eds., *Best Science Fiction Stories: 1952.* (N.Y.: Garden City, 1952).

Paul Frederic BOWLES (1911-   )
'A Gift for Kinza.' XXXV (March, 1951), 56, 119-121. Short story; uncollected.

Ernest Augustus BOYD (1887-1946)
'Songs that Mother Used to Sing.' II (July, 1935), 34, 119-120. Article; uncollected. [Boyd was then one of the editors of *American Spectator.*]

'Did the Germans Fool Us?' XV (January, 1941), 24-25. Article; uncollected.

Ray BRADBURY (1920-   )
'The Illustrated Man.' XXXIV (July, 1950), 49, 132-136. Short story; collected in Bradbury, *The Illustrated Man* (N.Y.: Doubleday, Doran, 1951); and in *The Esquire Treasury.*

'The Great Hallucination.' XXXIV (November, 1950), 68, 151-155. Short story; uncollected.

'Mars Is Heaven.' XXXIV (December, 1950), 96-97, 163-164, 166, 168, 170, 172. Short story; collected in Bleiler and Dikty, eds., *Science Fiction Omnibus: The Best Science Fiction Stories, 1949, 1950* (N.Y.: Garden City, 1951).

'The Last Night of the World.' XXXV (February, 1951), 41. Short story; collected in *The Illustrated Man,*

'The Immortality of Horror.' XXXVI (November, 1951), 102, 153-157. Short story; uncollected.

'A Piece of Wood.' XXXVII (June, 1952), 63, 125. Short story; uncollected.

'The Gift.' XXXVIII (December, 1952), 111. Short short story; uncollected.

'The Playground.' XL (October, 1953), 58-59, 129-133. Short story; collected in Bradbury, *Fahrenheit 451* (N.Y.: Houghton Mifflin, 1953).

'The Meadow.' XL (December, 1953), 85, 185-186, 188, 190. Short story; collected in Bradbury, *The Golden Apples of the Sun* (N.Y.: Doubleday Doran, 1953).

'Interval in Sunlight.' XLI (March, 1954), 46, 96, 98-99. Short story; uncollected.

'The Dragon.' XLIV (August, 1955), 61. Short short story; uncollected.

Roark BRADFORD (1896-1948)
'Three Times Seven.' IV (September, 1935), 32-33, 169-170. Short story; uncollected.

Note: in all, Bradford published eight pieces in *Esquire*, 1935-1948.

Louis BROMFIELD (1896-1956)
'The Shame of Our Colleges.' XXXIX (March, 1953), 33-34, 94. Article; uncollected.

Thomas Kite BROWN, III (1916-   )
'The Valley of the Shadow,' XXIV (July, 1945), 32-33, 112, 114. Short story; collected in *The Best American Short Stories of 1946* (Boston: Houghton Mifflin, 1946); and in *The Esquire Treasury.*

N

'Holy Day,' XLV (May, 1956), 82, 84. Short story; uncollected.

'A Drink of Water.' XLVI (September, 1956), 50, 89, 91, 94, 96, 103-104. Short story; uncollected.

Ivan BUNIN (1870-1953)
'A Night at Sea.' I (May, 1934), 30, 156, 162. Short story; collected in Bunin, *Grammar of Love* (N.Y.: Smith & Haas, 1934). [Trans. John Cournos.]

Whit BURNETT (1899-)
'One of Those Literary Guys.' I (February, 1934), 89, 93. Short story; collected in Burnett, *The Maker of Signs* (N.Y.: Smith & Haas, 1934).

'Whither the Beard?' XLIII (April, 1955), 75, 136. Article; uncollected.

William Riley BURNETT (1899-)
'For Charity's Sake.' II (June, 1934), 29, 141-142. Short story; uncollected.

'Greyhound Racing.' V (February, 1936), 81, 134, 136. Article; uncollected.

Witter Harold BYNNER (1881-)
'A Quartet of Males.' II (August, 1934), 35. Four Poems: 'Benedick', 'Oats', 'Philanderer', and 'Widower'; 'Widower' collected in Bynner, *Selected Poems*, ed. Robert Hunt (N.Y.: Knopf, 1943).

James Mallahan CAIN (1892-)
'Pay-Off Girl.' XXXVIII (August, 1952), 30, 108-109. Short story; uncollected.

Erskine Preston CALDWELL (1903-)
'August Afternoon.' I (Autumn, 1933), 22, 89, 110. Short story; collected in H. S. Canby, ed., *Stories by Erskine Caldwell* (N.Y.: Duell, Sloan and Pearce, 1944); and in *Caldwell Caravan* (Cleveland: World, 1946).

'The Sick Horse.' I (March, 1934), 32, 138. Short story; collected in *The Complete Stories of Erskine Caldwell* (N.Y.: Duell, Sloan and Pearce, 1941).

'Martha Jean.' III (January, 1935), 50, 140. Short story; collected in *Kneel to the Rising Sun* (N.Y.: Viking, 1935); and in *Complete Stories*.

'Candy-Man.' III (February, 1935), 39, 146. Short story; collected as 'Candy-Man Beechum' in *Kneel to the Rising Sun* and in *Complete Stories*.

'Return to Lavinia.' IV (December, 1935), 50, 185-186. Short story; collected in Caldwell, *Southways* (N.Y.: Viking, 1938); and in *Complete Stories*.

'The People vs. Abe Lathan, Colored.' XII (August, 1939), 26-27, 145. Short story; collected in E. J. O'Brien, ed., *The Best Short Stories of 1940* (Boston: Houghton Mifflin, 1940); and in *Complete Stories*.

'Squire Dinwiddy.' XV (January, 1941), 33, 131. Short story; collected in *Complete Stories*.

'Figurines of Love.' XXXIX (May, 1953), 56, 108-109. Short story; collected as 'Girl with Figurines' in Caldwell, *Gulf Coast Stories* (Boston: Little, Brown, 1956).

'To the Chaparral.' XL (December, 1953), 151, 236-237. Short story; collected in *Gulf Coast Stories*.

'My Twenty-Five Years of Censorship.' L (October, 1958), 176-178. Article; on the censorship history of *God's Little Acre*; uncollected.

Morley Edward CALLAGHAN (1903-)
'Let Me Promise You.' I (Autumn, 1933), 15, 86. Short story; collected in Callaghan, *Now That April's Here* (N.Y.: Random House, 1936). Note: in all, Callaghan published sixteen stories in *Esquire*, 1933-1952.

Albert CAMUS (1913-)
'The Spirit of Algiers.' XL (December, 1953), 92, 191-192. Article; collected in *The Armchair Esquire*.

'The Growing Stone.' XLIX (February, 1958), 111-121. Short story; collected in *Exile and the Kingdom* (N.Y.: Knopf, 1958).

Carl Lamson CARMER (1893-)
'And It Shall Be Given.' IV (August, 1935), 56-57, 103. Short story; uncollected.

Paul Vincent CARROLL (1900-)
'Home Sweet Home.' XI (January, 1939), 41, 153-154. Short story; uncollected.

Joyce CARY (1888-1957)
'Christmas in Africa.' XL (December, 1953), 101, 208. Article; uncollected.

'The Limit.' XLI (June, 1954), 43. Short short story; uncollected.

'Rush River.' XLII (July, 1954), 40, 106-107. Short story; uncollected.

R. V. CASSILL (1919-)
'The Sunday Painter.' XLVIII (November, 1957), 164-171. Short story; uncollected.

James CHARTERS (1897-)
'The White Winers.' II (August, 1934), 42-43, 126. Article; autobiographic; the last of a series by a Paris bartender in which he chats about Norman Douglas, Hemingway, Gordon Craig, Pound, Sinclair Lewis, and Ford Madox Ford; collected in Charters, *This Must be the Place*: Memoirs of Montparnasse (London: M. Joseph, 1934). Intro. by Ernest Hemingway. [A caricature of the principals is printed with the article, pp. 42-43.]

Paddy CHAYEFSKY (1923-)
'The Goddess.' XLIX (March, 1958), 96-129. Screenplay; uncollected.

Ann CHIDESTER (1919-)
'The Quality of Revenge.' XXXIX (June, 1953), 107, 132-134. Short story; uncollected.

Allen CHURCHILL (1911-)
'Portrait of a Nobel Prize Winner as a Bum.' XLVII (June, 1957), 98-101.

Article; on Eugene O'Neill; uncollected.

Stuart CLOETE (1897-)
'The Number 4 Gun.' XVII (April, 1942), 34, 107. Short story; uncollected. Note: in all, Cloete published nine stories in *Esquire*, 1942-1956.

Robert Myron COATES (1897-)
'The Cows Jumped over the Moon.' XXIX (February, 1948), 71. Short story; uncollected.

'Saturday and the Past.' XXXIII (June, 1950), 89, 128. Short story; uncollected.

'The Subject of a Dream: A Fable.' XLIX (June, 1958), 150-156. Short story; uncollected.

Irvin Shrewsbury COBB (1876-1944)
'The Moral Leopard.' I (January, 1934), 50, 111-112. Short story; collected in Cobb, *Faith, Hope and Charity*, (Indianapolis: Bobbs, 1934).

'Ace, Deuce, Ten Spot, Joker.' I (February, 1934), 48-49, 114; Part One: 'The Ten Spot.' I (March, 1934), 64-65; Part Two: 'The Deuce.' Short story; collected in *Faith, Hope and Charity*.

Robert Peter Tristram COFFIN (1892-1955)
'Christmas in New England.' XXXII (December, 1949), 75-77. Article; uncollected.

Lester COHEN (1901-)
'The Man Who Laughed Too Much.' XLIII (February, 1955), 99-106. Novelette; uncollected.

Padraic COLUM (1881-)
'George Moore, Esquire.' V (March, 1936), 62, 127. Article; uncollected.

Evan S. CONNELL, Jr. (1924-)
'Crash Landing.' XLIX (February, 1958), 59-63. Short story; uncollected.

Barnaby CONRAD (1922-   )
'The Greatest Bullfight Ever.' XXIX (April, 1948), 62, 142-143. Article; collected in *The Esquire Treasury.*

'The Visitors.' XXXVIII (November, 1952), 51, 111-112. Short story; uncollected.

Jack CONROY (1899-   )
'Happy Birthday for You.' VII (January, 1937), 74, 156. Short story; uncollected.

Alfred Edgar COPPARD (1878-1957)
'Lucy in her Pink Jacket.' XL (December, 1953), 149, 169-170, 172, 174, 176. Short story; uncollected.

Norman Lewis CORWIN (1910-   )
'Candid Cameragraphs. Three Poems.' V (January, 1936), 112. Poems: 'Boy Retiring', 'Street Corner', and 'Realist Reading a Sonnet Sequence'; uncollected.

Malcolm COWLEY
'The Leopard in Hart Crane's Brow.' L (October, 1958). Article; on Hart Crane; uncollected.

Ted CRONER (1922-   )
'The Mind of the Playwright: A Conversation with Elmer Rice.' XLVII (April, 1957), 66-67, 140. Article; an interview with the playwright; uncollected.

'The Mind of the Playwright: A Conversation with Lindsay and Crouse.' XLVIII (July, 1957), 36-38. Article; an interview with the playwrights; uncollected.

Edward Estlin CUMMINGS (1894-   )
'Five Poems.' III (May, 1935), 39, Poems: 'that which we who're alive', 'sh estiffl', 'o', 'sonnet entitled how to run the world', and 'IN / all those who got'; collected in Cummings, *No Thanks* (N.Y.: Golden Eagle Press, 1935), and in Cummings, *Poems: 1923-1954* (N.Y.: Harcourt, 1954).

'Exit the Boob." III (June, 1935), 33, 155. Article; collected in *The Armchair Esquire.*

Roald DAHL (1916-1953)
'Parson's Pleasure.' XLIX (April, 1958), 148-161. Short story; uncollected.

Salvador DALI (1904-   )
'Total Camouflage for Total War.' XVIII (August, 1942), 65-66, 130. Article; uncollected.

Clarence DARROW (1857-1938)
'Attorney for the Defense.' V (May, 1936), 36-37, 211-213. Article; collected in W. H. and K. C. Cordell, eds., *American Points of View, 1936* (N.Y.: Doubleday, Doran, 1937); and in *Bedside Esquire.*

Rhys DAVIES (1903-   )
'Mourning for Ianto.' VII (February, 1937), 92-93, 148. Short story; collected in E. J. O'Brien, ed., *The Best British Short Stories of 1937* (Boston: Houghton Mifflin, 1937); and in Davies, *Boy with a Trumpet* (N.Y.: Doubleday, 1951).

Gen. Charles André Joseph Marie DE GAULLE (1890-   )
'De Gaulle on Willkie, F.D.R., and Ike.' L (October, 1958), 119-120. Sections, in advance of publication, from his *Memoirs de Guerre, Vol. II.*

David Cornel DE JONG (1905-   )
'Going the Whole Way.' I (May, 1934), 76, 128, 131. Short story; uncollected.

'Calling in the Night.' VI (October, 1936), 80-81, 166-168. Short story; collected in De Jong, *Snow-on-the-Mountain* (N.Y.: Reynal & Hitchcock, 1946).

'Minding the Calves.' XII (August, 1939), 38-39, 119. Short story; collected as 'Calves' in Harry Hansen, ed., *O. Henry Memorial Prize Stories of 1939* (N.Y.: Doubleday, Doran, 1939). [Awarded 3rd Prize.]

'A Point of Honor.' XIII (January, 1940), 73, 164-165. Short story; uncollected.

Alexander Procofieff DE SEVERSKY (1894-   )
'Mitchell Memorial.' XVIII (December, 1942), 141-166. Article; reproductions of newspaper clippings of Mitchell's career with commentary by the author; uncollected.

Peter DE VRIES (1910-   )
'Art's a Funny Thing.' V (February, 1936), 59, 124, 127. Satirical sketch; uncollected.

'I, Voluptuary.' VI (December, 1936), 82, 245-246, 248, 250. Short story; uncollected.

'Man on the Street.' VII (April, 1937), 100, 140, 142. Satirical sketch; uncollected.

'Rhapsody for a Girl on a Bar Stool.' VIII (November, 1937), 48-49. Poem; uncollected.

'Songs for Eight O'Clock.' IX (February, 1938), 40-41. Four untitled poems; uncollected.

'Song for a Bride.' IX (June, 1938), 36. Poem; uncollected.

'Lament at Thirty.' XI (January, 1939), 38. Poem; uncollected.

'The Floorwalker Attends a Slide Lecture on Gauguin.' XII (September, 1939), 28. Poem; uncollected.

'Teach a Child the Way.' XVI (November, 1941), 42-43, 126. Satirical sketch; uncollected.

'Conversion of Thunderpuss.' XVIII (October, 1942,) 87, 113-116. Short story; uncollected.

'Larder Ex Libris.' XXX (December, 1948), 130. Article; uncollected.

Reuel DENNEY
'Individuality and the New Leisure.' L (October, 1958), 78, 91. Article; uncollected.

Pietro DI DONATO (1911-   )
'Christ in Concrete.' VII (March, 1937), 40-41, 194-196. Short story; first version of the novel by the same name; collected in *The Best Short Stories of 1938*; and in E. J. O'Brien, ed., *Fifty Best American Short Stories, 1915-1939* (Boston: Houghton Mifflin, 1939); and in *Bedside Esquire*.

'It's Cheaper to Be . . .' X (November, 1938), 49, 101-102. Short story; uncollected.

'La Smorfia.' XLIV (December, 1955), 105, 240-241. Short story; uncollected.

'Geremio.' XLIX (June, 1958), 88-90. Short story; uncollected.

James Frank DOBIE (1888-   )
'A Boy and His Horse.' XXIV (September, 1945), 88-89. Article; uncollected.

John Roderigo DOS PASSOS (1896-   )
'Back Home in 1919.' I (Autumn, 1933), 10, 107, 115. Short story; incorporated in Dos Passos, *The Big Money* (N.Y.: Harcourt, Brace, 1936) as the first Charley Anderson episode. [On p. 11 is a full-colour reproduction of a water colour by Dos Passos, 'Port of New York.']

'Man with a Watch in His Hand.' I (January, 1934), 55, 108. Article; short biography of F.W. Taylor; incorporated into *The Big Money* as 'The American Plan.'

'Brooklyn to Helsingfors.' I (February, 1934), 38, 136, 142. Article; revised and incorporated, with same title, into Dos Passos, *In All Countries* (N.Y.: Harcourt, Brace, 1934).

'Another Redskin Bites the Dust.' I (March, 1934), 38, 115, 143. Article; revised and incorporated into *In All Countries* as 'Emiliana Zapata.'

'Facing a Bitter World. A Portfolio of Etchings.' III (February, 1935), 25. Article; short commentary on Luis Quintanilla; uncollected. [Not listed in previous bibliographies of Dos Passos; cf. Ernest HEMINGWAY.]

'The Celebrity.' IV (August, 1935), 22, 92. Short story; in revised form this appears as part of the third Charley Anderson episode in *The Big Money*. Collected in *The Armchair Esquire*.

'The Bitter Drink.' IV (September, 1935), 20-21, 174-175. Article; short biography of Veblen; revised and incorporated, with same title, into *The Big Money*.

'None but the Brave.' V (January, 1936), 42, 170. Short story; uncollected.

'Personal Appearance.' V (February, 1936), 32, 181-182. Article; short biography of Valentino; revised and incorporated into *The Big Money* as 'Adagio Dancer.'

'Art and Isadora.' V (March, 1936), 41, 196-197. Article; short biography of Duncan; revised and incorporated, with same title, into *The Big Money*.

'The Camera Eye.' V (April, 1936), 51, 112. Article; autobiographic; revised and incorporated into *The Big Money* as 'The Camera Eye (43)', 'Newsreel XLVII', 'The Camera Eye (44)', 'The Camera Eye (45)', 'The Camera Eye (46)', and part of 'Newsreel XLV.'

'The Big Director.' V (May, 1936), 50, 217. Short story; incorporated into *The Big Money* as the fifth Margo Dowling episode.

'The Poor Whites of Cuba.' V (May, 1936), 110. Article; short commentary on Antonio Gattorno, a Cuban painter; uncollected. [*Cf.* Ernest HEMINGWAY.]

'Grosz Comes to America.' VI (September, 1936), 105, 128, 131. Article; un-collected. [Illustrated with five etchings by Grosz.]

'Introduction to Civil War.' VIII (October, 1937), 53, 141-142, 144. Article; incorporated into Dos Passos, *Journeys Between Wars* (N.Y.: Harcourt, Brace, 1938) as 'A Spring Month in Paris'.

'Spanish Diary; Coast Road.' VIII (November, 1937), 47, 202, 204, 206. Article; incorporated into *Journeys Between Wars* as part of 'Coast Road South', pp. 345-353.

'The Road to Madrid.' VIII (December, 1937), 62, 238, 240, 243. Article; incorporated into *Journeys Between Wars* as part of 'Coast Road South,' pp. 353-360, and as 'Valencia-Madrid'.

'Room and Bath at the Hotel Florida.' IX (January, 1938), 35, 131-132, 134. Article; incorporated into *Journeys Between Wars* as 'Madrid Under Siege.'

'The Villages are the Heart of Spain.' IX (February, 1938), 32-33, 151-153. Article; published separately as a 15-p. pamphlet by Esquire-Coronet, Inc., in 1938; incorporated, with same title, into *Journeys Between Wars*. [All articles incorporated into *Journeys Between Wars* were revised slightly.]

'Most Likely to Succeed.' XL (September, 1953), 48, 124-125. Short story; incorporated into Dos Passos, *Most Likely to Succeed* (N.Y.: Prentice-Hall, 1953).

'The Death of James Dean.' L (October, 1958), 121-123. Article; uncollected. A short biography using the techniques of *The Big Money*, as a retrospective feature for *Esquire's* 25th Anniversary issue.

Theodore Herman Albert DREI-SER (1871-1945)

'Mathewson.' I (May, 1934), 20-21, 125; Part One. II (June, 1934), 24-25, 114; Part Two. Short story; uncollected.

'An Address to Caliban.' II (September, 1934), 20-21, 158D. Article; an attack on Chicago; collected in E. A. Walter, ed., *Essay Annual, 1935* (N.Y.: Scott, 1935), pp. 78-86.

'You the Phantom.' II (November, 1934), 25-26. Article; collected in Arnold Gingrich, ed., *Bedside Esquire* (N.Y.: McBride, 1940).

'The Epic Sinclair.' II (December, 1934), 32-33, 178-179. Article; on Upton Sinclair; uncollected. [EPIC: End Poverty in California.]

'Kismet.' III (January, 1935), 29, 175-176. Article; uncollected.

'Five Moods in Minor Key.' III (March, 1935), 25. Five Poems: 'Tribute', 'The Loafer', 'Improvisation', 'Machine', and 'Escape'; collected in Dreiser, *Moods, Philosophic and Emotional* (N.Y.: Simon & Schuster, 1935).

'Overland Journey.' IV (September, 1935), 24, 97. Article; uncollected.

'Mark Twain: Three Contacts.' IV (October, 1935), 22, 162-162B. Article; uncollected.

'The Tithe of the Lord.' X (July, 1938), 36-37, 150, 155-158. Short story; collected in *The Armchair Esquire*.

'Myself and the Movies.' XX (July, 1943), 50, 159. Article; autobiographical account of writer's service in Hollywood; uncollected.

'Black Sheep Number One: Johnny.' XXII (October, 1944), 39, 156-160. Sketch; "Introducing a series of unregenerate characters, each a bad piece of work, ranging from worthless to pernicious"; uncollected.

'Black Sheep Number Two: Otie.' XXII (November, 1944), 65. Sketch; uncollected.

'Black Sheep Number Three: Bill.' XXII (December, 1944), 118, 296-297. Sketch; uncollected.

'Black Sheep Number Four: Ethelda.' XXIII (January, 1945), 85, 127. Sketch; uncollected.

'Black Sheep Number Five: Clarence.' XXIII (February, 1945), 49, 129-130. Sketch; uncollected.

'Black Sheep Number Six: Harrison Barr.' XXIII (March, 1945), 49, 131. Sketch; uncollected.

'Background for An American Tragedy.' L (October, 1958), 155-157. An incident in the childhood of Clyde Griffiths; one of nine chapters excised from *An American Tragedy* before its publication. A part of the 'Titans Revisited' section of *Esquire's* 25th Anniversary issue.

Lord DUNSANY [Edward John Moreton Drax Plunkett, 18th Baron] (1878-1957)

'A Matter of Honour.' II (July, 1934), 56. One-act play; collected in Dunsany, *Plays for Earth and Air* (London: Heinemann, 1937).

'The New Moon.' XXXVII (March, 1952), 60, 106-107. Short story; uncollected.

Walter DURANTY (1884-1957)

'Life with a Dream Girl.' XVIII (December, 1942), 61, 264-265. Short story; uncollected.

'The Taking of Sanski Most.' XX (September, 1943), 80, 165-166. Short story; uncollected.

'Gifts of the Greeks.' XXXII (August, 1949), 37, 115-116. Short story; uncollected.

Walter Dumaux EDMONDS (1903-)

'The Resurrection of Solly Moon.' II (August, 1934), 47, 111, 150. Short story; collected in *Bedside Esquire*.

George Paul ELLIOTT (1918-)

'Among the Dangs.' XLIX (June, 1958), 128, 130, 132, 134-135, 137-140

'The Lost Decade.' XII (December, 1939), 113, 228. Short story; collected in *The Stories.*

'Pat Hobby's Christmas Wish.' XIII (January, 1940), 45, 170-172. Short story; uncollected. [The first of seventeen stories in which Pat Hobby, a jaded Hollywood script writer, appears as the main character.]

'A Man in the Way.' XIII (February, 1940), 40, 109. Short story; uncollected. [Pat Hobby.]

' 'Boil Some Water—Lots of it.' ' XIII (March, 1940), 30, 145, 147. Short story; collected in *Afternoon of an Author.* [Pat Hobby.]

'Teamed With Genius.' XIII (April, 1940), 44, 195-197. Short story; collected in *Afternoon of an Author.* [Pat Hobby.]

'Pat Hobby and Orson Welles.' XIII (May, 1940), 38, 198-199. Short story; uncollected.

'Pat Hobby's Secret.' XIII (June, 1940), 30, 107. Short story; uncollected.

'Pat Hobby, Putative Father.' XIV (July, 1940), 36, 172-174. Short story; uncollected.

'The Homes of the Stars.' XIV (August, 1940), 28, 120-121. Short story; uncollected. [Pat Hobby.]

'Pat Hobby Does His Bit.' XIV (September, 1940), 41, 104. Short story; uncollected.

'Pat Hobby's Preview.' XIV (October, 1940), 30, 118, 120. Short story; uncollected.

'No Harm Trying.' XIV (November, 1940), 30, 151-153. Short story; collected in *Afternoon of an Author.* [Pat Hobby.]

'A Patriotic Short.' XIV (December, 1940), 62, 269. Short story; collected in *The Stories.* [Pat Hobby]

'On the Trail of Pat Hobby.' XV (January, 1941), 36, 126. Short story; uncollected.

'Fun in an Artist's Studio.' XV (February, 1941), 64, 112. Short story; uncollected. [Pat Hobby]

'On an Ocean Wave.' XV (February, 1941), 59, 141-142. Short story; uncollected. [Written under the pseudonym of 'Paul Elgin'; see Arthur Mizener, *The Far Side of Paradise* (Boston: Houghton Mifflin, 1951), p. 356.]

'Two Old-Timers.' XV (March, 1941), 53, 143. Short story; collected in *The Stories.* [Pat Hobby]

'Mightier than the Sword.' XV (April, 1941), 36, 183. Short story; uncollected. [Pat Hobby]

'Pat Hobby's College Days.' XV (May, 1941), 55, 168-169. Short story; uncollected. [The last of the Pat Hobby stories.]

'The Woman from Twenty-One.' XV (June, 1941), 29, 164. Short story; uncollected.

'Three Hours Between Planes.' XVI (July, 1941), 41, 138-139. Short story; collected in *The Stories.*

'Advice to a Young Writer.' L (October, 1958), 158-159. Three unpublished letters of Fitzgerald's with accompanying text by Andrew Turnbull. A part of the 'Titans Revisited' section of *Esquire's* 25th Anniversary issue.

John Gould FLETCHER (1886-1950) 'Forever upon the Prairie.' I (March, 1934), 19. Poem; revised and collected as 'Shadow on the Prairie,' in Fletcher, *The Burning Mountain* (N.Y.: Dutton, 1946).

'Requiem for a Twentieth-Century Outlaw.' III (April, 1935), 26. Poem; revised and collected in *The Burning Mountain.*

Robert Louis FONTAINE (1912?-)
'The Loud and Vehement Prayer.'
XXII (July, 1944), 48-49, 148. Short
story; incorporated, with revisions, as
'The Loud Prayer' in Fontaine, *The
Happy Time* (N.Y.: Simon & Schuster,
1945).

'Geralde and the Good Green Earth.'
XXVIII (September, 1947), 94-95.
Short story; uncollected.

Shelby FOOTE (1916-)
'Shiloh.' XXXIX (February, 1953),
75-94, 96. Complete novel; with
Mathew B. Brady photographs; published previously, without photographs,
as Foote, *Shiloh* (N.Y.: Dial, 1952).

Ford Madox FORD [Ford Madox
Hueffer] (1873-1939)
'See, They Return!' III (June, 1935),
37, 164-166. Article; revised and incor-
porated into Ford, *Great Trade Route*
(N.Y.: Oxford, 1937) as Chapter
Three, 'Voyage Outwards.'

Cecil Scott FORESTER (1899-)
'To My Darling.' IV (September,
1935), 70, 106. Short story; uncollected.

'The Last Three Seconds.' V (March,
1936), 78, 128, 130. Short story; uncollected.

' "You Are Welcome!" ' XX (September, 1943), 48-49, 123. Short story; uncollected.

Waldo David FRANK (1889-)
'A Place to Lay One's Head.' III
(January, 1935), 35, 99. Short story;
collected in Charles Grayson, ed., *Half
a Hundred* (N.Y.: Garden City, 1945);
and in *Bedside Esquire*.

'Stepan and Natasha.' VII (June,
1937), 80, 158. Short story; uncollected.

Sidney FRANKLIN (1903-)
'There Was a Man: Joselito.' XXXIII
(June, 1950), 64, 120. Article; Joselito
the matador; uncollected.

Peter FREUCHEN (1886-1957)
'Nauja the Desired.' IV (December,

1935), 92, 146, 149. Short story; uncollected.

'Casanova on Ice.' V (January, 1935),
56, 198-201. Short story; uncollected.

Mavis GALLANT
'Thieves and Rascals.' XLVI (July,
1956), 82, 85-86. Short story; uncollected.

Martha Ellis GELLHORN
(1908-)
'About Shorty.' XXXIII (January,
1950), 52, 128-131. Short story; collected in Gingrich, ed., *Girls From
Esquire* (N.Y.: Random House, 1952);
Esquire Treasury; and in Gellhorn,
Honeyed Peace; Stories (N.Y.: Doubleday, 1953).

'Darling, Believe Me.' XXXVI (September, 1951), 45, 122, 124, 127. Short
story; uncollected.

'Man in a Trap.' XXXVIII (December, 1952), 128, 174, 176, 178, 181-
182, 184. Short story; uncollected.

Brendan GILL (1914-)
'A Home with the Latest Gadgets.'
XXIII (January, 1945), 70-71. Short
story; uncollected.

'The Night Bus to Atlanta.' XXIII
(March, 1945), 32, 140-145. Short
story; collected in *Girls From Esquire*.

Oliver St. John GOGARTY
(1878-1957)
'A Picture of Oscar Wilde.' XXIV
(August, 1945), 40-41, 149-152. Article;
uncollected.

Maxim GORKI (1868-1936)
'The Pogrom.' IV (July, 1935), 24-25,
164. Short story; uncollected. [This
story appeared to have been written
c. 1903.]

'Life in a Prison Cell.' VII (April,
1937), 44-45, 217-219. Short story; collected in *The Armchair Esquire*.

Robert GRAVES (1895-)
'The American Poet as a Businessman.

364

L (October, 1958), 22, 24, 26, 28.
Article; uncollected.

Paul GREEN (1894-   )
"Austin Honey and the Buzzards.'
XXV (March, 1946), 99, 178-179.
Short story; collected in Green, *Salvation on a String* (N.Y.: Harper, 1946).

Graham GREENE (1904-   )
'Her Uncle vs. His Father.' XVIII
(July, 1942), 30, 116-119. Short story;
uncollected.

William Lindsay GRESHAM
(1909-   )
'The Long Drop.' XXVIII (August,
1947), 59, 134. Short story; uncollected.
Note: in all, Gresham published eight
pieces in *Esquire*, 1947-1954.

John Joseph GUNTHER (1901-   )
'I Dub You Sir Knight.' XXXI
(March, 1949), 34, 126-128. Short
story; uncollected.

Alfred Bertram GUTHRIE, Jr.
(1901-   )
'The Last Snake.' XXXII (November,
1949), 57, 109-110, 112, 114, 116.
Short story; uncollected.

'Bargain at Moon Dance.' XXXVIII
(October, 1952), 72, 127-130. Short
story; uncollected.

James B. HALL
'The Claims Artist.' XL (September,
1953), 42-43, 105. Short story; uncollected.

'The Fall and the Twilight.' XLVIII
(September, 1957), 100-104. Short
story; uncollected.

Albert HALPER (1904-   )
'Hot Night in Rockford.' II (August,
1934), 66-67, 117. Short story; uncollected.

'Model Wanted.' V (January, 1936),
41, 182B. Short story; uncollected.

Samuel Dashiell HAMMETT
(1894-   )
'Albert Pastor at Home.' I (Autumn,

1933), 34. Short short story; uncollected.

Knut HAMSUN (1859-1952)
'Son of the Sun.' I (March, 1934), 30,
120. Short story; uncollected.

'The Conqueror.' II (October, 1934),
65, 112. Short story; uncollected.

Michael HASTINGS (1937-   )
'The Game.' XLIX (April, 1958), 135-
147. Sampler from novel, *The Game*
(N.Y.: McGraw-Hill, 1958).

Ben HECHT (1893-   )
'Snowfall in Childhood.' II (November, 1934), 40-41, 122. Short story; collected in Hecht, *Actor's Blood* (N.Y.:
Covici, 1936); and in *Bedside Esquire*.

'A Champion in Chains.' XVIII (October, 1942), 36, 168-169. Article; uncollected.

'John Decker's Hollywood.' XXIV
(December, 1945), 132. Article; uncollected.

'Dr. Romeo and Juliet.' XXXVII
(June, 1952), 47, 49, 109-110, 112-114.
Short story; uncollected.

'Sex in Hollywood.' XLI (May, 1954),
35, 120-121. Article; uncollected.

'The Tired Horse.' XLII (September,
1954), 42-43. Short short story; uncollected.

'Sic Transit.' XLII (December, 1954),
87. Short short story; uncollected.

'Bosoms Away.' XLVIII (July, 1957),
73-74. Article; uncollected.

Robert Louis HEILBRONER
(1919-   )
'The Murder of the Man Who Was
Shakespeare.' XLII (December, 1954),
115-122. Article; 'Calvin Hoffman's
case for Christopher Marlowe'; uncollected; Hoffman's book published in
New York, 1955.

Ernest Miller HEMINGWAY
(1899-   )
'Marlin off the Morro. A Cuban

Letter.' I (Autumn, 1933), 8-9, 39, 97. Article; with numerous photographs; collected as 'Marlin off Cuba' in E. V. Connett, ed., *American Big Game Fishing* (N.Y.: Derrydale, 1935).

'The Friend of Spain. A Spanish Letter.' I (January, 1934), 26, 136. Article; illustrated by a reproduction, in full colour, of a water colour by John DOS PASSOS, p. 27; uncollected.

'A Paris Letter.' I (February, 1934), 22, 156. Article; uncollected.

'a.d. in Africa. A Tanganyika Letter.' I (April, 1934), 19, 146. Article; uncollected. ['a.d.': amoebic dysentery.]

'Shootism Versus Sport. The Second Tanganyika Letter.' II (June, 1934), 19, 150. Article; uncollected.

'Notes on Dangerous Game. The Third Tanganyika Letter.' II (July, 1934), 19, 94. Article; important background material for *Green Hills of Africa*, 'The Short Happy Life of Francis Macomber,' and 'The Snows of Kilimanjaro'; uncollected.

'Out in the Stream. A Cuban Letter.' II (August, 1934), 19, 156, 158. Article; uncollected.

'Defense of Dirty Words. A Cuban Letter.' II (September, 1934), 19, 158B, 158D. Article; criticism of Ring Lardner and others; uncollected.

'Genio After Josie. A Havana Letter.' II (October, 1934), 21-22. Article; uncollected.

'Old Newsman Writes.' II (December, 1934), 25-26. Article; attack on "proletarian writers"; uncollected.

'Notes on Life an Letters. Or a Manuscript Found in a Bottle.' III (January, 1935), 21, 159. Article; excoriation of William SAROYAN; uncollected.

'Remembering Shooting-Flying. A Key West Letter.' III (February, 1935), 21, 152. Article; collected in *Esquire's First Sports Reader.*

'Facing a Bitter World. A Portfolio of Etchings by Luis Quintanilla.' III (February, 1935), 26-27. Article; a commentary on Quintanilla; uncollected [*Cf.* John DOS PASSOS.]

'Sailfish off Mombasa. A Key West Letter.' III (March, 1935), 21, 156. Article; uncollected.

'The Sights of Whitehead Street. A Key West Letter.' III (April, 1935), 25, 156. Article; uncollected.

'a.d. Southern Style. A Key West Letter.' III (May, 1935), 25, 156. Article; uncollected.

'On Being Shot Again. A Gulf Stream Letter.' III (June, 1935), 25, 156-157. Article; uncollected.

'The President Vanishes. A Bimini Letter.' IV (July, 1935), 23, 167. Article; uncollected.

'He Who Gets Slap Happy. A Bimini Letter.' IV (August, 1935), 19, 182. Article; account of the veterans in a Key West saloon is similar to the episode in Chapter 22, *To Have and Have Not*; uncollected.

'Notes on the Next War.' IV (September, 1935), 19, 156. Article; violently isolationist; collected in W. H. Cordell and K. C. Cordell, eds., *American Points of View, 1936* (N.Y.: Doubleday, Doran, 1937).

'Monologue to the Maestro. A High Seas Letter.' IV (October, 1936), 21, 174A-174B. Article; strictures on the art of fiction; uncollected.

'The Malady of Power. A Second Serious Letter.' IV (November, 1935), 31, 198-199. Article; another anti-war piece; collected in *American Points of View, 1936.*

'Million Dollar Fright. A New York Letter.' IV (December, 1935), 35, 190B. Article; on heavyweight boxing; uncollected.

'Wings Always Over Africa. An Ornithological Letter.' V (January, 1936), 31, 174-175. Article; on Italo-Ethiopian war; uncollected.

'The Tradesman's Return.' V (February, 1936), 27, 193-196. Short story; incorporated, with revisions, into *To Have and Have Not* as Chapters 6-8; and in *The Esquire Treasury*.

'On the Blue Water. A Gulf Stream Letter.' V (April, 1936), 31, 184-185. Article; on marlin-fishing; contains a 178-word anecdote which is the 'germ' of *The Old Man and the Sea*; collected in Eric Devine, ed., *Blow the Man Down* (N.Y.: Doubleday, Doran, 1937); and in *Bedside Esquire*.

'There She Breaches! Or Moby Dick off the Morro.' V (May, 1936), 35, 203-205. Article; uncollected.

'Gattorno: Program Note.' V (May, 1936), 111, 141. Article; short commentary on the Cuban painter Antonio Gattorno; uncollected. [A reprint of the original program note, Havana, April, 1935; cf. John DOS PASSOS.]

'The Horns of the Bull.' V (May, 1936), 31, 190-193. Short story; revised and collected as 'The Capital of the World' in Hemingway, *The Fifth Column and the First Forty-Nine Stories* (N.Y.: Scribner's 1938).

'The Snows of Kilimanjaro.' VI (August, 1936), 27, 194-201. Short story; the name 'Scott Fitzgerald' appears, instead of 'Julian', in this first version; collected in *The Fifth Column and the First Forty-Nine Stories*; and in E. J. O'Brien, ed., *The Best Short Stories of 1937* (Boston; Houghton Mifflin, 1937); and in *Bedside Esquire*.

'The Denunciation' X (November, 1938), 39, 111-114. Short story; uncollected; first of a series of three stories about Chicote's Bar in Madrid during the Spanish Civil War.

'The Butterfly and the Tank.' X (December, 1938), 51, 186, 188, 190. Collected in *The Armchair Esquire*.

'Night Before Battle.' XI (February, 1939), 27-29, 91-92, 95, 97. Uncollected.

James HILTON (1900-1954)
'Challenge of Mt. Everest.' XXX (July, 1948), 58, 145. Article; uncollected.

Chester B. HIMES (1909-   )
'Crazy in the Stir.' II (August, 1934), 28, 114, 117. Short story; early story with prison setting by the Negro novelist; uncollected. Note: in all, Himes published ten pieces in *Esquire*, 1934-1946.

Stewart Hall HOLBROOK (1893-   )
'The Unholy Horatio Alger.' XIX (January, 1943), 69, 177-180. Article; uncollected.

John Clellon HOLMES (1926?-   )
'The Philosophy of the Beat Generation.' XLIX (February, 1958), 35-38. Article; uncollected. [*Cf.* John KEROUAC.]

Geoffrey HOUSEHOLD (1900-   )
'The Idealist.' XXXIX (June, 1953), 58, 135-136. Short story; uncollected.

Laurence HOUSMAN (1865-1959)
'The Fall of the Sparrow.' IV (December, 1935), 69, 155. Short story; collected in Housman, *What Next?* (London: Cape, 1938).

James Langston HUGHES (1902-   )
'A Good Job Gone.' I (April, 1934), 46, 142, 144. Short story; collected in Hughes, *The Ways of White Folks* (N.Y.: Knopf, 1934); and in *Bedside Esquire*.

'The Folks at Home.' I (May, 1934), 56-57, 93-94. Short story; collected as 'Home' in *The Ways of White Folks*.

'The Little Old Spy.' II (September, 1934), 47, 150, 152. Short story; collected in Hughes, *Laughing to Keep From Crying* (N.Y.: Holt, 1952).

'On the Road.' III (January, 1935), 92, 154. Short story; collected in *Laughing to Keep From Crying*.

'Tragedy at the Baths.' IV (October, 1935), 80, 122. Short story; collected in *Laughing to Keep From Crying*.

'Slice 'em Down.' V (May, 1936), 44-45, 190-193. Short story; collected in *Laughing to Keep From Crying*.

'Let America Be America Again.' VI (July, 1936), 92. Poem; uncollected.

'Air Raid: Barcelona.' X (October, 1938), 40. Poem; uncollected.

'Seven Moments of Love. An Un-Sonnet Sequence in Blues.' XIII (May, 1940), 60-61. Seven Poems: 'Twilight Reverie', 'Supper Time', 'Bed Time', 'Daybreak', 'Sunday', 'Pay Day', and 'Letter'; collected in Hughes, *Shakespeare in Harlem* (N.Y.: Knopf, 1942).

John HUSTON (1906-   )
'Moulin Rouge.' XXXVIII (December, 1952), 103-106. Article; notes on making the film *Moulin Rouge*, with photographs of Toulouse-Lautrec and two excellent reproductions of his work; uncollected.

Robert Maynard HUTCHINS
(1899-   )
'The Lesson of Khrushchev's Little Red Schoolhouse.' XLIX (June, 1958), 84-87. Article; uncollected.

'The Age of the Interchangeable Man.' L (October, 1958), 66, 70. Article; uncollected.

Aldous Leonard HUXLEY
(1894-   )
'Visiting Stranger.' IV (November, 1935), 32-33, 197. Short story; uncollected.

'Time's Revenge.' XXXVI (October, 1951), 49, 131-138. Short story; uncollected.

'Sludge and Sanctity.' XXXIX (June, 1953), 53, 127-131. Article; cleanliness and sewage; uncollected.

'The French of Paris.' XL (December, 1953), 121, 123-124, 127-128. Article; uncollected.

'Usually Destroyed.' XLIV (July, 1955), 42, 112-113. Article; collected in Huxley, *Tomorrow and Tomorrow and Tomorrow* (N.Y.: Harper, 1956).

'Miracle in Lebanon.' XLIV (August, 1955), 23-24. Article; commences a series entitled 'From the Study of Aldous Huxley'; collected in *Tomorrow and Tomorrow and Tomorrow*.

'Doodles in the Dictionary.' XLIV (September, 1955), 44, 135-136. Article; on Toulouse-Lautrec; collected in *Tomorrow and Tomorrow and Tomorrow*.

'Censorship and Spoken Literature.' XLIV (October, 1955), 55-56. Article; on political and economic censorship; collected in *Tomorrow and Tomorrow and Tomorrow*.

'Liberty, Quality, Machinery.' XLIV (November, 1955), 67-68. Article; the individual's place in a technological society; collected in *Tomorrow and Tomorrow and Tomorrow*.

'Canned Fish.' XLIV (December, 1955), 93, 252. Article; on work; collected in *Tomorrow and Tomorrow and Tomorrow*.

'Variations on a Musical Theme.' XLV (January, 1956), 43-44, 122, 124, 125A. Article; uncollected.

'Mother.' XLV (February, 1956), 31-32. Article; collected in *Tomorrow and Tomorrow and Tomorrow*.

'Tomorrow and Tomorrow and Tomorrow.' XLV (March, 1956), 43-44. Article; collected in *Tomorrow and Tomorrow and Tomorrow*.

'Back Numbers.' XLV (April, 1956), 49, 140-142. Article; uncollected.

'Where Do You Live?' XLV (May, 1956), 43-44, 108. Article; uncollected.

'Madness, Badness, Sadness.' XLV (June, 1956), 50, 146-148. Article; uncollected.

'Brave New World Revisited.' XLVI (July, 1956), 31-32. Article; collected in *The Armchair Esquire*.

'Genius.' XLVI (August, 1956), 24, 114. Article; uncollected.

'Facts and Fetishes.' XLVI (September, 1956), 43, 115-116. Article; uncollected.

'A Case of Voluntary Ignorance.' XLVI (October, 1956), 47, 124, 127-128, 130. Article; uncollected.

'Paradoxes of Progress.' XLVI (November, 1956), 55-56. Article; uncollected.

'Can We Be Well Educated?' XLVI (December, 1956), 112, 216, 218, 220. Article; uncollected.

'Post-Mortem on Bridey.' XLVII (January, 1957), 45, 128, 130. Article; uncollected.

'Pleasures.' XLVII (February, 1957), 27-28. Article; uncollected.

'The Oddest Science.' XLVII (March, 1957), 33-34, 123. Article; on psychology; uncollected.

'Politics and Biology.' XLVII (April, 1957), 46-45. Article; England and Suez; ends the series 'From the Study'; uncollected.

Charles Reginald JACKSON (1903-)
'Millstones.' XXXIX (May, 1953), 79. Short short story; uncollected.

'Don't Call Me Sonny.' XL (July, 1953), 42, 109. Short story; uncollected.

'Landscape with Figures.' XL (December, 1953), 156. Short short story; uncollected.

Cyril Edwin Mitchinson JOAD (1891-1953)
'The Higher Escapism.' XV (June, 1941), 27, 159-163. Article; uncollected.

James JONES (1921-)
'Two Legs for the Two of Us.' XXXVI (September, 1951), 43, 100, 103. Short story; collected in *Girls From Esquire* and in *Esquire Treasury*.

'The Tennis Game.' XLIX (January, 1958), 60-64. Short story; uncollected.

Garson KANIN (1912-)
'All Through the House.' XLIV (December, 1955), 167-174. Long short story; uncollected.

'The Damnedest Thing.' XLV (February, 1956), 63-64. Short story; uncollected.

'Flowers of Friendship.' XLVI (August, 1956), 31, 110, 113. Short story; uncollected.

MacKinlay KANTOR (1904-)
'The Widow Kelvey's Curse.' XXII (September, 1944), 30-31, 164. Short story; uncollected.

'All Night with My Darling.' XXII (December, 1944), 64-65. Short story; uncollected.

'Old Times There Are Not Forgotten.' XXIII (February, 1945), 43. Short short story; uncollected.

'Time to Wake Up Now.' XXIV (October, 1945), 48-49, 135. Article; semi-autobiographical war narrative; uncollected.

'Dear Old Ghost of Mine.' XXIV (November, 1945), 40-41, 171-174. Article; on ghosts; uncollected.

'And the Armies that Remained Suffered.' XXIV (December, 1945), 100-101, 307. Article; on the death of F. D. R. and the men overseas; uncollected.

'Pretty Pictures for Tooey.' XXV (February, 1946), 46-47, 154-166. Article; World War II; uncollected.

'To Have Dominion.' XXXIII (April 1950), 57. Short short story; uncollected.

'How to Tell Dirty Stories.' XLI (February, 1954), 31, 90, 92. Article; uncollected.

Rockwell KENT (1882-   )
'Cinderella in Greenland.' II (July, 1934), 32, 151-152. Short story; first of a series of three short stories, each accompanied by a full-page reproduction in colour of a water colour by the author; uncollected.

'Skaal Salamina!' II (August, 1934), 26, 136, 138, 141.

'The Blonde Eskimo.' II (September, 1934), 29, 130-131.

John KEROUAC (1922-   )
'Aftermath: The Philosophy of the Beat Generation.' XLIX (March, 1958), 24-26. Article; uncollected.

'Ronnie on the Mound.' XLIX (May, 1958), 87-88. Short story; uncollected.

Gerald KERSH (1909-   )
'The Undefeated Radetski.' XXIV (August, 1945), 28-29, 126-130. Short story; collected as 'Undefeated' in Kersh, *The Horrible Dummy and Other Stories* (London: Heinemann, 1944). Note: in all, Kersh published twenty-six pieces in *Esquire*, 1944-1957.

Eric Mowbray KNIGHT (1897-1943)
'Mary Ann and the Duke.' VIII (December, 1937), 92, 214, 216, 218, 220. Short story; collected in Knight, *Sam Small Flies Again* (N.Y.: Harper, 1942); and in E. J. O'Brien, ed., *The Best British Short Stories of 1938* (Boston: Houghton Mifflin, 1938).

'Never Come Monday.' IX (March, 1938), 36-37, 183-186. Short story; collected in *Sam Small Flies Again;* and in *Bedside Esquire,*

'Strong in the Arms.' IX (April, 1938), 56-57, 193, 195-197. Short story; collected in *Sam Small Flies Again.*

'Time for the Pie-Boy.' IX (June, 1938), 37, 169, 171-172. Short story; uncollected.

'I Knew They'd Never Make It.' XI (May, 1939), 81, 164. Short story; uncollected.

'Bison Bill and Johnnie Bull.' XIV (November, 1940), 48-49, 166-168. Short story; uncollected.

Manuel KOMROFF (1890-   )
'Invitation to Danger.' I (Autumn, 1933), 44. Short short story; collected in Komroff, *All In Our Day* (N.Y.: Harper, 1942). Note: in all, Komroff published seventy-eight stories in *Esquire,* 1933-1944.

Alfred KREYMBORG (1883-   )
'No More War.' XXIX (February, 1948), 72-73. Poem; uncollected.

Christopher LA FARGE (1897-1956)
'Don Juan Miscarried.' XXXVIII (October, 1952), 58, 115-120. Short story; uncollected.

Oliver Hazard Perry LA FARGE (1901-   )
'Kittens Can Climb.' I (March, 1934), 43, 82, 152. Short story; material appeared, in different form, in the novel *The Copper Pot* (N.Y.: Houghton Mifflin 1942).

'A Family Matter.' III (January, 1935), 25, 157. Short story; collected in La Farge, *All the Young Men* (Boston: Houghton Mifflin, 1935).

'Introduction to Mexico.' III (June, 1935), 34, 179-180. Sketch; uncollected.

'Interior of Mexico.' IV (September, 1935), 50-51, 128. Article; uncollected.

'Backwoods of Mexico.' IV (October, 1935), 43, 176-176B. Article; uncollected.

'Guatemalan Goodbye.' V (January, 1936), 88-89, 130. Sketch; uncollected.

'Divinely Fair.' V (February, 1936), 76, 111. Short story; uncollected.

'News By Lip Service.' V (May, 1936), 101, 136. Article; uncollected.

'The Natives Are Friendly.' VI (August, 1936), 76-77, 146. Sketch; uncollected.

'Thick on the Bay.' VII (January, 1937), 58, 126, 128. Short story; uncollected.

'The Girl and the Tiponi.' VII (April, 1937), 72-73, 136, 139. Short story; uncollected.

'Independent Research.' VIII (August, 1937), 32, 203-208. Short story; uncollected.

'The Little Flower.' IX (January, 1938), 74-75, 162, 164-166. Short story; uncollected.

'The Young Warrior.' X (December, 1938), 95, 219-220. Short story; uncollected.

'Old Men's Plans.' XVI (July, 1941), 66-67, 100, 102. Short story; uncollected.

'The Saga of Zela.' XVII (February, 1942), 40, 111-113. Short story; uncollected.

'Dog Boy.' XLII (December, 1954), 134, 213-215. Short story; uncollected·

Ringgold Wilmer LARDNER (1885-1933)
'Greek Tragedy.' I (February, 1934), 18-19, 85, 147. Short story; the last story written before his death ('Backstage with Esquire,' p. 16); collected in *Bedside Esquire*. [Not included in Robert H. Goldsmith, 'Ring W. Lardner; A Check-list of His Published Work,' *Bulletin of Bibliography*, XXI (September-December, 1954), 104-106.]

Ringgold Wilmer LARDNER, Jr. (1915-   )
'Princeton Panorama.' I (Autumn, 1933), 68, 80. Article; uncollected.

Richard Edward LAUTERBACH (1914-1950)
'The Legend of Dorothy Parker.' XXII (October, 1944), 93, 139-146. Article; biographical; collected in *Girls From Esquire*.

David Herbert LAWRENCE (1885-1930)
'Strike Pay.' II (June, 1934), 54-55, 100. Short story; a story "left unpublished"; collected in Lawrence, *Modern Lover* (N.Y.: Viking, 1934).

'Turnabout is Fair.' II (August, 1934), 50, 156. Short story; collected as 'Her Turn' in *Modern Lover*; and in *The Armchair Esquire*.

'The Witch à la Mode.' II (September, 1934), 42-43, 131-132. Short story; collected in *Modern Lover*.

Meyer LEVIN (1905-   )
'Dr, Fabian's One Man Show.' XLII (July, 1954), 38, 104-105. Short story; uncollected.

'The Gift of Mr. Rubius.' XLV (January, 1956), 64, 66, 68. Short story; uncollected.

'The Seven Scrolls of Professor Sukenik.' XLVII (January, 1957), 65, 142, 144-145. Article; on the Dead Sea Scrolls; uncollected.

'His Clever Wife.' XLIX (February, 1958), 81-82. Short story; uncollected.

Harry Sinclair LEWIS (1885-1951)
'Gentlemen, this is Revolution.' XXIII (June, 1945), 76-77. Article; discussion of Wright's *Black Boy*, Whites *A Rising Wind*, Myrdal's *An American Dilemma*, and *What the Negro Wants*; collected in *The Armchair Esquire*.

'Obscenity and Obscurity.' XXIV (July, 1945), 51, 140. Article; the "feeble violence" of obscenity, the "coy snootiness" of obscurity, and the distinguished writing of Eudora Welty; uncollected.

'What the Young Joe Should Write.' XXIV (August, 1945), 67, 137. Article; advice to authors of war books and praise for Barzun's *Teacher in America*; uncollected.

'Wolfes and Wolves.' XXIV (September, 1945), 81, 129. Article; comments on twenty novels most of which need a "more rigorous use of the blue pencil and far more rigorous avoidance of the influences of Tom Wolfe and William Faulkner and Mary McCarthy"; uncollected.

'The Boxers of M. Voltaire.' XXIV (October, 1945), 78-79. Article; unfavourable commentary on Louis Bromfield's *Pleasant Valley*; uncollected.

'The Sac of Fortune.' XXIV (November, 1945), 78-80. Article; lively discussion of Wallace Stegner, August Derleth and James T. Farrell; uncollected.

'Are Women Better?' XXIV (December, 1945), 148, 239. Article; discussion of Maritta Wolff and Ann Chidester; uncollected.

'A Minnesota Diary.' L (October, 1958), 160-162. A section of a journal Lewis kept between 1942 and 1946; with an introductory note by Mark Schorer. A part of the 'Titans Revisited' section of *Esquire's* 25th Anniversary issue.

Ludwig LEWISOHN (1883-1955)
'The Endless Test.' XXVII (June, 1947), 88-89, 229-231. Short story; uncollected.

Abbott Joseph LIEBLING (1904-   )
'Who Did They Lick?' XXVI (November, 1946), 82-83. Book Review; uncollected. Note: in all, Liebling did sixteen monthly book reviews for *Esquire*, November, 1946–February, 1948.

Yu-t'ang LIN (1895-   )
'The Last of the Confucianists.' XV (March, 1941), 27, 122-123. Article; uncollected.

Robert James Collas LOWRY (1919-   )
'Possessed.' XLV (April, 1956), 61, 151-154. Short story; uncollected.

Emil LUDWIG (1881-1948)
'Portrait of a Comedian.' I (January, 1934), 23. Article on Chaplin; uncollected.

'Man whose Name is Steel.' I (February, 1934), 24, 141. [Trans. Ernest Boyd.] Article; uncollected.

'The Paradox of Hollywood.' I (March, 1934), 29, 145. [Trans. Ernest Boyd.] Article; uncollected.

'Teleprejudice.' I (April, 1934), 26. [Trans. Ernest Boyd.] Article; uncollected.

'The Fate of Political Exiles.' II (July, 1935), 36-37, 140. [Trans. Ernest Boyd.] Article; uncollected.

Robie MACAULAY (1919-1959)
'The Academic Style.' XLVII (June, 1957), 116, 159-160, 162, 164. Short story; uncollected.

Dwight MACDONALD (1906-   )
'The Bright Young Men in the Arts.' L (September, 1958), 38-40. Article; uncollected. This article appeared as part of a supplement on 'The Bright Young Men of 1958', in which Dr. Paul Klopsteg wrote on the field of Science; Senator Paul Douglas on Politics; and Robert Weaver on Business.

William Morley Punshon McFEE (1881-   )
'Bellissima.' I (Autumn, 1933), 19, 77. Short story; uncollected.

'Perishable Freight.' I (February, 1934), 52-53, 111. Short story; uncollected.

'Little Angevine.' I (April, 1934), 40, 111, 115; Part One. I (May, 1934), 54-55, 132, 134; Part Two. Short story; uncollected.

'The Kid Across the River.' II (August, 1934), 56. Short short story; collected in *Bedside Esquire*.

'Donald McKay of the Clippers.' XIII (April, 1940), 42-43, 165-166, 168. Article; uncollected.

Siobhan McKENNA (1932-   )
'An Imaginary Conversation with George Bernard Shaw.' XLVIII (December, 1957), 194-195. Article; the 'conversation' of G.B.S. consists of quotations from his plays; uncollected.

Maurice MAETERLINCK (1862-1949)
'Science into Fantasy.' I (March, 1934), 24, 147, 150. [Trans. Ernest Boyd.] Article; uncollected.

Norman Kingsley MAILER (1923-   )
'The Language of Men.' XXXIX (April, 1953), 61, 115-117. Short story; collected in *The Armchair Esquire*.

Klaus MANN (1906-1949)
'Le Dernier Cri.' XV (May, 1941), 28-29, 147-148, 150. Short story; uncollected.

'Three German Masters.' XXV (January, 1946), 50, 197-203. Article; uncollected.

Thomas MANN (1875-1955)
'The Hungry.' III (March, 1935), 22-23. Short story; collected in Mann, *Stories of Three Decades* (N.Y.: Knopf, 1936).

'The Godly Warrior.' V (April, 1936), 32-33, 203-206. Short story; collected as 'Gladius Dei' in Mann, *Stories of Three Decades*; and in *The Armchair Esquire*.

'That Man is My Brother.' XI (March, 1939), 31, 132-133. Article; collected

as 'A Brother' in Mann, *Order of the Day* (N.Y.: Knopf, 1942).

William MARCH [William Edward March Campbell] (1894-1955)
'Mrs. Joe Cotton.' II (July, 1934), 38, 127. Short story; revised and collected as 'Woollen Drawers' in March, *Trial Balance* (N.Y.: Harcourt, Brace, 1945).

'The Slate and the Sorrow.' XXII (November, 1944), 84, 186-189. Short story; collected in *Trial Balance*; and in *The Esquire Treasury*.

'A Great Town for Characters.' XXV (May, 1946), 86, 143-146. Short story; uncollected.

Edgar Lee MASTERS (1868-1950)
'Two Views of a Rainy Night.' II (June, 1934), 131. Two poems; uncollected.

'Battery Park in January.' III (January, 1935), 24. Poem; collected in Masters, *More People* (N.Y.: Appleton-Century, 1939).

'Dreiser at Spoon River.' XI (May, 1939), 66, 146, 151-152, 154, 156, 158. Article; collected in *The Armchair Esquire*.

'William Marion Reedy: Feaster.' XII (October, 1939), 67, 148, 150. Article; uncollected.

'The Time of Ruby Robert.' XIII (February, 1940), 33, 152-155. Article; collected in Gingrich, ed., *Esquire's 2nd Sports Reader* (N.Y.: Barnes, 1946).

'Fiddlers of the Ozarks.' XXII (November, 1944), 47, 142-145. Article; autobiographical; uncollected.

William Somerset MAUGHAM (1874-   )
'The Old Party Goes to London.' XXXVIII (December, 1952), 91. Article; personal reminiscence; uncollected.

André MAUROIS [Emile Salomon Wilhelm Herzog] (1885-   )
'Forgive Me, Irene.' I (January, 1934), 53. Short short story; revised and col-

lected as 'Irene' in Maurois, *Ricochets* (N.Y.: Harper, 1935).

'On the Rebound.' I (February, 1934), 67. Short short story; revised and collected as 'Ricochets' in *Ricochets*.

'An Idea for a Story.' II (July, 1934), 26, 138. Article; collected in *Bedside Esquire*.

'Young Girl in the Snow.' IV (December, 1935), 53, 208-209. Short story; uncollected.

'The Odd Dollar.' VI (October, 1936), 53, 200B-203. Short story; uncollected.

'Here, Kitty, Kitty.' VII (April, 1937), 59, 184, 186. Short story; uncollected.

'A Case of Conscience.' IX (April, 1938), 39, 152-153. Short story; uncollected.

'The Devil in the Mine.' X (September, 1938), 34, 99-100. Short story; uncollected.

'The Schoolboy's Return.' X (October, 1938), 51, 168. Short story; collected in Anne Freemantle, ed., *Maurois Reader* (N.Y.: Didier, 1949).

'The Role of Myrrhine.' XXIV (December, 1945), 65, 310-314. Short story; collected in *Maurois Reader*.

'How to Get Along with the Americans.' XXXVII (April, 1952), 54, 130-131. Article; uncollected.

Martin MAYER (1928-   )
'Igor Makes a Record.' XL (December, 1953), 145, 209-213. Article; on recording Stravinsky's *The Rake's Progress*; uncollected.

'A Profile of *The Daily Worker*.' XLVIII (August, 1957), 113-114, 116. Article; uncollected.

'Wall Street: Men and Money.' XXXVIII (September, 1952), 52-57, 89-90, 92. Article; uncollected. Mayer expanded this into the book, *Wall Street: Men and Money* (N.Y.: Harpers, 1955).

Note: Mayer did regular pieces on musical subjects for *Esquire*, 1954-1958.

Henry Louis MENCKEN (1880-1956)
'Downfall of a Revolutionary.' XIV (September, 1940), 27, 122. Article; autobiographic; collected in Mencken, *Heathen Days, 1890-1936* (N.Y.: Knopf, 1943).

'An Evening on the House.' XX (December, 1943), 63, 233-234, 236, 238-239. Article; autobiographical; collected in *The Armchair Esquire*.

'Obsequies in the Grand Manner.' XXI (January, 1944), 43, 133-135. Article; autobiographical; uncollected.

'The Crime of McSwane.' XXXII (October, 1949), 74, 132. Short story; reprinted from *Leslie's Popular Monthly*, July, 1902; as a literary curiosity, being a youthful imitation of a Kipling adventure tale.

Gian-Carlo MENOTTI (1911-   )
'Vanessa.' XLVIII (December, 1957), 114-122. Libretto to opera of the same name, with music by Samuel Barber; with illustrations and photographs in inset; opera produced in New York City, 1958.

James Albert MICHENER (1907-   )
'Siva Tonight!' XXXV (March, 1951), 40-41, 99. Article; the South Pacific; uncollected.

'Proud Queen.' XXXV (April, 1951), 76, 141. Short story; uncollected.

'The Precious Drop.' XXXVI (December, 1951), 121, 193-199. Short story; collected in *The Esquire Treasury*.

'On the Sendai Train.' XXXVII (April, 1952), 48-49. Short short story; uncollected.

Arthur MILLER (1915-   )
'A Regular Death Call.' XXXII (August, 1949), 35, 106. Short story; uncollected.

374

'The Misfits.' XLVIII (October, 1957), 158, 160-166. Short story; collected in *The Armchair Esquire*.

'Bridge to a Savage World.' L (October, 1958), 185-190. Article; on juvenile delinquency, originally prepared as a memorandum for a documentary film; uncollected.

Gilbert MILLSTEIN (1915-   )
'The Dark at the Top of William Inge.' XLIX (August, 1958), 62-65. Article; uncollected.

Ferenc MOLNÁR (1878-1952)
'Heavenly and Earthly Love.' IX (April, 1938), 43, 141. A satirical 'dialogue'; collected in *The Armchair Esquire*.

Nicholas John Turney MONSAR-RAT (1910-   )
'The Man Who Wanted a Mark IX.' XLI (June, 1954), 41, 129-136. Short story; uncollected.

Alberto MORAVIA [Alberto Pincherle] (1907-   )
'The Chinese Dog.' XLV (January, 1956), 55, 116. Short story; collected in *The Armchair Esquire*.

Wright MORRIS (1910-   )
'The Cat in the Picture.' XLIX (May, 1958), 91, 93-94. Short story; uncollected.

Romano MUSSOLINI (1927-   )
'How I Remember Papa.' L (October, 1958), 183-184. Article; autobiographical; uncollected.

George Jean NATHAN (1882-1958)
'First Nights & Passing Judgments.' VI (October, 1936), This is the first of a monthly series of dramatic reviews which regularly appeared up to September, 1946, and which were variously and frequently incorporated into Nathan, *The Theatre Book of the Year, 1942-1943, et seq.*, published by Knopf.

'Reflections After the Curtains Fall.' XLIV (August, 1955). This is the first of a monthly series of dramatic essays which regularly appeared up to January, 1957, about such subjects as burlesque, a plea for a theatrical stage, and such writers as O'Casey, O'Neill, and Anouilh.

'. . . On Eugene O'Neill.' XLVII (June, 1957), 101. Article; on *Long Day's Journey Into Night*; uncollected.

'The Happiest Days of H. L. Mencken.' XLVIII (October, 1957), 146-150. Article; collected in *The Armchair Esquire*.

'The Golden Boy of the Twenties.' 'The Owner of Main Street's Soap Box,' and 'The Elephant that Whistled the Polka.' L (October, 1958), 148-154. Memoirs of F. Scott Fitzgerald, Sinclair Lewis, and Theodore Dreiser; a part of the 'Titans Revisited' section of *Esquire's* 25th Anniversary issue.

Richard Lewis NEUBERGER (1912-   )
'Madison Avenue in Politics.' XLVIII (August, 1957), 78-80, 82, 84. Article; uncollected.

Frank O'CONNOR [Michael O'Donovan] (1903-   )
'Orpheus and His Lute.' V (January, 1936), 92-93, 111. Short story; collected in O'Connor, *Bones of Contention* (N.Y.: Macmillan, 1936).

'The Paragon.' XLVIII (October, 1957), 116, 119-120, 123-125. Short story; collected in O'Connor, *Domestic Relations* (N.Y.: Knopf, 1957).

Seán O'FAOLÁIN (1900-   )
'The Tall Coorter.' V (April, 1936), 36, 166, 168, 171-172. Short story; collected in *Bedside Esquire*.

Liam O'FLAHERTY (1897-   )
'All Things Come of Age.' III (January, 1935), 43, 184. Short story; uncollected.

'The Water Hen.' X (August, 1938), 59, 147. Short story; collected in O'Flaherty, *Two Lovely Beasts* (N.Y.: Devin-Adair, 1950).

'Good Soldiers Play Safe.' XVII (May, 1942), 23, 120-122. Article; uncollected.

'The Test of Courage.' XIX (February, 1943), 28, 129-130, 132, 134. Short story; uncollected.

'Village Ne'er-Do-Well.' XXIV (September, 1945), 53-54. Article; autobiographic; uncollected.

'The Flute Player.' XXVII (March, 1947), 41, 127-129. Short story; collected in *Two Lovely Beasts*.

'I Go to Sea.' XXXVIII (September, 1952), 38-39, 85-86, 88. Short story; uncollected.

'The Mirror.' XL (November, 1953), 58, 146. Short story; collected in O'Flaherty, *The Stories* (N.Y.: Devin-Adair, 1956).

'The Fanatic.' XL (December, 1953), 90, 194, 196, 198. Short story; uncollected.

'The Blow.' XLII (July, 1954), 32-33, 110-113. Short story; collected in *The Stories*.

John Henry O'HARA (1905-   )
'Little 'Chita.' VI (August, 1936), 41, 168. Short story; uncollected.

Dorothy Rothschild PARKER (1893-   )
'Best Fiction of 1957.' XLVIII (December, 1957), 60, 62, 64, 66. Article; uncollected. Note: beginning May, 1958, Dorothy Parker contributed a monthly book review column to *Esquire*.

Elliot Harold PAUL (1891-1958)
'Gertrude, Alas, Alas.' XXVI (July, 1946), 62, 189-193. Article; on Gertrude Stein; collected in *The Esquire Treasury*.

Louis PAUL (1901-   )
'No More Trouble for Jedwick.' I (March, 1934), 58-59, 148. Short story; collected in Harry Hansen, ed., *O. Henry Memorial Award Prize Stories of 1934* (N.Y.: Doubleday, Doran, 1934). [Awarded 1st Prize.]

Luigi PIRANDELLO (1867-1936)
'With Other Eyes,' II (July, 1934), 54-55. Short story; collected in *The Armchair Esquire*.

Ezra Loomis POUND (1885-   )
'Gaudier: A Postscript.' II (August, 1934), 73-74. Article; uncollected. [Photographic reproduction of G-B's 'Hieratic Head' of Pound, p. 16.]

'Riposte from Rapallo.' II (October, 1934), 12. Letter to the editor, in which Pound corrects, among other things, errors in his article on Gaudier [August, 1934]; uncollected.

'Reflexshuns on Iggurunce.' III (January, 1935), 55, 133. Article; on international credit; collected in *The Armchair Esquire*.

'Mug's Game?' III (February, 1935), 35, 148. Article; uncollected.

'A Matter of Modesty.' III (May, 1935), 31, Article; uncollected.

'Hickory—Old and New.' III (June, 1935), 40, 156. Article; uncollected.

'A Thing of Beauty.' IV (November, 1935), 49, 195-197. Article; uncollected.

'How to Save Business.' V (January, 1936), 35, 195-196. Article; uncollected.

Fletcher PRATT (1897-1956)
'The Ordeal of John Paul Jones.' XXIV (December, 1945), 66. Article; uncollected.

Theodore PRATT (1901-   )
'The Owl that Kept Winking.' XXI (June, 1944), 48, 124-125. Short story; collected in Martha Foley, ed., *The Best American Short Stories of 1945* (Boston: Houghton Mifflin, 1945).

Frederic PROKOSCH (1908-   )
'The Murderer.' IV (July, 1935), 64, 144. Short story; uncollected.

'The Trip to Granada.' XXVII (February, 1947), 41, 157-160. Short story; uncollected.

James PURDY (1923-   )
'Night and Day.' L (July, 1958), 108-112. Short story; uncollected.

Samson RAPHAELSON (1896-   )
'Design in Confetti.' XXIX (January, 1948), 62, 171-174. Short story; uncollected.

Quentin James REYNOLDS (1902-   )
'Holbein's Star Performance.' XXIX (March, 1948), 33, 121-125. Short story; uncollected.

'A Glass of Orange Juice.' XXXI (January, 1949), 36, 101-102, 104, 106-108, 111. Short story; collected in H. U. Ribalow, ed., *The World's Greatest Boxing Stories* (N.Y.: Twain, 1952).

'The Third Vase.' XXXII (December, 1949), 78, 181-182. Short story; uncollected.

'The Third Act.' XXXIV (December, 1950), 86, 151-152, 154, 156, 158, 160. Short story; uncollected.

Kenneth REXROTH (1905-   )
'Jazz and Poetry.' XLIX (May, 1958), 20, 22. Article; uncollected.

Diego RIVERA (1886-1957)
'Stalin Undertaker of the Revolution.' XIII (May, 1940), 35, 114. Article; uncollected.

Henry Morton ROBINSON (1898-   )
'The Curious Case of Thornton Wilder.' XLVII (March, 1957), 71, 124-126. Article; uncollected.

Selden RODMAN (1909-   )
'Consuelo at the Country Club.' X (July, 1938), 38. Poem; uncollected.

James ROOSEVELT (1907-   )
'Life Because of Father.' XLVIII (November, 1957), 43-46. Article; autobiographical; uncollected.

Phillip ROTH (1933-   )
'Heard Melodies Are Sweeter.' L (August, 1958), 60. Short story; uncollected.

Richard Halworth ROVERE (1915-   )
'The Question of Ezra Pound.' XLVIII (September, 1957), 66, 68, 71-72, 74-75, 78, 80. Article; E.P.'s sanity and incarceration; collected in *The Armchair Esquire*.

'Aftermath: The Question of Ezra Pound.' XLVIII (December, 1957), 12, 14, 16, 18, 20. Letters to the editor; Rovere's article on E.P. produced such a spirited reply, that the letters were grouped separately. Letters are from John Dos Passos, Van Wyck Brooks, Marianne Moore, Osbert Sitwell, Howard Nemerov, Richard Wilbur, Wallace Fowlie, Mark Schorer, Norman Mailer, Kenneth Rexroth, Robert Graves, and Patrick Murphy Malin.

'Best Nonfiction of 1957.' XLVIII (December, 1957), 68, 70, 72, 76, 80. Article; uncollected.

'Aftermath: The Question of Ezra Pound.' XLVIII (January, 1958), 135, 136. Letters to the editor from Babette Deutsch, J. V. Cunningham, Andrew Lytle, William Carlos Williams.

'Aftermath: The Question of Ezra Pound.' XLIX (February, 1958), 22B, 24-26. Letters to the editor from Robert L. Allen, Richard Chase, T. D. Horton, Selden Rodman.

'The Last Days of Joe McCarthy.' L (August, 1958), 29-34. Article; uncollected.

Alfred Damon RUNYON (1884-1946)
'They Saw that They Were Naked.' XXXIX (May, 1953), 58, 114. Article; 'the last piece he wrote'; uncollected.

'The Breaking Point.' XXX (December, 1948), 78, 215-218. Short story; collected in *Some Faces in the Crowd* and in *Girls From Esquire*.

'The Dare.' XXXI (May, 1949), 38, 97-98, 100-101. Short story; collected in *Some Faces in the Crowd*.

'The Legend that Walks Like a Man.' XXXIV (August, 1950), 41, 99-100. Short story; collected in *Some Faces in the Crowd*.

'What Made Tiger Rag?' XXXIV (September, 1950), 57. Article; uncollected.

'A Free Man.' XL (August, 1953), 32. Short short story; uncollected.

'Hollywood vs. Chris Samuels, at Nine.' XL (December, 1953), 109. Short story; uncollected.

William Buehler SEABROOK (1886-1945)
'The Yatanga Naba.' IV (November, 1935), 43, 161-164. Short story; uncollected.

Allan SEAGER (1906-   )
'As a Little Child.' XI (March, 1939), 65, 168-170. Short story; uncollected.
'Jersey, Guernsey, Alderney, Sark.' XVI (August, 1941), 40, 120-121. Short story; collected in Seager, *The Old Man of the Mountain* (N.Y.: Simon & Schuster, 1950).

'The Half Dollar with the Hole in it and the Little Candy Hearts.' XLVIII (September, 1957), 118. Short short story; uncollected.

'It's Hard to Recognize a Drowning Man.' XLIX (March, 1958), 63-64. Short story; uncollected.

George Bernard SHAW (1857-1950)
'The Love Letters of Bernard Shaw.' XLIX (April, 1958), 63-65. Letters to Alice Lockett; collected in *The Armchair Esquire*.

Irwin SHAW (1913-   )
'The Monument.' XI (June, 1939), 40, 132, 134. Short story; collected in Shaw's *Sailor off the Bremen* (N.Y.: Random House, 1939).

'Residents of Other Cities.' XII (July, 1939), 32-33, 155. Short story; collected in *Sailor off the Bremen*.

'It Happened in Rochester.' XII (December, 1939), 128, 280-282. Short story; collected in Shaw, *Welcome to the City* (N.Y.: Random House, 1942).

'The House of Pain.' XIV (November, 1940), 95, 189-190. Short story; collected in *Welcome to the City*.

'Triumph of Justice.' XIV (December, 1940), 99, 270-273. Short story; collected in *Welcome to the City;* and in E. J. O'Brien, ed., *Best Short Stories of 1941* (N.Y.: Houghton Mifflin, 1941).

'The Eighty-Yard Run.' XV (January, 1941), 23, 164-167. Short story; collected in *Welcome to the City*.

'The Convert.' XXVIII (September, 1947), 42-43, 143-146. Short story; collected in *Girls From Esquire*.

'The Singing Brute.' XXVIII (October, 1947), 64-65, 147-148, 150. Short story; uncollected.

'The Circle of Light.' L (October, 1958), 226-ff. Short story; uncollected.

James Vincent SHEEAN (1899-   )
'Three Dead Geese.' IV (July, 1935), 26, 170. Article; uncollected.

'Over Mozart's Memory.' IV (November, 1935), 38, 178. Article; uncollected.

'The New Road.' IV (December, 1935), 43, 212-216. Short story; collected in Sheean, *The Pieces of a Fan* (N.Y.: Doubleday, Doran, 1937).

Max SHULMAN (1919-   )
'Spanish Spoken Here.' XXIII (Janu-

ary, 1945), 52-53, 145-147. Short story; collected in *The Esquire Treasury*.

'My Regards to Morpheus.' XXIII (March, 1945), 71, 138-139. Short story; uncollected.

'One Shoe Off.' XXXVIII (September, 1952), 40, 108-111. Short story; uncollected.

Georges SIMENON (1903-)
'The Case of Dr. Ceccioni.' IV (November, 1935), 84. Short short story; uncollected.

Jo SINCLAIR [Ruth Seid] (1913-)
'Children at Play.' IX (January, 1938), 45, 124. Short story; collected in J. DeL. Ferguson, et al., *Theme and Variation in the Short Story* (N.Y.: Dryden, 1938).

Upton Beall SINCLAIR (1878-)
'We Choose Our Future.' IV (August, 1935), 20, 167-168. Article; uncollected.

Sacheverell SITWELL (1897-)
'Les Châteaux de la Loire.' L (September, 1958), 48-51. Article; uncollected.

Harry Allen SMITH (1907-)
'The Admirable Avery.' XL (December, 1953), 131, 240-241. Short story; uncollected.

Robert Paul SMITH (1915-)
'About a Place Called Gabrielle's.' XLIX (March, 1958), 85-86. Short story; uncollected.

Laurence STALLINGS (1894-)
'The Youth in the Abyss.' XXXVI (October, 1951), 47, 107-111. Article; F. Scott Fitzgerald in Hollywood; uncollected.

'Last Talk with Damon Runyon.' XLVIII (November, 1957), 61. Article; uncollected.

'Hitler Did Not Dance That Jig.' L (October, 1958), 264.

Vincent STARRETT (1886-)
'Alibi in a Roadhouse.' I (Autumn, 1933), 73, 89. Short story; uncollected.

'A Note on Mr. Sherlock Holmes.' I (May, 1934), 59, 96, 98. Article; uncollected.

'Prolific Papas.' XLIV (July, 1955), 92, 118. Article; uncollected.

Wallace Earle STEGNER (1909-)
'He Who Spits at the Sky.' XLIX (March, 1958), 140, 143-154. Short story; uncollected.

John Ernst STEINBECK (1902-)
'The Lonesome Vigilante.' VI (October, 1936), 35, 186A-186B. Short story; collected as 'The Vigilante' in Steinbeck, *The Long Valley* (N.Y.: Viking, 1938); and in *Esquire Treasury*.

'The Ears of Johnny Bear.' VIII (September, 1937), 35, 195-200. Short story; collected as 'Johnny Bear' in *The Long Valley*.

'A Snake of One's Own.' IX (February, 1938), 31, 178-180. Short story; collected as 'The Snake' in *The Long Valley*.

'The Case of Arthur Miller.' XLVII (June, 1957), 86. Article; collected in *The Armchair Esquire*.

James STERN (1904-)
'Strangers Defeated.' XIX (January, 1943), 74, 185-188. Short story; uncollected.

'The Man Behind the Bar.' XXIII (June, 1945), 52-53, 116. Short story; revised and collected as 'The Face Behind the Bar' in Stern, *The Man Who Was Loved* (N.Y.: Harcourt, Brace, 1951).

George Rippey STEWART (1895-)
'Melodrama in the Forties.' XXIII (March, 1945), 100-102. Article; on naming towns, rivers, and mountains in the 1840s; uncollected.

'McGinnity's Rock.' XXVII (January, 1947), 102-103. Short story; uncollected.

Leonard Alfred George STRONG (1896-   )
'Over the Toast.' II (September, 1934), 44, 141-142. A dialogue; uncollected.

'The Escape.' III (January, 1935), 79, 126. Short story; uncollected.

'The Come-back.' III (June, 1935), 39, 167-170. Short story; collected in *Esquire's 2nd Sports Reader*.

'The Ails of Clonbocketty.' X (August. 938), 38, 140-141. Article; uncollected.

'A Marriage of Convenience.' XV (May, 1941), 30, 172-173. Short story; uncollected.

Jesse Hilton STUART (1907-   )
'The Ballad of Lonesome Waters.' V (June, 1936), 32-33. Poem; uncollected.

'Uncle Fonse Laughed.' VI (September, 1936), 32-33, 182,184, 186. Short story; collected in *Bedside Esquire*. Note: in all, Stuart published sixty-two stories and poems in *Esquire*, 1936-1956.

Harvey B. SWADOS (1920-   )
'Year of Grace.' XLIX (June, 1958), 157-169. Short story; uncollected.

Robert Myron SWITZER (1923-   )
'The Big Bout.' XXVIII (August, 1947), 26-27, 126. Short story; uncollected.

'Death of a Prize Fighter.' XXXI (June, 1949), 39, 109-110. Short story; collected in H. Brickell, ed., *Prize Stories of 1950* (N.Y.: Doubleday, Doran 1950); and in H. Ribalow, ed., *World's Greatest Boxing Stories* (N.Y.: Twain, 1952); and in *The Esquire Treasury*. Note: in all, Switzer published seven stories in *Esquire*, 1947-1952.

Harry SYLVESTER (1908-   )
'The Crazy Guy.' IX (April, 1936), 102, 188-189. Short story; collected in Sylvester, *All Your Idols* (N. Y.: Holt, 1948); and in *The Best Stories of 1939*.

Dylan Marlais THOMAS (1914-1953)
'A Child's Christmas in Wales.' XLIV (December, 1955), 95-102. Short story. 'A Child's Christmas in Wales' first appeared in *Quite Early One Morning* (N. Y.: New Directions, 1954). This printing appeared simultaneously with a gift book, limited edition, published by New Directions in December, 1955.

Jim TULLY (1888-1947)
'The Worm That Turned.' I (May, 1934), 24, 110. Short story; uncollected.

'The Last Carnival.' II (June, 1934), 27, 98, 102. Article; autobiographic; comment on Faulkner in Hollywood; uncollected.

'The Manly Art.' II (July, 1934), 63-64, 114. Article; uncollected.

'Señor Diego Rivera.' II (August, 1934), 48-49, 168-169. Article; revised and collected in Tully, *A Doxen and One* (Hollywood: Murray & Gee, 1943).

'Over a Barrel.' II (October, 1934), 54, 139. Article; autobiography as related to Tully by W. C. Fields; uncollected.

'Glancing Backward.' II (December, 1934), 59, 146, 149. Article; autobiography as related to Tully by Paul Muni; uncollected.

'A Harvest Memory.' VI (December, 1936), 59, 308, 310-13. Article; uncollected.

'Case of Convict 1174.' VII (February, 1937), 48, 203-204. Short story; uncollected.

'The Dying Hobo.' VII (April, 1937), 101. Poem; uncollected.

'The King of Laughter.' VII (June, 1937), 47, 231-235. Article; collected as 'Charlie Chaplin' in *A Dozen and One*.

'Portrait of My Father.' XII (November, 1939), 90-91, 120. Article; uncollected.

'The Saga of the Big Dane.' XX (August, 1943), 124. Article; on Hollywood; uncollected.

John Roberts TUNIS (1889-   )
'The Great Depression of 1965.' XLVIII (October, 1957), 108. Short short story; uncollected.

Leon TROTZKY [Lev Davidovitch Trotskii né Bronstein] (1879-1940)
'Clouds in the Far East.' II (August, 1934), 20-21. Article; uncollected.

Louis UNTERMEYER (1885-   )
'Sinderella, Incorporated.' XXVI (December, 1946), 101, 249-250, 252. Article; uncollected.

'My Own Five-Foot Shelf.' XXVIII (August, 1947), 34, 120-125. Article; a list of 50 great books; uncollected.

'Plot Luck or Situations Wanted.' XXX (July, 1948), 78, 144. Article; uncollected.

Roger VAILLAND (1907-   )
'The Game of the Law.' L (October, 1958), 191-198. Episode from 1957 Prix Goncourt novel *La Loi*. Translated by Peter Wiles as *The Law* (N.Y.: Knopf, 1958).

John WAIN (1925-   )
'Rafferty.' XLIX (April, 1958), 84-86. Short story; uncollected.

Frederic WAKEMAN (1909-   )
'You Have to Sell Yourself.' XL (August, 1953), 46, 108-109. Short story; uncollected.

'The Cossacks and the Violin.' XL (December, 1953), 87, 201-207. Short story; uncollected.

Jakob WASSERMANN (1873-1934)
'Geronimo de Aguilar.' II (June, 1934), 30-31, 158B, 160. [Trans. Eric Posselt and Michel Kraika.] Short story; collected in *Bedside Esquire*.

Alec WAUGH (1898-   )
'The Wicked Baronet.' XXXV (March 1951), 37, 100, 102. Short story; uncollected.

'Something Worth Waiting For.' XXXIX (February, 1953), 25, 103-105. Short story; uncollected.

'Small Back Room in St. Marylebone.' XXXIX (March, 1953), 35-37, 98, 101. Short story; uncollected.

'Nearing Sixty.' XLVIII (July, 1957), 98, 100, 103-104. Article; autobiographical reflections; uncollected.

Evelyn Arthur St. John WAUGH (1903-   )
'St. Francis Xavier's Bones.' XL (December, 1953), 83, 226-229. Article; the saint's bones in Goa; collected in *The Armchair Esquire*.

Joseph WECHSBERG (1907-   )
'Honorable Composer Big Click.' XXI (March, 1944), 45, 157-161. Article; collected in *The Esquire Treasury*.

'Sports Writer's Nightmare.' XXII (November, 1944), 82-83, 175-177. Article; uncollected.

'New Year's at Boeuf Stroganoff.' XXII (December, 1944), 186, 283-285. Article; uncollected.

'A Visitor from America.' XXIII (January, 1945), 54, 148-152. Article; uncollected.

'The Terrors of Law.' XXIV (December, 1945), 81, 283-287. Article; uncollected.

'Opening in Algiers.' XXV (January, 1946), 90-91, 170, 172. Article; uncollected.

'Revolt with Strings.' XXVIII (July, 1947), 59, 201-203. Short story; uncollected.

'East on the Sealed Express.' XXXVIII (November, 1952), 47, 117-120. Article; uncollected.

'The Emperor's Folly.' XL (November, 1953), 54-55, 115-116. Short story; uncollected.

'All Quiet on the Eastern Front,' XLI (January, 1954), 39, 120-125. Article; uncollected.

'Apfelstrudel and Old Lace.' XLIII (March, 1955), 51, 120-123. Article; uncollected.

'Three Times Zero.' XLIII (April, 1955), 57, 139-142. Article; uncollected.

'This is Vienna.' XLIV (September, 1955), 58, 137-139. Article; uncollected.

'The Gothic Murals Scandal.' XLIV (December, 1955), 141, 244-246. Article; art forgery; uncollected.

'Budapest Revisited.' XLV (April, 1956), 58, 124, 127-128. Article; uncollected.

'Laughter in the Wrong Place.' XLVI (September, 1956), 49, 132-134. Article; uncollected.

'Monsieur Tranquille.' XLVII (May, 1957), 55, 115-116, 118. Article; the Vienna Staatsoper; uncollected.

Jerome WEIDMAN (1913-   )
'Everybody Wants to be a Lady.' VII (May, 1937), 63, 244, 245. Short story; collected in Weidman, *The Horse that could Whistle Dixie* (N. Y.: Simon & Schuster, 1939).

'Foreign Exchange.' XLI (April, 1954), 51, 113-115. Short story; uncollected.

Franz WERFEL (1890-1945)
'The Bulletproof Hidalgo.' XV (February, 1941), 28, 151-155. Short story; collected in Herman Kesten and Klaus Mann, eds., *Best of Modern European*

Literature (Philadelphia: Blakiston, 1945).

Heinz WERNER (1901-   )
'Black Tobias and the Empire.' IX (May, 1938), 36-37, 107. Short story; collected in *Best Short Stories of 1939*.

Anthony C. WEST (1910-   )
'Narcissus unto Echo.' XLV (May, 1956), 51, 134-137. Short story; collected in West, *River's End and Other Stories* (N. Y.: McDowell-Obolensky, 1958).

'The Turning Page.' XLVI (December, 1956), 117-122. Short story; collected in *River's End*.

'River's End.' XLVII (March, 1957), 39-58. Long short story; collected in *River's End*.

'Not Isaac.' XLVIII (September, 1957), 114-115. Short story; collected in *River's End*.

'Song of the Barrow.' L (July, 1958), 82-84. Short story; collected in *River's End*.

Theodore Harold WHITE (1915-   )
'The Mountain Road.' XLIX (May, 1958), 122, 124, 126, 128, 131-132, 134, 136, 138, 140, 143-146. Episode from novel, *The Mountain Road* (N. Y.: Morrow-Sloane, 1958).

Edward Reed WHITTEMORE (1919-   )
'Nice Fireplace, Good Beach.' XLVIII (July, 1957), 108-110. Short story; uncollected.

'The Cuteness of Well-Being: The Gift Shoppe.' L (October, 1958), 280, 283-284. Article; uncollected.

Percival WILDE (1887-1953)
'Salt for Savor.' XL (December, 1953), 158-160, 162, 164-166. A play; a comedy in one act; uncollected.

Ben Ames WILLIAMS (1889-1953)
'The Jawbreaker.' XXXIII (June

1950), 75, 111-114, 116. Short story; uncollected.

Tennessee WILLIAMS [Thomas Lanier] (1914-   )
'A Perfect Analysis Given by a Parrot.' L (October, 1958), 131-134. Short play for subsequent presentation on television; uncollected.

Thomas WILLIAMS
'Goose Pond.' XLVIII (November, 1957), 149-154. Short story; collected in P. Engle and K. Harnac, eds., *Prize Stories of 1959* (N. Y.: Doubleday, 1958).

'The Buck in Trotevale's .'L (August, 1958), 102-108, 110, 113-115. Short story; uncollected.

Angus Frank Johnstone WILSON (1913-   )
'Ten Minutes to Twelve.' XLVIII (December, 1957), 162, 164-166. 168-169, 171. Short story; collected in Wilson, *A Bit off the Map* (N. Y.: Viking, 1957).

Thomas Clayton WOLFE (1900-1938)
'Arnold Pentland.' III (June, 1935), 26, 150-152. Short story; collected as 'A Kinsman of His Blood' in Wolfe, *The Hills Beyond* (N. Y.: Harper, 1941); and in *The Armchair Esquire*.

'The Hollow Men.' XIV (October, 1940), 27, 115, 116. Short story; incorporated into Wolfe, *You Can't Go Home Again* (N. Y.: Harper, 1940), pp. 460-463, 467-469, 470-475, 476-477, 478, 479. [See George R. Preston, Jr., *Thomas Wolfe, A Bibliography* (N. Y.: Boesen, 1943), p. 74.]

'Welcome to Our City.' XLVIII (October, 1957), 58-82. A play: in ten scenes; published here for the first time; uncollected.

Ira WOLFERT (1908-   )
'Off the Highway.' VIII (October, 1937), 65, 190-192, 194. Short story; collected in *The Best Short Stories of 1938*.

'The Indomitable Blue.' XL (December, 1953), 94-95, 217-224. Short story; collected in P. Engle and H. Martin, eds., *Prize Stories of 1955* (N. Y.: Doubleday, 1955).

Herman WOUK (1915-   )
'Irresistible Force.' XXXVIII (August, 1952), 27, 96. Short story; collected in *The Esquire Treasury*.

Frank Lloyd WRIGHT (1869-1959)
'Away with the Realtor.' L (October, 1958), 179-180. Article; uncollected.

Richard WRIGHT (1909-   )
'Big, Black, Good Man.' XLVIII (November, 1957), 74-76, 78, 80. Short story; uncollected.

Ida Alexa Ross WYLIE (1885-   )
'End of Season.' XLI (March, 1954), 38-39, 90. Short story; uncollected.

Francis Brett YOUNG (1884-1954)
'It's an Ill Wind.' IV (September, 1935), 56-57, 119. Short story; collected in Young, *The Ship's Surgeon's Yarn* (N. Y.: Reynal & Hitchcock, 1940).

Lajos ZILAHY (1891-   )
'But for This . . .'' IV (October, 1935), 103. Short story; his first to be translated into English; collected in *Bedside Esquire*.

'The Silver Winged Windmill.' V (June, 1936), 61, 150. Short story; uncollected.

Arnold ZWEIG (1887-   )
'The Pogeins.' II (July, 1935), 30-31. Short story; uncollected.

'The Old Man of the Sea.' V (March, 1936), 32-33. Short story; uncollected.